IEE Support for BS 7671 : 200

The Institution of Engineering and Technology publishes a range of b
and runs courses and services for industry to support the use and ap

GUIDANCE NOTES

The Institution of Engineering and Technology's series of **IEE Guidance Notes** offers extensive, industry-endorsed guidance to designers and installers in the effective use of BS 7671.

Seven **IEE Guidance Notes** are currently available:

1. Selection and Erection of Equipment
2. Isolation and Switching
3. Inspection and Testing
4. Protection against Fire
5. Protection against Electric Shock
6. Protection against Overcurrent
7. Special Locations

ON-SITE GUIDE

A convenient, practical guide for electricians which covers domestic installations and smaller industrial and commercial installations up to 100 A, 3-phase. The most widely used guide in the industry, it removes the need for detailed calculations and outlines a detailed inspection and testing regime for installations. Comprehensive checklists and procedures are provided.

COMMENTARY ON BS 7671 : 2001

Written for designers and managers, this title provides clear interpretations of and guidance to the Regulations.

CODES OF PRACTICE

The **IEE Code of Practice for In-Service Inspection and Testing of Electrical Equipment** offers guidance for the inspection, testing and maintenance of electrical appliances, plus advice on compliance with health and safety legislation.

The **IEE Electrical Maintenance – Code of Practice** offers guidance on electrical aspects of building maintenance, including electrical installation, fire alarms, emergency lighting and more, plus detailed guidance on legal responsibilities.

CD-ROM OF IEE WIRING REGULATIONS

The CD-ROM version of BS 7671 (incorporating all amendments) is a fully-structured electronic reference tool, hyperlinked and fully cross-referenced. As well as BS 7671, the CD-ROM contains the **On-Site Guide**, all seven **IEE Guidance Notes** and both **IEE Codes of Practice**.

To order any of these publications, please contact
The Institution of Engineering and Technology:

- by telephone: +44 (0)1438 767328
- by email: **sales@theiet.org**
- by fax: +44 (0)1438 742792
- via our website: **www.theiet.org/shop**

For free downloads, updates and to join our email list, visit **www.theiet.org/technical**

Please send me further information on the following products and/or courses:

☐ BS 7671 IEE Wiring Regulations / CD-ROM   ☐ On-Site Guide

☐ Guidance Notes / Commentary   ☐ Codes of Practice

☐ Training Courses

☐ Please add my details to your mailing list for future product news / updates

Name _____

Company _____

Address _____

_____

Post code _____ E-mail_____

TRAINING AND SHORT COURSES

The Institution of Engineering and Technology offers a full range of training for BS 7671 and its amendments. Both public and in-company courses are available.

Design – Three-day course

Level 3 Certificate in Requirements for Electrical Installations BS 7671 – Three-day course (Qualifying C & G 2381)

Testing of Electrical Installations – One-day course

Level 3 Certificate in Inspection, Testing and Certification of Electrical Installations – Three-day course (Qualifying C & G 2391)

Portable Appliance Testing – Two one-day courses
(Incorporating Management of Electrical Equipment qualifying C & G 2377-001 and Inspection and Testing of Electrical Equipment qualifying C & G 2377-002)

Electrical Maintenance – Two-day course

Electricity at Work – One-day course

Dates and venues for these and other courses can be found from The Institution of Engineering and Technology:

- by telephone: +44 (0)1438 767289
- by email: **courses@theiet.org**
- by fax: +44 (0)1438 767291
- via the web: **www.theiet.org/courses**

BRITISH STANDARD

BS 7671 : 2001

incorporating
Amendments
No 1 : 2002
and
No 2 : 2004

Requirements for Electrical Installations

IEE Wiring Regulations
Sixteenth Edition

Copies may be obtained from:
    The Institution of Engineering and Technology
    P.O. Box 96
    Stevenage
    SG1 2SD, UK
    Tel: +44 (0)1438 767328
    Email: sales@theiet.org

or BSI:

    BSI Customer Services
    389 Chiswick High Road
    London W4 4AL, UK
    Tel: +44 (0)20 8996 9001
    Email: orders@bsi-global.com

Published by: The Institution of Engineering and Technology, London, UK in agreement with BSI

 The Institution of Engineering and Technology is the new Institution formed by the joining together of the IEE (The Institution of Electrical Engineers) and the IIE (The Institution of Incorporated Engineers). The new Institution is the inheritor of the IEE brand and all its products and services, such as this one, which we hope you will find useful.

ISBN   (10-digit) 0 86341 373 0 (Paperback)
       (13-digit) 978 086341 373 5 (Paperback)

Printed in the United Kingdom by Page Bros, Norwich

CONTENTS

Foreword

This British Standard is published under the direction of the British Electrotechnical Committee (BEC) and The Institution of Engineering and Technology.

Following a full review, this standard replaced the 16th Edition of the IEE Wiring Regulations BS 7671 : 1992 as amended. Copyright is held jointly by The Institution of Engineering and Technology and BSI.

Technical authority for this standard is vested in the Joint IEE/BSI Technical Committee JPEL/64. This Joint Technical Committee, which is responsible for the work previously undertaken by the IEE Wiring Regulations Committee and the BSI Technical Committee PEL/64, meets the constitutional and operational requirements of both parent bodies. JPEL/64 has the responsibility for the contents of this British Standard under the joint authority of the Institution of Engineering and Technology and the BSI Standards Board.

All references in this text to the Wiring Regulations or the Regulation(s), where not otherwise specifically identified, shall be taken to refer to BS 7671 : 2001 (2004), Requirements for Electrical Installations.

Regulations changed owing to the issue of Amendments 1 and 2 are indicated by a side bar in the margin.

Introduction to BS 7671 : 2001

BS 7671 : 2001, Requirements for Electrical Installations was issued on 1 June 2001 and came into effect on 1 January 2002. Installations designed after 1 January 2002 are to comply with this edition.

BS 7671 : 2001 includes changes necessary to maintain technical alignment with CENELEC harmonization documents, including:
- an expanded Part 1: Scope, Object and Fundamental Principles
- Section 443: Protection against overvoltages of atmospheric origin or due to switching
- Section 482: Precautions where particular risks or dangers of fire exist
- amendments to Chapter 43, Chapter 46, Section 604 (Construction Site Installations) and Section 611 (Installation of Highway Power Supplies, Street Furniture and Street Located Equipment)

Changes of a national origin include:
- a revision of Section 607 (Earthing requirements for the installation of equipment having high protective conductor currents)

Introduction to Amendment No 1 : 2002 (AMD 13628)

Amendment No 1 : 2002 provides table ratings specifically for UK National Type insulated and sheathed flat twin cables with protective conductor (Table 4D5A). These ratings are generally greater than those ratings given in Table 4D2A.

Regulation 433-02-04 is amended to require the ratings of ring circuit cables to be not less than 20 A instead of 0.67 I_n.

Other, generally editorial, changes have been made.

This amendment comes into effect on 1st February 2002.

Introduction to Amendment No 2 : 2004 (AMD 14905)

Amendment No 2 : 2004 implements:
- the harmonized cable core colours and the alphanumeric marking of HD 308 S2: 2001 *Identification of cores in cables and flexible cords*, and BS EN 60446 : 2000 *Basic and safety principles for the man-machine interface, marking and identification. Identification of conductors by colours or numerals* and BS EN 60445 : 2000 *Basic and safety principles for man-machine interface, marking and identification of equipment terminals and of terminations;* a new Appendix 7 gives guidance on marking at the interface between old and harmonized marking, and
- changes necessitated by the Electricity Safety, Quality and Continuity Regulations 2002 generally of an editorial nature, although there is a prohibition on the use of TN-C systems other than for distribution systems.

The changes required by the Electricity Safety, Quality and Continuity Regulations 2002 being statutory requirements are for immediate implementation.

Installations commencing on site after 31st March 2006 are to comply with the marking requirements of Section 514 as amended, and as appropriate cores identified with the harmonized colours. Installations commencing on site after 31st March 2004 and before 1st April 2006 may be installed in accordance with Amendment No 2 : 2004 or Amendment No 1 : 2002, that is, they may use the harmonized colours or the old colours, but NOT both.

Editions

CONSTITUTION
as at December 2003

Eur Ing N C Friswell BSc(Eng) CEng FIEE (Chairman)

for IEE
J P Cutting CEng FIEE
P E Donnachie BSc CEng FIEE
Eur Ing J R Mackenzie BSc CEng DMS FIEE FIMgt
R Mellors-Bourne MA PhD
Eur Ing J Rickwood BSc(Eng) CEng FIEE
G G Willard DipEE CEng MIEE
W H Wright MA CEng FIEE

and
G B Lum BA(Hons) (Amalgamated Engineering & Electrical Union)
S A MacConnacher BSc CEng MIEE (Association of Manufacturers of Domestic Electrical Appliances)
S Archer MIDGTE (Association of Manufacturers of Power generating Systems)
C K Reed I Eng MIIE (British Cables Association)
A Cooper BSc CEng MIEE (BEAMA Installation Ltd)
Eur Ing M H Mullins BA CEng FIEE FIIE (BEAMA Installation Ltd)
S Willmore (BEAMA Installation Ltd)
P D Galbraith IEng MIIE MCM (British Electrotechnical & Allied Manufacturers Association Ltd)
R F B Lewington MIEE (British Electrotechnical & Allied Manufacturers Association Ltd)
P G Newbery BSc CEng MIEE (British Electrotechnical & Allied Manufacturers Association Ltd)
P D Stokes MA CEng MRAeS (British Electrotechnical Approvals Board)
M R Danvers (British Standards Institution)
I Cahill MA MIEE (British Telecommunications plc)
Eur Ing G Stokes BSc(Hons) CEng FIEE FCIBSE (Chartered Institution of Building Services Engineers)
H R Lovegrove IEng FIIE (City & Guilds of London Institute)
D Irwin BEng(Hons) (DC Power Users Forum)
B O'Connell BSc BA(Hons) MEng(Hons) CEng MIEE (Department of Health)
G Scott BEng ACGI MSc CEng MIEE (Department of Trade and Industry)
W R Berry IEng MIIE (Electrical Contractors' Association)
D Locke IEng MIIE ACIBSE (Electrical Contractors' Association)
D Millar IEng MIIE MILE (Electrical Contractors' Association of Scotland t/a SELECT)
D J Start BSc CEng MIEE (Electricity Association Limited)
R J Richman (Engineering Equipment & Materials Users' Association)
M W Coates BEng (ERA Technology Ltd)
F W Pearson CEng MIEE (Federation of the Electronics Industry)
K A Morriss BSc CEng MIEE (The GAMBICA Association Ltd)
Eur Ing J A McLean BSc CEng FIEE FIOSH (Health & Safety Executive)
I P Andrews (Heating, Ventilation and Air Conditioning Manufacturers' Association)
G P Bowles MIFire (HM Fire Service Inspectorate, ODPM)
P Tootill IEng MIIE (Institution of Incorporated Engineers)
G C T Pritchard BTech(Hons) IEng FILE (Institution of Lighting Engineers)
K R Kearney IEng MIIE (Lighting Association)
B Pratley (Lighting Industry Federation Ltd)
B Dunn BEng CEng MIEE (MOD)
J C McLuckie BSc(Eng) FIEE (NHS Scotland)
M C Clark BSc(Eng) MSc CEng FIEE FIMechE FCIBSE (National Inspection Council for Electrical Installation Contracting)
J Reed ARIBA (Royal Institute of British Architects)
E N King CEng FCIBSE (Office of the Deputy Prime Minister)
J Reed ARIBA (Royal Institute of British Architects)
P Wilson MIMechE (Safety Assessment Federation Limited)
C J Tanswell CEng MIEE MCIBSE (Society of Electrical and Mechanical Engineers serving Local Government)
J Pettifer BSc CEng MIEE FIQA (United Kingdom Accreditation Scheme)

Secretary
P R L Cook CEng FIEE MCIBSE

Preface

BS 7671, Requirements for Electrical Installations takes account of the technical substance of agreements reached in CENELEC. In particular, the technical intent of the following CENELEC Harmonization Documents are included:

CENELEC Harmonization Document reference			**BS 7671 reference**
HD 193	1982	Voltage bands	Part 1 and Definitions
HD 308 S2	2001	Identification of cores in cables and flexible cords	Part 5, Section 514
HD 384.1	2000	Scope, Object and Fundamental Principles	Part 1
HD 384.2	1986 (1997)	Definitions	Part 2
HD 384.3	1995	Assessment of general characteristics	Part 3
HD 384.4.41	1996	Protection against electric shock	Part 4, Chapter 41
HD 384.4.42	1985 (1992), (1994)	Protection against thermal effects	Part 4, Chapter 42
HD 384.4.43	1980 (1999)	Protection against overcurrent	Part 4, Chapter 43
HD 384.4.443	1999	Protection against overvoltages of atmospheric origin or due to switching	Part4, Section 443
HD 384.4.45	1989	Protection against undervoltage	Part 4, Chapter 45
HD 384.4.46	1999	Isolation and switching	Part 4, Chapter 46
HD 384.4.47	1988 (1995)	Application of measures for protection against electric shock	Part 4, Section 470
HD 384.4.473	1980	Application of measures for protection against overcurrent	Part 4, Section 473
HD 384.4.482	1997	Protection against fire where particular risks of danger exist	Part 4, Section 482
HD 384.5.51	1996	Selection and erection of equipment, common rules	Part 5, Chapter 51
HD 384.5.52	1995 (1998)	Wiring systems	Part 5, Chapter 52 and Appendix 4
HD 384. 5.523	1991	Wiring systems, current-carrying capacities	Part 5, Section 523 and Appendix 4
HD 384.5.537	1998	Switchgear and controlgear, devices for isolation and switching	Part 5, Section 537
HD 384.5.54	1988	Earthing arrangements and protective conductors	Part 5, Chapter 54
HD 384.5.551	1997	Other equipment, low voltage generating sets	Part 5, Section 551
HD 384.5.56	1985	Safety services	Part 5, Chapter 56
HD 384.6.61	1992	Initial verification	Part 7, Chapter 71
HD 384.7.702	1992	Special location - Swimming pools	Part 6, Section 602
HD 384.7.703	1991	Special location - Locations containing a hot air sauna heater	Part 6, Section 603
HD 384.7.704	1999	Construction and demolition site installations	Part 6, Section 604
HD 384.7.705	1991	Special location - Agricultural and horticultural premises	Part 6, Section 605
HD 384.7.706	1991	Special location - Restrictive conductive locations	Part 6, Section 606
HD 384.7.708	1992	Special location - Caravan parks and caravans	Part 6, Section 608
HD 384.7.714	1999	Outdoor lighting installations	Part 6, Section 611

The dates in brackets refer to the year of issue of amendments to the Harmonization Document (HD).

BS 7671 will continue to be amended from time to time to take account of the publication of new or amended CENELEC standards. The opportunity has been taken to revise Regulations that experience has shown require clarification or to allow for new technology and methods.

Reference is made throughout BS 7671 to publications of the British Standards Institution, both specifications and codes of practice. Appendix 1 lists these publications and gives their full titles whereas throughout BS 7671 they are referred to only by their numbers.

Where reference is made in BS 7671 to a British Standard which takes account of a CENELEC Harmonization Document or European Norm, it is understood that the reference also relates to any European national standard similarly derived from the CENELEC standard, although account needs to be taken of any national exemptions.

Note by the Health and Safety Executive

The Health and Safety Executive (HSE) welcomes the publication of BS 7671 : 2001 (2004), Requirements for Electrical Installations, IEE Wiring Regulations, 16th Edition. The IEE Wiring Regulations and BS 7671 have been extensively referred to in HSE guidance over the years. Installations which conform to the standards laid down in BS 7671 : 2001 (2004) are regarded by HSE as likely to achieve conformity with the relevant parts of the Electricity at Work Regulations 1989. Existing installations may have been designed and installed to conform to the standards set by earlier editions of the IEE Wiring Regulations or BS 7671. This does not mean that they will fail to achieve conformity with the relevant parts of the Electricity at Work Regulations 1989.

Notes on the plan of the 16th Edition

The edition is based on the plan agreed internationally for the arrangement of safety rules for electrical installations.

In the numbering system used, the first digit signifies a Part, the second digit a Chapter, the third digit a Section and the subsequent digits the Regulation number. For example, the Section number 413 is made up as follows:

> PART 4 – PROTECTION FOR SAFETY
> Chapter 41 (first chapter of Part 4) – Protection against electric shock.
> Section 413 (third section of Chapter 41) – Protection against indirect contact.

Part 1 sets out the scope, object and fundamental principles.

Part 2 defines the sense in which certain terms are used throughout the Regulations.

The subjects of the subsequent parts are as indicated below:

Part	Subject
3	Identification of the characteristics of the installation that will need to be taken into account in choosing and applying the requirements of the subsequent Parts. These characteristics may vary from one part of an installation to another and should be assessed for each location to be served by the installation.
4	Description of the basic measures that are available for the protection of persons, property and livestock, and against the hazards that may arise from the use of electricity.
5	Precautions to be taken in the selection and erection of the equipment of the installation.
6	Special installations or locations – particular requirements.
7	Inspection and testing.

The sequence of the plan should be followed in considering the application of any particular requirement of the Regulations. The general index provides a ready reference to particular regulations by subject, but in applying any one regulation the requirements of related regulations should be borne in mind. Cross references are provided, and the index is arranged to facilitate this.

In many cases, a group of associated regulations is covered by a side heading which is identified by a two-part number, e.g. 547-03. Throughout the Regulations where reference is made to such a two-part number, that reference is to be taken to include all the individual regulation numbers which are covered by that side heading and include that two-part number.

PART 1

SCOPE, OBJECT AND FUNDAMENTAL PRINCIPLES

CONTENTS

PART 1

SCOPE, OBJECT AND FUNDAMENTAL PRINCIPLES

CHAPTER 11

SCOPE

110-01   General

110-01-01   The Regulations apply to electrical installations such as those of:
  (i)   residential premises
 (ii)   commercial premises
 (iii)   public premises
 (iv)   industrial premises
  (v)   agricultural and horticultural premises
 (vi)   prefabricated buildings
 (vii)   caravans, caravan parks and similar sites
 (viii)   construction sites, exhibitions, fairs and other installations in temporary buildings
 (ix)   highway power supplies and street furniture, and outdoor lighting.

The Regulations include requirements for:
  (x)   circuits supplied at nominal voltages up to and including 1000 V a.c. or 1500 V d.c. For a.c., the preferred frequencies which are taken into account in this standard are 50 Hz, 60 Hz and 400 Hz. The use of other frequencies for special purposes is not excluded
 (xi)   circuits, other than the internal wiring of apparatus, operating at voltages exceeding 1000 V and derived from an installation having a voltage not exceeding 1000 V a.c., e.g. discharge lighting, electrostatic precipitators
 (xii)   any wiring systems and cables not specifically covered by an appliance standard
 (xiii)   all consumer installations external to buildings
 (xiv)   fixed wiring for communication and information technology, signalling, control and the like (excluding internal wiring of apparatus)
 (xv)   the addition to or alteration of installations and also parts of existing installations affected by the addition or alteration.

The Regulations are intended to be applied to electrical installations generally but, in certain cases, they may need to be supplemented by the requirements or recommendations of other British Standards or by the requirements of the person ordering the work.

Such cases include the following:

 (xvi)   electric signs and high voltage luminous discharge tube installations - BS 559
 (xvii)   emergency lighting - BS 5266
 (xviii)   electrical apparatus for explosive gas atmospheres - BS EN 60079 and BS EN 50014
 (xix)   electrical apparatus for use in the presence of combustible dust - BS EN 50281
 (xx)   fire detection and alarm systems in buildings - BS 5839
 (xxi)   installations subject to the Telecommunications Act 1984 - BS 6701 Part 1
 (xxii)   electric surface heating systems - BS 6351
 (xxiii)   electrical installations for open cast mines and quarries - BS 6907

110-02   Exclusions from scope

110-02-01   The Regulations do not apply to the following installations:

  (i)   'distributor's equipment' as defined in the Electricity Safety, Quality and Continuity Regulations 2002
 (ii)   railway traction equipment, rolling stock and signalling equipment
 (iii)   equipment of motor vehicles, except those to which the requirements of the Regulations concerning caravans are applicable
 (iv)   equipment on board ships
  (v)   equipment of mobile and fixed offshore installations
 (vi)   equipment of aircraft
 (vii)   those aspects of mines and quarries specifically covered by Statutory Regulations
 (viii)   radio interference suppression equipment, except so far as it affects safety of the electrical installation

(ix) lightning protection of buildings covered by BS 6651

 (x) those aspects of lift installations covered by BS 5655.

110-03   Equipment

110-03-01   The Regulations apply to items of electrical equipment only so far as selection and application of the equipment in the installation are concerned. The Regulations do not deal with requirements for the construction of assemblies of electrical equipment, which are required to comply with appropriate standards.

110-04   Relationship with Statutory Regulations

110-04-01   The Regulations are non-statutory regulations. They may, however, be used in a court of law in evidence to claim compliance with a statutory requirement. The relevant statutory provisions are listed in Appendix 2 and include Acts of Parliament and Regulations made thereunder. In some cases Regulations may be accompanied by Codes of Practice approved under Section 16 of the Health and Safety at Work etc. Act 1974. The legal status of these Codes is explained in Section 17 of the 1974 Act.

For a supply given in accordance with the Electricity Safety, Quality and Continuity Regulations 2002, it shall be deemed that the connection with earth of the neutral of the supply is permanent. Outside Great Britain, confirmation shall be sought from the distributor that the supply conforms to requirements corresponding to those of the Electricity Safety, Quality and Continuity Regulations 2002, in this respect.

110-05   Installations in premises subject to licensing

110-05-01   For installations in premises over which a licensing or other authority exercises a statutory control, the requirements of that authority shall be ascertained and complied with in the design and execution of the installation.

CHAPTER 12

OBJECT AND EFFECTS

120-01   General

120-01-01   This standard contains the rules for the design and erection of electrical installations so as to provide for safety and proper functioning for the intended use.

120-01-02   Chapter 13 of this standard states the fundamental principles. It does not include detailed technical requirements which may be subject to modifications because of technical developments.

120-01-03   This standard sets out technical requirements intended to ensure that electrical installations conform to the fundamental principles of Chapter 13, as follows:

     Part 3   Assessment of general characteristics

     Part 4   Protection for safety

     Part 5   Selection and erection of equipment

     Part 6   Special installations or locations

     Part 7   Inspection and testing

Any intended departure from these Parts requires special consideration by the designer of the installation and shall be noted on the Electrical Installation Certificate specified in Part 7.

120-02   New materials and inventions

120-02-01   Where the use of a new material or invention leads to departures from the Regulations, the resulting degree of safety of the installation is to be not less than that obtained by compliance with the Regulations. Such use is to be noted on the Electrical Installation Certificate specified in Part 7.

CHAPTER 13

FUNDAMENTAL PRINCIPLES

130   PROTECTION FOR SAFETY

130-01   General

130-01-01   The requirements of this section are intended to provide for the safety of persons, livestock and property against dangers and damage which may arise in the reasonable use of electrical installations.

In electrical installations, risk of injury may result from:

   (i)   shock currents

   (ii)   excessive temperatures likely to cause burns, fires and other injurious effects

   (iii)   mechanical movement of electrically actuated equipment, in so far as such injury is intended to be prevented by electrical emergency switching or by electrical switching for mechanical maintenance of non-electrical parts of such equipment

   (iv)   explosion.

130-02   Protection against electric shock

Protection against direct contact (normal conditions)

130-02-01   Persons and livestock shall be protected so far as is reasonably practicable against dangers that may arise from contact with live parts of the installation.

This protection can be achieved by one of the following methods.

   (i)   preventing a current from passing through the body of any person or any livestock

   (ii)   limiting the current which can pass through a body to a value lower than the shock current.

Protection against indirect contact (under single fault conditions)

130-02-02   Persons and livestock shall be protected against dangers that may arise from contact with exposed-conductive-parts during a fault.

This protection can be achieved by one of the following methods:

   (i)   preventing current passing through the body of any person or any livestock

   (ii)   limiting the fault current which can pass through a body to a value lower than the shock current

   (iii)   automatic disconnection of the supply in a determined time on the occurrence of a fault likely to cause a current to flow through a body in contact with exposed-conductive-parts, where the value of that current is equal to or greater than the shock current.

In connection with the protection against indirect contact, the application of the method of equipotential bonding is one of the important principles for safety.

130-03   Protection against thermal effects

130-03-01   So far as is reasonably practicable the electrical installation shall be so arranged that the risk of ignition of flammable materials due to high temperature or electric arc is reduced. In addition, during normal operation of the electrical equipment, the risk of burns to persons or livestock shall be reduced so far as is reasonably practicable.

130-03-02   Persons, fixed equipment and fixed materials adjacent to electrical equipment shall be protected against harmful effects of heat or thermal radiation emitted by electrical equipment, particularly the following consequences:

   (i)   combustion, ignition, or degradation of materials

   (ii)   risk of burns

   (iii)   impairment of the safe function of installed equipment.

Electrical equipment shall not present a fire hazard to adjacent materials.

130-04   Protection against overcurrent

130-04-01 So far as is reasonably practicable, persons or livestock shall be protected against injury and property shall be protected against damage due to excessive temperatures or electromechanical stresses caused by any overcurrents likely to arise in live conductors.

130-05   Protection against fault current

130-05-01 Conductors, and any other parts likely to carry a fault current, shall be capable of carrying that current without attaining an excessive temperature.

For live conductors, compliance with Regulation 130-04 assures their protection against overcurrents caused by faults.

130-06   Protection against overvoltage

130-06-01 So far as is reasonably practicable, persons or livestock shall be protected against injury and property shall be protected against any harmful effects as a consequence of a fault between live parts of circuits supplied at different voltages.

130-06-02 So far as is reasonably practicable, persons, livestock and property shall be protected against the consequence of overvoltages likely to arise due to atmospheric phenomena and switching.

130-07   Additions and alterations to an installation

130-07-01 No addition or alteration, temporary or permanent, shall be made to an existing installation, unless it has been ascertained that the rating and the condition of any existing equipment, including that of the distributor, which will have to carry any additional load is adequate for the altered circumstances and the earthing and bonding arrangements are also adequate.

131   DESIGN

131-01   General

131-01-01 The electrical installation shall be designed to provide for:

(i)   the protection of persons, livestock and property in accordance with Section 130

(ii) the proper functioning of the electrical installation for the intended use.

The information required as a basis for design is listed in Regulations 131-02 to 131-05. The requirements with which the design shall comply are stated in Regulations 131-06 to 131-14.

131-02   Characteristics of available supply or supplies

131-02-01 Information on the characteristics of the available supply or supplies as below shall be determined by calculation, measurement, enquiry, or inspection:

(i)   Nature of current: a.c. and/or d.c.

(ii) Purpose and number of conductors:

    – for a.c.   phase conductor(s)

                     neutral conductor

                     protective conductor

                     PEN conductor

    – for d.c.   conductors equivalent to those listed above (outer/middle/earthed live conductors, protective conductor, PEN conductor)

(iii) Values and tolerances:

    – nominal voltage and voltage tolerances

    – nominal frequency and frequency tolerances

    – maximum current allowable

    – prospective short-circuit current

    – earth fault loop impedance

(iv)   Protective measures inherent in the supply, e.g. earthed neutral or mid-wire

(v)   Particular requirements of the distributor.

131-03   Nature of demand

131-03-01   The number and type of circuits required for lighting, heating, power, control, signalling, communication and information technology, etc shall be determined from knowledge of:

(i)   location of points of power demand

(ii)   loads to be expected on the various circuits

(iii)   daily and yearly variation of demand

(iv)   any special conditions

(v)   requirements for control, signalling, communication and information technology, etc.

131-04   Emergency supply or supplies for safety services

131-04-01   Where a supply for safety services is specified the following shall be determined:

(i)   characteristics of the supply

(ii)   circuits to be supplied by the safety source.

131-05   Environmental conditions

131-05-01   Equipment likely to be exposed to weather, corrosive atmospheres or other adverse conditions, shall be so constructed or protected as may be necessary to prevent danger arising from such exposure.

131-05-02   Equipment in surroundings susceptible to risk of fire or explosion shall be so constructed or protected and such other special precautions shall be taken to prevent, so far as is reasonably practicable, danger.

131-06   Cross-sectional area of conductors

131-06-01   The cross-sectional area of conductors shall be determined according to:

(i)   the admissible maximum temperature

(ii)   the voltage drop limit

(iii)   the electromechanical stresses likely to occur due to short-circuit and earth fault currents

(iv)   other mechanical stresses to which conductors are likely to be exposed

(v)   the maximum impedance for operation of short-circuit and earth fault protection.

131-07   Type of wiring and method of installation

131-07-01   The choice of the type of wiring system and the method of installation shall include consideration of the following:

(i)   the nature of the location

(ii)   the nature of the structure supporting the wiring

(iii)   accessibility of wiring to persons and livestock

(iv)   voltage

(v)   the electromechanical stresses likely to occur due to short-circuit and earth fault currents

(vi)   other stresses (e.g. mechanical, thermal and those associated with fire) to which the wiring is likely to be exposed during the erection of the electrical installation or in service.

131-08   Protective equipment

131-08-01   The characteristics of protective equipment shall be determined with respect to their function including protection against the effects of:

(i)   overcurrent (overload, short-circuit)

(ii)   earth fault current

(iii)   overvoltage

(iv)   undervoltage and no-voltage.

The protective devices shall operate at values of current, voltage and time which are suitably related to the characteristics of the circuits and to the possibilities of danger.

131-09   Emergency control

131-09-01   Where in case of danger there is necessity for immediate interruption of supply, an interrupting device shall be installed in such a way that it can be easily recognised and effectively and rapidly operated.

131-10   Disconnecting devices

131-10-01   Disconnecting devices shall be provided so as to permit disconnection of the electrical installation, circuits or individual items of apparatus as required for maintenance, testing, fault detection and repair.

131-11   Prevention of mutual detrimental influence

131-11-01   The electrical installation shall be arranged in such a way that no mutual detrimental influence will occur between different electrical installations and non-electrical installations of the building. Electromagnetic interference shall be taken into account.

131-12   Accessibility of electrical equipment

131-12-01   Electrical equipment shall be arranged so as to afford as may be necessary:

  (i)   sufficient space for the initial installation and later replacement of individual items

  (ii)   accessibility for operation, inspection, testing, maintenance and repair.

131-13   Protective devices and switches

131-13-01   A single-pole fuse, switch or circuit-breaker shall be inserted in the phase conductor only.

131-13-02   No switch or circuit-breaker, except where linked, or fuse shall be inserted in an earthed neutral conductor and any linked switch or linked circuit-breaker inserted in an earthed neutral conductor shall be arranged to break all the related phase conductors.

131-14   Isolation and switching

131-14-01   Effective means, suitably placed for ready operation, shall be provided so that all voltage may be cut off from every installation, from every circuit thereof and from all equipment, as may be necessary to prevent or remove danger.

131-14-02   Every fixed electric motor shall be provided with an efficient means of switching off, readily accessible, easily operated and so placed as to prevent danger.

132   SELECTION OF ELECTRICAL EQUIPMENT

132-01   General

132-01-01   Every item of equipment shall comply with the appropriate EN or HD or National Standard implementing the HD. In the absence of an EN or HD, the equipment shall comply with the appropriate National Standard. In all other cases, reference shall be made to the appropriate IEC Standard or to an appropriate National Standard of another country.

132-01-02   Where there is no applicable standard, the item of equipment concerned shall be selected by special agreement between the person specifying the installation and the installer.

Voltage

132-01-03   The rated voltage of electrical equipment shall be suitable for the nominal voltage. Such equipment shall be suitable for the overvoltage category envisaged. For certain equipment as appropriate the lowest voltage likely to occur shall be taken into account.

Current

132-01-04   Electrical equipment shall be selected with respect to the maximum steady current (rms value for a.c.) which it has to carry in normal service, and with respect to the current likely to be carried in abnormal conditions and the period (e.g. operating time of protective devices if any) during which it may be expected to flow.

Frequency

132-01-05 Equipment shall be suitable for the frequencies likely to occur in the circuit.

Power

132-01-06 Electrical equipment which is selected on the basis of its power characteristics shall be suitable for the duty demanded of the equipment, taking into account the load factor and the normal service conditions.

Conditions of installation

132-01-07 Electrical equipment shall be selected so as to withstand safely the stresses, the environmental conditions (see Regulation 131-05) and the characteristics of its location. An item of equipment which does not by design have the properties corresponding to its location may be used where additional protection is provided.

Prevention of harmful effects

132-01-08 Electrical equipment shall be selected so that it will not cause, so far as is reasonably practicable, harmful effects on other equipment or impair the supply during normal service including switching operations.

133   ERECTION, VERIFICATION, AND PERIODIC INSPECTION AND TESTING OF ELECTRICAL INSTALLATIONS

133-01   Erection

133-01-01 Good workmanship and proper materials shall be used.

133-01-02 The characteristics of the electrical equipment, as determined in accordance with Section 132, shall not be impaired by the process of erection.

133-01-03 Conductors shall be identified in accordance Section 514.

133-01-04 Every electrical joint and connection shall be of proper construction as regards conductance, insulation, mechanical strength and protection.

133-01-05 Electrical equipment shall be installed in such a manner that the design temperatures are not exceeded.

133-01-06 Electrical equipment likely to cause high temperatures or electric arcs shall be placed or guarded so as to minimise the risk of ignition of flammable materials.

Where the temperature of an exposed part of electrical equipment is likely to cause injury to persons or livestock that part shall be so located or guarded as to prevent accidental contact therewith.

133-02   Verification

133-02-01 On completion of an installation or an addition or alteration to an installation, appropriate inspection and testing shall be carried out to verify so far as is reasonably practicable that the requirements of this standard have been met.

133-03   Periodic inspection and testing

133-03-01 The person carrying out inspection and testing shall make a recommendation for subsequent periodic inspection and testing as detailed in Chapter 73.

PART 2

DEFINITIONS

For the purposes of the Regulations, the following definitions shall apply. Some of these definitions are aligned with those given in BS 4727 - 'Glossary of electrotechnical, power, telecommunication, electronics, lighting and colour terms'. Other terms not defined herein are used in the sense defined in BS 4727.

Accessory. A device, other than current-using equipment, associated with such equipment or with the wiring of an installation.

Ambient temperature. The temperature of the air or other medium where the equipment is to be used.

Appliance. An item of current-using equipment other than a luminaire or an independent motor.

Arm's reach. A zone of accessibility to touch, extending from any point on a surface where persons usually stand or move about to the limits which a person can reach with a hand in any direction without assistance.

This zone of accessibility is illustrated by figure 1 in which the values refer to bare hands without any assistance, e.g. from tools or a ladder.

fig 1 **Arm's reach**

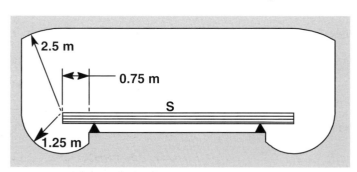 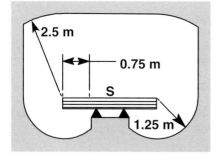

S = surface expected to be occupied by persons

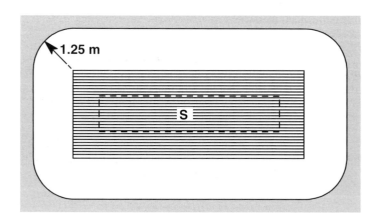 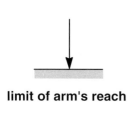

limit of arm's reach

Barrier. A part providing a defined degree of protection against contact with live parts from any usual direction of access.

Basic insulation. Insulation applied to live parts to provide basic protection against electric shock and which does not necessarily include insulation used exclusively for functional purposes.

Bonding conductor. A protective conductor providing equipotential bonding.

Building void, accessible. A space within the structure or the components of a building accessible only at certain points. Such voids include the space within partitions, suspended floors, ceilings and certain types of window frame, door frame and architrave.

Building void, non-accessible. A space within the structure or the components of a building which has no ready means of access.

Bunched. Cables are said to be bunched when two or more are contained within a single conduit, duct, ducting, or trunking or, if not enclosed, are not separated from each other by a specified distance.

Cable bracket. A horizontal cable support system, consisting of elements fixed at one end only, spaced at intervals along the length of the cable and on which the cable rests.

Cable channel. An enclosure situated above or in the ground, ventilated or closed, and having dimensions which do not permit the access of persons but allow access to the conduits and/or cables throughout their length during and after installation. A cable channel may or may not form part of the building construction.

Cable cleat. A component of a support system, which consists of elements spaced at intervals along the length of the cable or conduit and which mechanically retains the cable or conduit.

Cable coupler. A means of enabling the connection or disconnection, at will, of two flexible cables. It consists of a connector and a plug.

Cable ducting. An enclosure of metal or insulating material, other than conduit or cable trunking, intended for the protection of cables which are drawn in after erection of the ducting.

Cable ladder. A cable support consisting of a series of transverse supporting elements rigidly fixed to main longitudinal supporting members.

Cable tray. A cable support consisting of a continuous base with raised edges and no covering. A cable tray may or may not be perforated.

Cable trunking. A closed enclosure normally of rectangular cross-section, of which one side is removable or hinged, used for the protection of cables and for the accommodation of other electrical equipment.

Cable tunnel. A corridor containing supporting structures for cables and joints and/or other elements of wiring systems and whose dimensions allow persons to pass freely throughout the entire length.

Caravan. A trailer leisure accommodation vehicle, used for touring, designed to meet the requirements for the construction and use of road vehicles (see also definition of Motor caravan and Leisure accommodation vehicle).

Caravan park. An area of land which contains two or more caravan pitches.

Caravan pitch. A plot of ground upon which a single leisure accommodation vehicle or leisure home may stand.

Caravan pitch electrical supply equipment. Equipment which provides means of connecting and disconnecting supply cables from a leisure accommodation vehicle to a fixed external power supply.

Cartridge fuse link. A device comprising a fuse element or several fuse elements connected in parallel enclosed in a cartridge usually filled with arc-extinguishing medium and connected to terminations (see fuse link).

Circuit. An assembly of electrical equipment supplied from the same origin and protected against overcurrent by the same protective device(s).

Circuit-breaker. A device capable of making, carrying and breaking normal load currents and also making and automatically breaking, under pre-determined conditions, abnormal currents such as short-circuit currents. It is usually required to operate infrequently although some types are suitable for frequent operation.

Circuit-breaker, linked. A circuit-breaker the contacts of which are so arranged as to make or break all poles simultaneously or in a definite sequence.

Circuit protective conductor (cpc). A protective conductor connecting exposed-conductive-parts of equipment to the main earthing terminal.

Class I equipment. Equipment in which protection against electric shock does not rely on basic insulation only, but which includes means for the connection of exposed-conductive-parts to a protective conductor in the fixed wiring of the installation (see BS 2754).

Class II equipment. Equipment in which protection against electric shock does not rely on basic insulation only, but in which additional safety precautions such as supplementary insulation are provided, there being no provision for the connection of exposed metalwork of the equipment to a protective conductor, and no reliance upon precautions to be taken in the fixed wiring of the installation (see BS 2754).

Class III equipment. Equipment in which protection against electric shock relies on supply at SELV and in which voltages higher than those of SELV are not generated (see BS 2754).

Conduit. A part of a closed wiring system for cables in electrical installations, allowing them to be drawn in and/or replaced, but not inserted laterally.

Connector. The part of a cable coupler or of an appliance coupler which is provided with female contacts and is intended to be attached to the end of the flexible cable remote from the supply.

Consumer unit (may also be known as a consumer control unit or electricity control unit). A particular type of distribution board comprising a co-ordinated assembly for the control and distribution of electrical energy, principally in domestic premises, incorporating manual means of double-pole isolation on the incoming circuit(s) and an assembly of one or more fuses, circuit-breakers, residual current operated devices or signalling and other devices purposely manufactured for such use.

Current-carrying capacity of a conductor. The maximum current which can be carried by a conductor under specified conditions without its steady state temperature exceeding a specified value.

Current-using equipment. Equipment which converts electrical energy into another form of energy, such as light, heat or motive power.

Danger. Risk of injury to persons (and livestock where expected to be present) from:
   (i) fire, electric shock and burns arising from the use of electrical energy, and
   (ii) mechanical movement of electrically controlled equipment, in so far as such danger is intended to be prevented by electrical emergency switching or by electrical switching for mechanical maintenance of non-electrical parts of such equipment.

Data processing equipment. Electrically operated machine units which, separately or assembled in systems, accumulate, process and store data. Acceptance and divulgence of data may or may not be by electronic means.

Design current (of a circuit). The magnitude of the current (rms value for a.c.) to be carried by the circuit in normal service.

Direct contact. Contact of persons or livestock with live parts.

Disconnector. A mechanical switching device which, in the open position, complies with the requirements specified for isolation. A disconnector is otherwise known as an isolator.

Distribution board. An assembly containing switching or protective devices (e.g. fuses, circuit-breakers, residual current operated devices) associated with one or more outgoing circuits fed from one or more incoming circuits, together with terminals for the neutral and protective circuit conductors. It may also include signalling and other control devices. Means of isolation may be included in the board or may be provided separately.

Distribution circuit. A band II circuit connecting the origin of the installation to:
   (i) an item of switchgear, or
   (ii) an item of controlgear, or
   (iii) a distribution board
to which one or more final circuits or items of current-using equipment are connected (see also definition of Final circuit).

A distribution circuit may also connect the origin of an installation to an outlying building or separate installation, when it is sometimes called a sub-main.

Distributor. A person who distributes electricity to consumers using electrical lines and equipment that he owns or operates.

Double insulation. Insulation comprising both basic insulation and supplementary insulation.

Duct. A closed passageway formed underground or in a structure and intended to receive one or more cables which may be drawn in.

Ducting (see Cable ducting).

Earth. The conductive mass of the Earth, whose electric potential at any point is conventionally taken as zero.

Earth electrode. A conductor or group of conductors in intimate contact with, and providing an electrical connection to, Earth.

Earth electrode resistance. The resistance of an earth electrode to Earth.

Earth fault current. A fault current which flows to Earth.

Earth fault loop impedance. The impedance of the earth fault current loop starting and ending at the point of earth fault. This impedance is denoted by the symbol Z_s.

The earth fault loop comprises the following, starting at the point of fault:
- the circuit protective conductor, and
- the consumer's earthing terminal and earthing conductor, and
- for TN systems, the metallic return path, and
- for TT and IT systems, the earth return path, and
- the path through the earthed neutral point of the transformer, and
- the transformer winding, and
- the phase conductor from the transformer to the point of fault.

Earth leakage current. *Deleted by BS 7671 : 2001 (see Protective conductor current).*

Earthed concentric wiring. A wiring system in which one or more insulated conductors are completely surrounded throughout their length by a conductor, for example a metallic sheath, which acts as a PEN conductor.

Earthed equipotential zone. A zone within which exposed-conductive-parts and extraneous-conductive-parts are maintained at substantially the same potential by bonding, such that, under fault conditions, the differences in potential between simultaneously accessible exposed- and extraneous-conductive-parts will not cause electric shock.

Earthing. Connection of the exposed-conductive-parts of an installation to the main earthing terminal of that installation.

Earthing conductor. A protective conductor connecting the main earthing terminal of an installation to an earth electrode or to other means of earthing.

Electric shock. A dangerous physiological effect resulting from the passing of an electric current through a human body or livestock.

Electrical equipment (abbr: *Equipment*). Any item for such purposes as generation, conversion, transmission, distribution or utilisation of electrical energy, such as machines, transformers, apparatus, measuring instruments, protective devices, wiring systems, accessories, appliances and luminaires.

Electrical installation (abbr: *Installation*). An assembly of associated electrical equipment supplied from a common origin to fulfil a specific purpose and having certain co-ordinated characteristics.

Electrically independent earth electrodes. Earth electrodes located at such a distance from one another that the maximum current likely to flow through one of them does not significantly affect the potential of the other(s).

Electrode boiler (or electrode water heater). Equipment for the electrical heating of water or electrolyte by the passage of an electric current between electrodes immersed in the water or electrolyte.

Emergency stopping. Emergency switching intended to stop an operation.

Emergency switching. An operation intended to remove, as quickly as possible, danger, which may have occurred unexpectedly.

Enclosure. A part providing protection of equipment against certain external influences and in any direction protection against direct contact.

Equipment *(see Electrical equipment).*

Equipotential bonding. Electrical connection maintaining various exposed-conductive-parts and extraneous-conductive-parts at substantially the same potential.

Equipotential zone *(see Earthed equipotential zone).*

Exposed-conductive-part. A conductive part of equipment which can be touched and which is not a live part but which may become live under fault conditions.

External influence. Any influence external to an electrical installation which affects the design and safe operation of that installation.

Extra-low voltage *(see Voltage, nominal).*

Extraneous-conductive-part. A conductive part liable to introduce a potential, generally earth potential, and not forming part of the electrical installation.

Fault. A circuit condition in which current flows through an abnormal or unintended path. This may result from an insulation failure or a bridging of insulation. Conventionally the impedance between live conductors or between live conductors and exposed- or extraneous-conductive-parts at the fault position is considered negligible.

Fault current. A current resulting from a fault.

Final circuit. A circuit connected directly to current-using equipment, or to a socket-outlet or socket-outlets or other outlet points for the connection of such equipment.

Fixed equipment. Equipment designed to be fastened to a support or otherwise secured in a specific location.

Flexible cable. A cable whose structure and materials make it suitable to be flexed while in service.

Flexible cord. A flexible cable in which the cross-sectional area of each conductor does not exceed 4 mm^2.

Flexible wiring system. A wiring system designed to provide mechanical flexibility in use without degradation of the electrical components.

Functional earthing. Connection to Earth necessary for proper functioning of electrical equipment.

Functional extra-low voltage (FELV). An extra-low voltage system in which not all of the protective measures required for SELV or PELV have been applied.

Functional switching. An operation intended to switch 'on' or 'off' or vary the supply of electrical energy to all or part of an installation for normal operating purposes.

Fuse. A device which by the melting of one or more of its specially designed and proportioned components, opens the circuit in which it is inserted by breaking the current when this exceeds a given value for a sufficient time. The fuse comprises all the parts that form the complete device.

Fuse carrier. The movable part of a fuse designed to carry a fuse link.

Fuse element. A part of a fuse designed to melt when the fuse operates.

Fuse link. A part of a fuse, including the fuse element(s), which requires replacement by a new or renewable fuse link after the fuse has operated and before the fuse is put back into service.

Gas installation pipe. Any pipe, not being a service pipe (other than any part of a service pipe comprised in a primary meter installation) or a pipe comprised in a gas appliance, for conveying gas for a particular consumer and including any associated valve or other gas fitting.

Harmonized Standard. A standard which has been drawn up by common agreement between national standards bodies notified to the European Commission by all member states and published under national procedures.

Hazardous-live-part. *Deleted by BS 7671 : 2001*

Highway. A highway means any way (other than a waterway) over which there is public passage and includes the highway verge and any bridge over which, or tunnel through which, the highway passes.

Highway distribution board. A fixed structure or underground chamber, located on a highway, used as a distribution point, for connecting more than one highway distribution circuit to a common origin. Street furniture which supplies more than one circuit is defined as a highway distribution board. The connection of a single temporary load to an item of street furniture shall not in itself make that item of street furniture into a highway distribution board.

Highway distribution circuit. A band II circuit connecting the origin of the installation to a remote highway distribution board or items of street furniture. It may also connect a highway distribution board to street furniture.

Highway power supply. An electrical installation comprising an assembly of associated highway distribution circuits, highway distribution boards and street furniture, supplied from a common origin.

Hot air sauna. A room or location in which air is heated, in service, to high temperatures where the relative humidity is normally low, rising only for a short period of time when water is poured over the heater.

Indirect contact. Contact of persons or livestock with exposed-conductive-parts which have become live under fault conditions.

Installation *(see Electrical installation).*

Instructed person. A person adequately advised or supervised by skilled persons to enable him/her to avoid dangers which electricity may create.

Insulation. Suitable non-conductive material enclosing, surrounding or supporting a conductor.

Isolation. A function intended to cut off for reasons of safety the supply from all, or a discrete section, of the installation by separating the installation or section from every source of electrical energy.

Isolator. A mechanical switching device which, in the open position, complies with the requirements specified for isolation. An isolator is otherwise known as a disconnector.

Ladder *(see Cable ladder).*

Leakage current. Electric current in an unwanted conductive path under normal operating conditions.

Leisure accommodation vehicle. Unit of living accommodation for temporary or seasonal occupation which may meet requirements for construction and use of road vehicles.

Live part. A conductor or conductive part intended to be energised in normal use, including a neutral conductor but, by convention, not a PEN conductor.

Low noise earth. An earth connection in which the level of conducted or induced interference from external sources does not produce an unacceptable incidence of malfunction in the data processing or similar equipment to which it is connected. The susceptibility in terms of amplitude/frequency characteristics varies depending on the type of equipment.

Low voltage *(see Voltage, nominal).*

Luminaire. Equipment which distributes, filters or transforms the light from one or more lamps, and which includes any parts necessary for supporting, fixing and protecting the lamps, but not the lamps themselves, and, where necessary, circuit auxiliaries together with the means for connecting them to the supply. For the purposes of the Regulations a lampholder, however supported, is deemed to be a luminaire.

Luminaire supporting coupler (LSC). A means, comprising an LSC outlet and an LSC plug, providing mechanical support for a luminaire and the electrical connection to and disconnection from a fixed wiring installation

LV switchgear and controlgear assembly. A combination of one or more low voltage switching devices together with associated control, measuring, signalling, protective, regulating equipment, etc., completely assembled under the responsibility of the manufacturer with all the internal electrical and mechanical interconnection and structural parts. The components of the assembly may be electromechanical or electronic. The assembly may be either type-tested or partially type-tested (see BS EN 60439-1).

Main earthing terminal. The terminal or bar provided for the connection of protective conductors, including equipotential bonding conductors, and conductors for functional earthing, if any, to the means of earthing.

Mechanical maintenance. The replacement, refurbishment or cleaning of lamps and non-electrical parts of equipment, plant and machinery.

Mobile and offshore installations. Installations used for the exploration or development of liquid or gaseous hydrocarbon resources.

Mobile home. A transportable leisure accommodation vehicle which includes means for mobility but does not meet the requirements for construction and use of road vehicles.

Motor caravan. Self-propelled leisure accommodation vehicle, used for touring, designed to meet requirements for the construction and use of road vehicles. The accommodation may be fixed or demountable (see also definition of Caravan).

Neutral conductor. A conductor connected to the neutral point of a system and contributing to the transmission of electrical energy. The term also means the equivalent conductor of an IT or d.c. system unless otherwise specified in the Regulations and also identifies either the mid-wire of a three-wire d.c. circuit or the earthed conductor of a two-wire earthed d.c. circuit.

Nominal voltage *(see Voltage, nominal).*

Obstacle. A part preventing unintentional contact with live parts but not preventing deliberate contact.

Ordinary person. A person who is neither a skilled person nor an instructed person.

Origin of an installation. The position at which electrical energy is delivered to an electrical installation.

Overcurrent. A current exceeding the rated value . For conductors the rated value is the current-carrying capacity.

Overcurrent detection. A method of establishing that the value of current in a circuit exceeds a predetermined value for a specified length of time.

Overload current. An overcurrent occurring in a circuit which is electrically sound.

PELV (protective extra-low voltage). An extra-low voltage system which is not electrically separated from earth, but which otherwise satisfies all the requirements for SELV.

PEN conductor. A conductor combining the functions of both protective conductor and neutral conductor.

Phase conductor. A conductor of an a.c. system for the transmission of electrical energy other than a neutral conductor, a protective conductor or a PEN conductor. The term also means the equivalent conductor of a d.c. system unless otherwise specified in the Regulations.

Plug. A device, provided with contact pins, which is intended to be attached to a flexible cable, and which can be engaged with a socket-outlet or with a connector.

Point (in wiring). A termination of the fixed wiring intended for the connection of current-using equipment.

Portable equipment. Electrical equipment which is moved while in operation or which can easily be moved from one place to another while connected to the supply.

Prospective fault current. The value of overcurrent at a given point in a circuit resulting from a fault of negligible impedance between live conductors having a difference of potential under normal operating conditions, or between a live conductor and an exposed-conductive-part.

Protective conductor. A conductor used for some measures of protection against electric shock and intended for connecting together any of the following parts:

  (i)   exposed-conductive-parts

  (ii)   extraneous-conductive-parts

  (iii) the main earthing terminal

  (iv)   earth electrode(s)

  (v)   the earthed point of the source, or an artificial neutral.

Protective conductor current. Electric current which flows in a protective conductor under normal operating conditions.

Protective multiple earthing (PME). An earthing arrangement, found in TN-C-S systems, in which the supply neutral conductor is used to connect the earthing conductor of an installation with Earth, in accordance with the Electricity Safety, Quality and Continuity Regulations 2002 (see also figure 5).

Reduced low voltage system. A system in which the nominal phase to phase voltage does not exceed 110 volts and the nominal phase to earth voltage does not exceed 63.5 volts.

Reinforced insulation. Single insulation applied to live parts, which provides a degree of protection against electric shock equivalent to double insulation under the conditions specified in the relevant standard. The term 'single insulation' does not imply that the insulation must be one homogeneous piece. It may comprise several layers which cannot be tested singly as supplementary or basic insulation.

Residual current. Algebraic sum of the currents in the live conductors of a circuit at a point in the electrical installation.

Residual current device. A mechanical switching device or association of devices intended to cause the opening of the contacts when the residual current attains a given value under specified conditions.

Residual operating current. Residual current which causes the residual current device to operate under specified conditions.

fig 2 ILLUSTRATION OF EARTHING AND PROTECTIVE CONDUCTOR TERMS

(see Chapter 54)

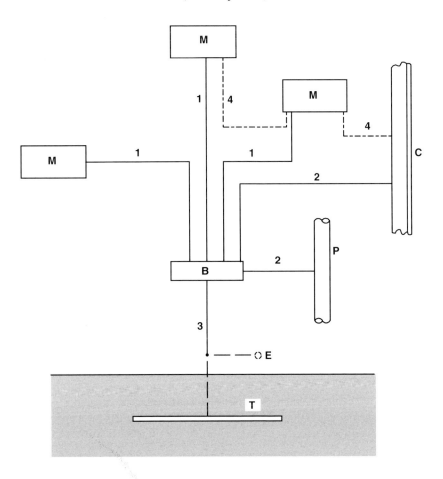

1,2,3,4,	=	protective conductors
1	=	circuit protective conductor
2	=	main equipotential bonding conductor
3	=	earthing conductor
4	=	supplementary equipotential bonding conductors (where required)
B	=	main earthing terminal
M	=	exposed-conductive-part
C	=	extraneous-conductive-part
P	=	main metallic water pipe (extraneous-conductive-part)
T	=	earth electrode (TT and IT systems)
E	=	other means of earthing (TN systems)

Resistance area (for an earth electrode only). The surface area of ground (around an earth electrode) on which a significant voltage gradient may exist.

Restrictive conductive location. A location comprised mainly of metallic or conductive surrounding parts, within which it is likely that a person will come into contact through a substantial portion of their body with the conductive surrounding parts and where the possibility of preventing this contact is limited.

Ring final circuit. A final circuit arranged in the form of a ring and connected to a single point of supply.

Safety service. An electrical system for electrical equipment provided to protect or warn persons in the event of a hazard, or essential to their evacuation from a location.

SELV (separated extra-low voltage). An extra-low voltage system which is electrically separated from Earth and from other systems in such a way that a single fault cannot give rise to the risk of electric shock.

Shock *(see Electric shock).*

Shock current. A current passing through the body of a person or livestock such as to cause electric shock and having characteristics likely to cause dangerous effects.

Short-circuit current. An overcurrent resulting from a fault of negligible impedance between live conductors having a difference in potential under normal operating conditions.

Simultaneously accessible parts. Conductors or conductive parts which can be touched simultaneously by a person or, in locations specifically intended for them, by livestock.

Simultaneously accessible parts may be: live parts, exposed-conductive-parts, extraneous-conductive-parts, protective conductors or earth electrodes.

Skilled person. A person with technical knowledge or sufficient experience to enable him/her to avoid dangers which electricity may create.

Socket-outlet. A device, provided with female contacts, which is intended to be installed with the fixed wiring, and intended to receive a plug. A luminaire track system is not regarded as a socket-outlet system.

Spur. A branch from a ring final circuit.

Stationary equipment. Electrical equipment which is either fixed, or equipment having a mass exceeding 18 kg and not provided with a carrying handle.

Street furniture. Fixed equipment, located on a highway, the purpose of which is directly associated with the use of the highway.

Street located equipment. Fixed equipment, located on a highway, the purpose of which is not directly associated with the use of the highway.

Supplementary insulation. Independent insulation applied in addition to basic insulation in order to provide protection against electric shock in the event of a failure of basic insulation.

Supplier. *Deleted by BS 7671 : 2001, Amendment No 2, 2004. (see Distributor)*

Supplier's works. *Deleted by BS 7671 : 2001, Amendment No 2, 2004.*

Switch. A mechanical device capable of making, carrying and breaking current under normal circuit conditions, which may include specified operating overload conditions, and also of carrying for a specified time currents under specified abnormal circuit conditions such as those of short-circuit. It may also be capable of making, but not breaking, short-circuit currents.

Switch, linked. A switch the contacts of which are so arranged as to make or break all poles simultaneously or in a definite sequence.

Switchboard. An assembly of switchgear with or without instruments, but the term does not apply to groups of local switches in final circuits.

Switchgear. An assembly of main and auxiliary switching apparatus for operation, regulation, protection or other control of an electrical installation.

System. An electrical system consisting of a single source of electrical energy and an installation. For certain purposes of the Regulations, types of system are identified as follows, depending upon the relationship of the source, and of exposed-conductive-parts of the installation, to Earth:

- **TN system,** a system having one or more points of the source of energy directly earthed, the exposed-conductive-parts of the installation being connected to that point by protective conductors,

- **TN-C system,** a system in which neutral and protective functions are combined in a single conductor throughout the system (see figure 3),

- **TN-S system,** a system having separate neutral and protective conductors throughout the system (see figure 4),

- **TN-C-S system,** a system in which neutral and protective functions are combined in a single conductor in part of the system (see figure 5),

- **TT system** a system having one point of the source of energy directly earthed, the exposed-conductive-parts of the installation being connected to earth electrodes electrically independent of the earth electrodes of the source (see figure 6),

- **IT system,** a system having no direct connection between live parts and Earth, the exposed-conductive-parts of the electrical installation being earthed (see figure 7).

Temporary supply unit. An enclosure containing equipment for the purpose of taking a temporary electrical supply safely from an item of street furniture.

Trunking *(see Cable trunking).*

Voltage bands

Band I
Band I covers:
- installations where protection against electric shock is provided under certain conditions by the value of voltage;
- installations where the voltage is limited for operational reasons (e.g. telecommunications, signalling, bell, control and alarm installations).

Extra-low voltage (ELV) will normally fall within voltage band I.

Band II
Band II contains the voltages for supplies to household, and most commercial and industrial installations. Low voltage (LV) will normally fall within voltage band II. Band II voltages do not exceed 1000 V a.c. rms or 1500 V d.c.

Voltage, nominal. Voltage by which an installation (or part of an installation) is designated. The following ranges of nominal voltage (rms values for a.c.) are defined:

- **Extra-low.** Normally not exceeding 50 V a.c. or 120 V ripple-free d.c., whether between conductors or to Earth,

- **Low.** Normally exceeding extra-low voltage but not exceeding 1000 V a.c. or 1500 V d.c. between conductors, or 600 V a.c. or 900 V d.c. between conductors and Earth.

The actual voltage of the installation may differ from the nominal value by a quantity within normal tolerances.

Voltage, reduced *(see Reduced low voltage system).*

Wiring system. An assembly made up of cable or busbars and parts which secure and, if necessary, enclose the cable or busbars.

fig 3   **TN-C system**.

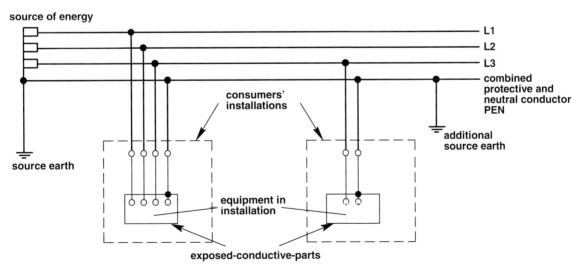

Neutral and protective functions combined in a single conductor throughout system.

All exposed-conductive-parts of an installation are connected to the PEN conductor.

Regulation 8(4) of the Electricity Safety, Quality and Continuity Regulations 2002 states that a consumer shall not combine the neutral and protective functions in a single conductor in his consumer's installation.

fig 4   TN-S system.

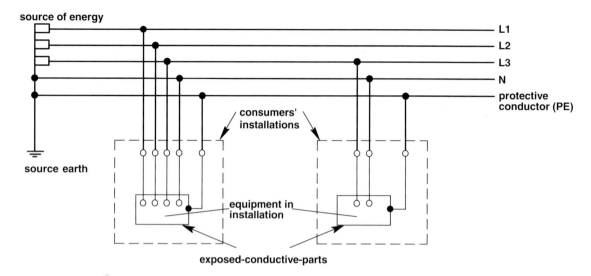

Separate neutral and protective conductors throughout the system.

The protective conductor (PE) is the metallic covering of the cable supplying the installations or a separate conductor.

All exposed-conductive-parts of an installation are connected to this protective conductor via the main earthing terminal of the installation.

fig 5   TN-C-S system.

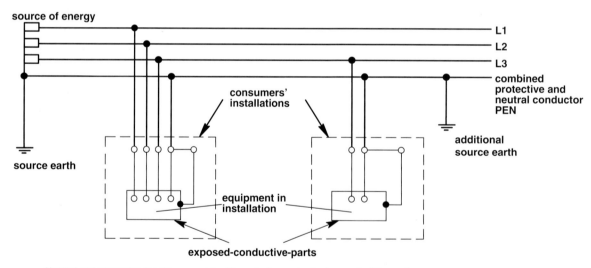

Neutral and protective functions combined in a single conductor in a part of the system.

The usual form of a TN-C-S system is as shown, where the supply is TN-C and the arrangement in the installations is TN-S.

This type of distribution is known also as protective multiple earthing and the PEN conductor is referred to as the combined neutral and earth (CNE) conductor.

The supply system PEN conductor is earthed at several points and an earth electrode may be necessary at or near a consumer's installation.

All exposed-conductive-parts of an installation are connected to the PEN conductor via the main earthing terminal and the neutral terminal, these terminals being linked together.

fig 6   TT system

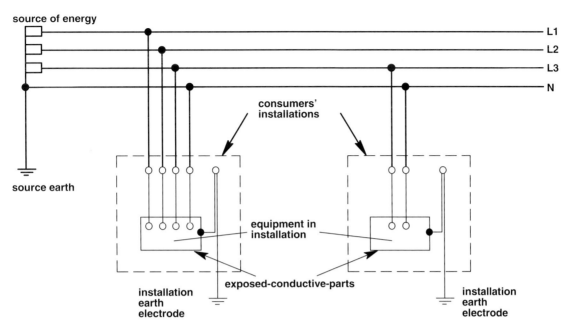

All exposed-conductive-parts of an installation are connected to an earth electrode which is electrically independent of the source earth.

fig 7   IT system

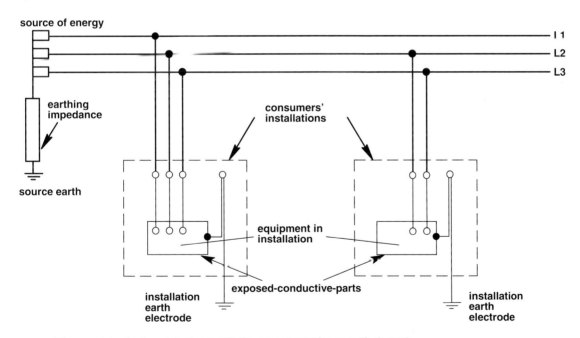

All exposed-conductive-parts of an installation are connected to an earth electrode.

The source is either connected to Earth through a deliberately introduced earthing impedance or is isolated from Earth.

Symbol	Description	Unit	Reference
C	correction factor - general		Appx 4, Sect 4
C_a	correction factor for ambient temperature		Appx 4, Sect 4
C_g	correction factor for grouping		Appx 4, Sect 4
C_i	correction factor for conductors embedded in thermal insulation		Appx 4, Sect 4
C_t	correction factor for operating temperature of conductor		Appx 4, Sect 4
D_e	overall cable diameter		Appx 4, Table 4A1
gG	class 'gG' utilisation category of fuses to BS 88 - general use		413-02-10
gM	class 'gM' utilisation category of fuses to BS 88 motor circuit applications		413-02-10
	frequency in cycles per second	Hz	Appx 4, Sect 1
I	current (general term)	A	
	fault current (general term)	A	434-03-03
I_a	current causing automatic operation of protective device within the time stated	A	413-02-08
I_b	design current of circuit	A	433-02-01(i)
I_d	fault current of first fault (IT system)	A	413-02-23
I_n	nominal current or current setting of protective device	A	Table 41B2
$I_{\Delta n}$	rated residual operating current of the protective device in amperes	A	412-06-02(ii)
I_t	tabulated current-carrying capacity of a cable	A	Appx 4, Sect 4
I_z	current-carrying capacity of a cable for continuous service under the particular installation conditions concerned	A	433-02-01(ii)
$I^2 t$	energy let-through value of device	A^2s	434-03-03
I_2	current causing effective operation of the overload protective device	A	433-02-01(iii)
λ	thermal conductivity	$Wm^{-1}K^{-1}$	523-04-01
k	material factor taken from Tables 43A and 54B to 54F	$As^{1/2}mm^{-2}$	434-03-03
$k^2 S^2$	energy withstand of cable	A^2s	434-03-03
$(mV/A/m)_r$	resistive voltage drop per ampere per metre	$mVA^{-1}m^{-1}$	Appx 4, Sect 7
$(mV/A/m)_x$	reactive voltage drop per ampere per metre	$mVA^{-1}m^{-1}$	Appx 4, Sect 7
$(mV/A/m)_z$	impedance voltage drop per ampere per metre	$mVA^{-1}m^{-1}$	Appx 4, Sect 7
R	resistance of supplementary bonding conductor	Ω	413-02-28
R_A	the sum of the resistances of the earth electrode and the protective conductor connecting it to the exposed-conductive-parts	Ω	413-02-20
R_a	*Deleted by BS 7671 : 1992, Amendment No 2.*		
R_b	*Deleted by BS 7671 : 1992, Amendment No 2.*		
R_1	resistance of phase conductor of a distribution or final circuit	Ω	Appx 6
R_2	resistance of circuit protective conductor (cpc) of a distribution or final circuit.	Ω	Appx 6
t_p	maximum permitted normal operating conductor temperature	°C	Appx 4, Sect 7
U	voltage between phases	V	Table 41E
U_o	nominal phase voltage (to earth for TN systems)	V	413-02-08
U_{oc}	open circuit voltage at the distribution transformer	V	Appx 3
Z_e	that part of the earth fault loop impedance which is external to the installation	Ω	313-01-01(iv)
Z_s	earth fault loop impedance	Ω	Part 2
Z^1_s	neutral-earth loop impedance (IT systems with distributed neutral only)	Ω	413-02-26
Ø	phase angle		Appx 4, Sect 7
cos Ø	power factor (sinusoidal)		Appx 4, Sect 7

PART 3

ASSESSMENT OF GENERAL CHARACTERISTICS

CONTENTS

PART 3

ASSESSMENT OF GENERAL CHARACTERISTICS

300-01   General

300-01-01   An assessment shall be made of the following characteristics of the installation in accordance with the chapters indicated:

   (i)   the purpose for which the installation is intended to be used, its general structure and its supplies (Chapter 31)

   (ii)   the external influences to which it is to be exposed (Chapter 32)

   (iii)   the compatibility of its equipment (Chapter 33)

   (iv)   its maintainability (Chapter 34).

These characteristics shall be taken into account in the choice of methods of protection for safety (see Part 4) and the selection and erection of equipment (see Part 5).

CHAPTER 31

PURPOSE, SUPPLIES AND STRUCTURE

311   MAXIMUM DEMAND

311-01-01   The maximum demand of an installation, expressed in amperes, shall be assessed. In determining the maximum demand of an installation or part thereof, diversity may be taken into account.

312   ARRANGEMENT OF LIVE CONDUCTORS AND TYPE OF EARTHING

312-01   General

312-01-01   The characteristics mentioned in Regulations 312-02-01 and 312-03-01 shall be ascertained and appropriate methods of protection for safety selected in compliance with Part 4.

312-02   Number and type of live conductors

312-02-01   The number and type of live conductors (e.g. single-phase two-wire a.c., three-phase four-wire a.c.) shall be determined, both for the source of energy and for each circuit to be used within the installation. Where the source of energy is provided by a distributor, the distributor shall be consulted if necessary.

312-03   Type of earthing arrangement

312-03-01   The type of earthing system to be used for the installation shall be determined, due account being taken of the characteristics of the source of energy, and in particular of any facilities for earthing.

Types of system are:

TN-C, TN-S, TN-C-S, TT and IT.

313   NATURE OF SUPPLY

313-01   General

313-01-01   The following characteristics of the supply or supplies, from whatever source, and where appropriate the normal range of those characteristics, shall be determined by calculation, measurement, enquiry or inspection:

(i)   the nominal voltage(s)

(ii)   the nature of the current and frequency

(iii)   the prospective short-circuit current at the origin of the installation

(iv)   the earth fault loop impedance (Z_e) of that part of the system external to the installation

(v)   the suitability for the requirements of the installation, including the maximum demand

(vi)   the type and rating of the overcurrent protective device acting at the origin of the installation.

313-02   Supplies for safety services and standby purposes

313-02-01   Where a supply for safety services or standby purposes is specified, the characteristics of the source or sources of any such supply shall be determined. Such supplies shall have adequate capacity, reliability and rating and appropriate changeover time for the operation specified.

Where the normal source of energy is to be provided by a distributor, the distributor shall be consulted regarding switching arrangements for safety and standby supplies and in particular where the various sources are intended to operate in parallel (or the sources must be prevented from so doing).

Supplies for safety services shall comply with the requirements of Chapter 56.

A source for safety services shall be classified as either automatic or non-automatic. The former may be continuously available (no break) or be available within a stated time delay.

314   INSTALLATION CIRCUIT ARRANGEMENT

314-01-01   Every installation shall be divided into circuits as necessary to:

(i)   avoid danger and minimize inconvenience in the event of a fault, and

(ii)   facilitate safe operation, inspection, testing and maintenance.

314-01-02   A separate circuit shall be provided for each part of the installation which needs to be separately controlled for compliance with the Regulations or otherwise to prevent danger, so that such circuits remain energised in the event of failure of any other circuit of the installation, and due account shall be taken of the consequences of the operation of any single protective device.

314-01-03   The number of final circuits required, and the number of points supplied by any final circuit, shall be such as to facilitate compliance with the requirements of Chapter 43 for overcurrent protection, Chapter 46 for isolation and switching and Chapter 52 as regards current-carrying capacities of conductors.

314-01-04   Where an installation comprises more than one final circuit, each final circuit shall be connected to a separate way in a distribution board. The wiring of each final circuit shall be electrically separate from that of every other final circuit, so as to prevent the indirect energising of a final circuit intended to be isolated.

CHAPTER 32

EXTERNAL INFLUENCES

At the time of issue of this Edition of the Regulations, the work on requirements for application of the classification of external influences for IEC Publication 364 is insufficiently advanced for adoption as a basis for national regulations. At a later stage, the IEC classification will be developed for adoption as Chapter 32 of these Regulations, together with the proposed IEC requirements for its application.

For the present, Appendix 5 contains information on the subject and a list of external influences which may need to be taken into account. The codes are utilised in Chapter 52.

CHAPTER 33

COMPATIBILITY

331-01   General

331-01-01   An assessment shall be made of any characteristics of equipment likely to have harmful effects upon other electrical equipment or other services, or be harmfully affected by them, or impair the supply. Those characteristics include the following:

> overvoltages;
> undervoltage;
> fluctuating loads;
> unbalanced loads;
> power factor;
> harmonic currents;
> starting currents;
> protective conductor currents;
> d.c. feedback;
> high-frequency oscillations;
> the necessity for additional connections to earth.

For an external source of energy the distributor shall be consulted regarding any equipment of the installation having a characteristic likely to have significant influence on the supply.

CHAPTER 34

MAINTAINABILITY

341-01   General

341-01-01   An assessment shall be made of the frequency and quality of maintenance that the installation can reasonably be expected to receive during its intended life. This assessment shall, wherever practicable, include consultation with the person or body who will be responsible for the operation and maintenance of the installation.

Having regard to the frequency and quality of maintenance expected, the requirements of Parts 4 to 7 shall be applied so that during the life of the installation:

(i)   any periodic inspection, testing, maintenance and repair likely to be necessary can be readily and safely carried out, and

(ii) any protective measure for safety remains effective, and

(iii) the reliability of equipment is sustained.

PART 4

PROTECTION FOR SAFETY

CONTENTS

PART 4

PROTECTION FOR SAFETY

CHAPTER 40

GENERAL

400-01   General

400-01-01   Every installation, either as a whole or in its several parts, shall comply with the requirements of this Part by the application in accordance with Chapter 47 of the protective measures described in Chapters 41 to 46.

The order in which the protective measures are listed shall not be taken to imply the relative importance of different measures.

400-02   Protective measures for installations and locations of increased shock risk

400-02-01   For any installation or part of an installation where the risk of electric shock is increased by a reduction in body resistance or by contact with earth potential, the relevant requirements of Part 6 of these Regulations shall be applied in addition to the requirements contained in other parts of the Regulations.

CHAPTER 41

PROTECTION AGAINST ELECTRIC SHOCK

CONTENTS

CHAPTER 41

PROTECTION AGAINST ELECTRIC SHOCK

410-01 General

410-01-01 Protection against electric shock shall be provided by the application, in accordance with Section 471, of:

(i) an appropriate measure specified in Section 411, for protection against both direct contact and indirect contact, or

(ii) a combination of appropriate measures specified in Section 412 for protection against direct contact and Section 413 for protection against indirect contact.

411 PROTECTION AGAINST BOTH DIRECT AND INDIRECT CONTACT

411-01 General

411-01-01 For protection against both direct contact and indirect contact, one of the following basic protective measures shall be used:

(i) protection by SELV according to Regulations 411-02 and 471-02

(ii) protection by limitation of discharge of energy according to Regulations 411-04 and 471-03.

411-01-02 Functional extra-low voltage alone shall not be used as a protective measure (see Regulation 471-14).

411-02 Protection by SELV

Sources for SELV

411-02-01 For protection by SELV, compliance with all the following requirements shall be provided:

(i) the nominal voltage of the circuit concerned shall not exceed extra-low voltage

(ii) the supply shall be from one of the safety sources listed in Regulation 411-02-02

(iii) the conditions of Regulations 411-02-03 to 411-02-11 shall be fulfilled.

411-02-02 The source for SELV shall be one of the following:

(i) a safety isolating transformer complying with BS 3535 in which there shall be no connection between the output winding and the body or the protective earthing circuit, if any, or

(ii) a source of current such as a motor-generator with windings providing electrical separation equivalent to that of the safety isolating transformer specified in (i) above, or

(iii) an electrochemical source (e.g. a battery) or another source independent of a higher voltage circuit (e.g. an engine driven generator), or

(iv) certain electronic devices complying with appropriate standards where measures have been taken so that even in the case of an internal fault the voltage at the output terminals cannot exceed the value specified by Regulation 411-02-01(i). A higher voltage at the output terminals is, however, permitted if, in the case of direct or indirect contact, the voltage at the output terminals is immediately reduced to the value specified by Regulation 411-02-01(i). Where such a higher voltage exists, compliance with this item (iv) is deemed to be met if the voltage at the output terminals is within the limit specified by Regulation 411-02-01(i) when measured with a voltmeter having an internal resistance of at least 3000 ohms.

411-02-03 A system supplied from a higher voltage system by other equipment which does not provide the necessary electrical separation, such as an autotransformer, potentiometer, semiconductor device etc., shall not be deemed to be a SELV system.

411-02-04 A mobile source for SELV shall be selected and erected in accordance with the requirements for protection by the use of Class II equipment or by equivalent insulation (see Regulations 413-03 and 471-09).

Arrangement of circuits for SELV

411-02-05 A live part of a SELV system shall:

(i) be electrically separated from that of any other higher voltage system. Except for cables the electrical separation shall be not less than that between the input and output of a safety isolating transformer

(ii) not be connected to Earth or to a live part or a protective conductor forming part of another system.

411-02-06 Circuit conductors of each SELV system shall be physically separated from those of any other system or, where compliance with this requirement is impracticable, installed in accordance with one of the following arrangements:

(i) SELV circuit conductors shall be insulated in accordance with the requirements of the Regulations for the highest voltage present

(ii) SELV circuit conductors shall be enclosed in an insulating sheath additional to their basic insulation

(iii) conductors of systems at voltages higher than SELV shall be separated from those at SELV by an earthed metallic screen or an earthed metallic sheath

(iv) where circuits at different voltages are contained in a multicore cable or other grouping of conductors, the conductors of SELV circuits shall be insulated, individually or collectively, for the highest voltage present in the cable or grouping.

In the arrangements (ii) and (iii) above, basic insulation of any conductor need be sufficient only for the voltage of the circuit of which it is a part.

In all electrical equipment of a SELV system, including relays, contactors and auxiliary switches, the electrical separation necessary between live parts of the SELV system and any other system shall be maintained.

411-02-07 No exposed-conductive-part of a SELV system shall be connected to any of the following:

(i) Earth

(ii) an exposed-conductive-part of another system

(iii) a protective conductor of any system

(iv) an extraneous-conductive-part, except that where electrical equipment is inherently required to be connected to an extraneous-conductive-part, measures shall be incorporated so that the parts cannot attain a voltage exceeding the appropriate value specified by Regulation 411-02-01(i).

411-02-08 If an exposed-conductive-part of an extra-low voltage system is liable to come into contact, either fortuitously or intentionally, with an exposed-conductive-part of any other system, the system shall not be deemed to be SELV and other protective measures shall be applied in accordance with Regulation 411-03.

411-02-09 If the nominal voltage of a SELV system exceeds 25 V a.c. rms or 60 V ripple-free d.c., protection against direct contact shall be provided by one or more of the following:

(i) a barrier or an enclosure (Regulation 412-03) affording at least the degree of protection IP2X or IPXXB

(ii) insulation (Regulation 412-02) capable of withstanding a type-test voltage of 500 V a.c. rms for 60 seconds.

If the nominal voltage does not exceed 25 V a.c. rms or 60 V ripple-free d.c., protection as described in items (i) and (ii) above is unnecessary.

For the purposes of this Regulation 'ripple-free' means, for sinusoidal ripple voltage, a ripple content not exceeding 10 % rms; the maximum peak value shall not exceed 140 V for a nominal 120 V ripple-free d.c. system and 70 V for a nominal 60 V ripple-free d.c. system.

411-02-10 A socket-outlet in a SELV system shall require the use of a plug which is not dimensionally compatible with those used for any other system in use in the same premises and shall not have a protective conductor contact.

411-02-11 A luminaire supporting coupler having a protective conductor contact shall not be installed in a SELV system.

411-03   Other extra-low voltage systems including functional extra-low voltage

411-03-01   Where, for functional reasons, extra-low voltage is used but not all of the requirements relating to SELV are fulfilled, other measures shall be applied to provide protection against direct and indirect contact, as specified in Regulation 471-14.

411-04   Protection by limitation of discharge of energy

411-04-01   For equipment complying with the appropriate British Standard, protection against both direct and indirect contact shall be deemed to be provided when the equipment incorporates means of limiting the current which can pass through the body of a person or livestock to a value lower than that likely to cause danger.

A circuit relying on this protective measure shall be separated from any other circuit in a manner equivalent to that specified in Regulations 411-02-05 and 411-02-06 for a SELV circuit.

412   PROTECTION AGAINST DIRECT CONTACT

412-01   General

412-01-01   For protection against direct contact one or more of the following basic protective measures shall be used in accordance with the relevant requirements of this section and the application rules specified in Section 471, including those indicated below:

   (i)   protection by insulation of live parts (Regulation 412-02 and Regulation 471-04)

   (ii)   protection by a barrier or an enclosure (Regulation 412-03 and Regulation 471-05)

   (iii)   protection by obstacles (Regulation 412-04 and Regulation 471-06)

   (iv)   protection by placing out of reach (Regulation 412-05 and Regulation 471-07).

Where supplementary protection by a residual current device is also provided, the requirements of Regulation 412-06 shall apply.

412-02   Protection by insulation of live parts (see also Regulation 471-04)

412-02-01   Live parts shall be completely covered with insulation which can only be removed by destruction and which is capable of durably withstanding the electrical, mechanical, thermal and chemical stresses to which it may be subjected in service. The insulation of factory-built equipment shall comply with the relevant standards for the electrical equipment. For other equipment, protection shall be provided by insulation capable of durably withstanding the stresses to which it may be subjected in service, such as mechanical, chemical, electrical and thermal influences. Paint, varnish, lacquer or similar products are generally not considered to provide adequate insulation for protection against direct contact in normal service

Where insulation is applied during the erection of the installation, the quality of the insulation shall be verified by tests equivalent to those specified in the British Standard for similar type-tested equipment.

412-03   Protection by barriers or enclosures (see also Regulation 471-05)

412-03-01   Live parts shall be inside enclosures or behind barriers providing at least the degree of protection IP2X or IPXXB except that, where an opening larger than that permitted for IP2X or IPXXB is necessary to allow the replacement of parts or to avoid interference with the proper functioning of electrical equipment both of the following requirements apply:

   (i)   suitable precautions shall be taken to prevent persons or livestock from touching a live part unintentionally, and

   (ii)   it shall be established, as far as practicable, that a person will be aware that a live part can be touched through the opening and should not be touched (see Regulation 471-05-02).

412-03-02   The horizontal top surface of a barrier or an enclosure which is readily accessible shall provide a degree of protection of at least IP4X.

412-03-03   Every barrier and enclosure shall be firmly secured in place and have sufficient stability and durability to maintain the required degree of protection and appropriate separation from any live part in the known conditions of normal service.

412-03-04 Where it is necessary to remove a barrier or to open an enclosure or to remove a part of an enclosure, one or more of the following requirements shall be satisfied:

(i) the removal or opening shall be possible only by use of a key or tool

(ii) the removal or opening shall be possible only after disconnection of the supply to the live part against which the barrier or enclosure affords protection, restoration of the supply being possible only after replacement or reclosure of the barrier or enclosure

(iii) an intermediate barrier shall be provided to prevent contact with a live part, such a barrier affording a degree of protection of at least IP2X or IPXXB and removable only by the use of a tool.

This regulation does not apply to:

a ceiling rose complying with BS 67
a pull cord switch complying with BS 3676
a bayonet lampholder complying with BS EN 61184
an Edison screw lampholder complying with BS EN 60238.

412-04 Protection by obstacles (see also Regulation 471-06)

412-04-01 An obstacle shall prevent, as appropriate, either of the following:

(i) unintentional bodily approach to a live part

(ii) unintentional contact with a live part when operating energised equipment.

412-04-02 An obstacle shall be so secured as to prevent unintentional removal, but may be removable without using a key or tool.

412-05 Protection by placing out of reach (see also Regulation 471-07)

412-05-01 A bare or insulated overhead line for distribution between buildings and structures shall be installed to the standard required by the Electricity Safety, Quality and Continuity Regulations 2002.

412-05-02 A bare live part other than an overhead line shall not be within arm's reach nor within 2.5 m of the following:

(i) an exposed-conductive-part

(ii) an extraneous-conductive-part

(iii) a bare live part of any other circuit.

412-05-03 If access to live equipment from a normally occupied position is restricted in the horizontal plane by an obstacle (e.g. handrail, mesh, screen) affording a degree of protection less than IP2X or IPXXB, the extent of arm's reach shall be measured from that obstacle.

412-05-04 In each place where any bulky or long conducting object is normally handled, the distances required by Regulations 412-05-02 and 412-05-03 shall be increased accordingly.

412-06 Supplementary protection by residual current devices

412-06-01 A residual current device shall not be used as the sole means of protection against direct contact.

412-06-02 The use of a residual current device is recognised as reducing the risk of electric shock where the following conditions are complied with:

(i) one of the protective measures specified in items (i) to (iv) of Regulation 412-01-01 shall be applied, and

(ii) the residual current device shall have a rated residual operating current ($I_{\Delta n}$) not exceeding 30 mA and an operating time not exceeding 40 ms at a residual current of 5 $I_{\Delta n}$, as provided by BS 4293, BS 7071, BS 7288, BS EN 61008-1 or BS EN 61009-1.

413 PROTECTION AGAINST INDIRECT CONTACT

413-01 General

413-01-01 For protection against indirect contact, one of the following basic measures shall be used in accordance with the relevant requirements of this section and the application rules specified in Section 471, including those indicated below:

(i) protection by earthed equipotential bonding and automatic disconnection of supply (Regulation 413-02 and Regulation 471-08)

(ii) protection by Class II equipment or by equivalent insulation (Regulation 413-03 and Regulation 471-09)

(iii) protection by non-conducting location (Regulation 413-04 and Regulation 471-10)

(iv) protection by earth-free local equipotential bonding (Regulation 413-05 and Regulation 471-11)

(v) protection by electrical separation (Regulation 413-06 and Regulation 471-12).

413-02 Protection by earthed equipotential bonding and automatic disconnection of supply
(see also Regulation 471-08)

General

413-02-01 This measure shall be applied in accordance with the requirements for the type of system earthing in use:

(i) TN systems: Regulations 413-02-06 to 413-02-17

(ii) TT systems: Regulations 413-02-18 to 413-02-20

(iii) IT systems: Regulations 413-02-21 to 413-02-26

413-02-02 In each installation main equipotential bonding conductors complying with Section 547 shall connect to the main earthing terminal extraneous-conductive-parts of that installation including the following:

(i) water service pipes

(ii) gas installation pipes

(iii) other service pipes and ducting

(iv) central heating and air conditioning systems

(v) exposed metallic structural parts of the building

(vi) the lightning protective system.

Where an installation serves more than one building the above requirement shall be applied to each building.

To comply with the Regulations it is also necessary to apply equipotential bonding to any metallic sheath of a telecommunication cable. However, the consent of the owner or operator of the cable shall be obtained.

413-02-03 Simultaneously accessible exposed-conductive-parts shall be connected to the same earthing system individually, in groups or collectively.

413-02-04 The characteristics of each protective device for automatic disconnection, the earthing arrangements for the installation and the relevant impedance of the circuit concerned shall be co-ordinated so that during an earth fault the voltages between simultaneously accessible exposed-conductive-parts and extraneous-conductive-parts occurring anywhere in the installation shall be of such magnitude and duration as not to cause danger.

Conventional means of compliance with this regulation are given in Regulations 413-02-06 to 413-02-26 inclusive according to the type of system earthing, but other equally effective means shall not be excluded.

Where the conditions for automatic disconnection of Regulations 413-02-08 to 413-02-14 (TN systems), 413-02-20 (TT systems), 413-02-22, 413-02-23, 413-02-25 and 413-02-26 (IT systems) cannot be fulfilled by using overcurrent protective devices, then either:

(i) local supplementary equipotential bonding shall be applied in accordance with Regulations 413-02-27 and 413-02-28, but the use of such bonding does not obviate the need to disconnect the supply for reasons other than protection against electric shock, such as thermal effects, or

(ii) protection shall be provided by means of a residual current device.

413-02-05 Account shall be taken of the increase of temperature and resistance of circuit conductors as a result of overcurrents. Circuits in which the overcurrent protective device complies with characteristics given in Appendix 3, and which comply with the loop impedance requirements of Regulations 413-02-10, 413-02-11 and 413-02-14, are deemed to comply with this regulation.

TN system

413-02-06 Each exposed-conductive-part of the installation shall be connected by a protective conductor to the main earthing terminal of the installation and that terminal shall be connected to the earthed point of the supply source in accordance with Regulations 542-01-02, 542-01-03 and 542-01-05, as appropriate.

413-02-07 One or more of the following types of protective device shall be used:

(i)   an overcurrent protective device

(ii)   a residual current device.

Where a residual current device is used in a TN-C-S system, a PEN conductor shall not be used on the load side. Connection of the protective conductor to the PEN conductor shall be made on the source side of the residual current device.

413-02-08 Regulation 413-02-04 is considered to be satisfied if the characteristic of each protective device and the earth fault loop impedance of each circuit protected by it are such that automatic disconnection of the supply will occur within a specified time when a fault of negligible impedance occurs between a phase conductor and a protective conductor or an exposed-conductive-part anywhere in the installation. This requirement is met where the following condition is fulfilled:

$$Z_s \leq \frac{U_o}{I_a}$$

where:

Z_s is the earth fault loop impedance.

I_a is the current causing the automatic operation of the disconnecting protective device within the time stated in Table 41A as a function of the nominal voltage U_o or, under the conditions stated in Regulations 413-02-12 and 413-02-13, within a time not exceeding 5 s.

U_o is the nominal voltage to Earth.

TABLE 41A
Maximum disconnection times for TN systems
(see Regulation 413-02-09)

Installation nominal voltage U_o (volts)	Maximum disconnection time t (seconds)
120	0.8
230	0.4
277	0.4
400	0.2
greater than 400	0.1

NOTES:

1.   For voltages which are within the supply tolerance band (230 ±10 % V) the disconnection time appropriate to the nominal voltage applies.

2.   For intermediate values of voltage, the next higher value of voltage in the table is to be used.

413-02-09 The maximum disconnection times of Table 41A shall apply to a circuit supplying socket-outlets and to other final circuits which supply portable equipment intended for manual movement during use, or hand-held Class I equipment.

This requirement does not apply to a final circuit supplying an item of stationary equipment connected by means of a plug and socket-outlet where precautions are taken to prevent the use of the socket-outlet for supplying hand-held equipment, nor to the reduced low voltage circuits described in Regulation 471-15.

413-02-10 Where a fuse is used to satisfy the requirements of Regulation 413-02-09, maximum values of earth fault loop impedance (Z_s) corresponding to a disconnection time of 0.4 s are stated in Table 41B1 for a nominal voltage to Earth (U_o) of 230 V. For types and rated currents of general purpose (gG) fuses other than those mentioned in Table 41B1, and for motor circuit fuses (gM), reference should be made to the appropriate British Standard to determine the value of I_a for compliance with Regulation 413 02-08.

TABLE 41B1
Maximum earth fault loop impedance (Z_s) for fuses, for 0.4 s disconnection time with U_o of 230 V
(see Regulation 413-02-10)

(a) General purpose (gG) fuses to BS 88-2.1 and BS 88-6

Rating (amperes)	6	10	16	20	25	32	40	50
Z_s (ohms)	8.89	5.33	2.82	1.85	1.50	1.09	0.86	0.63

(b) Fuses to BS 1361

Rating (amperes)	5	15	20	30	45
Z_s (ohms)	10.9	3.43	1.78	1.20	0.60

(c) Fuses to BS 3036

Rating (amperes)	5	15	20	30	45
Z_s (ohms)	10.0	2.67	1.85	1.14	0.62

(d) Fuses to BS 1362

Rating (amperes)	13
Z_s (ohms)	2.53

NOTE: The circuit loop impedances given in the table should not be exceeded when the conductors are at their normal operating temperature. If the conductors are at a different temperature when tested, the reading should be adjusted accordingly.

413-02-11 Where a circuit-breaker is used to satisfy the requirements of Regulation 413-02-09, the maximum value of earth fault loop impedance (Z_s) shall be determined by the formula of Regulation 413-02-08. Alternatively, for a nominal voltage to earth of 230 V and a disconnection time of 0.4 s, the values specified in Table 41B2 for the types and ratings of overcurrent devices listed may be used instead of calculation.

TABLE 41B2
Maximum earth fault loop impedance (Z_s) for circuit-breakers with U_0 of 230 V, for instantaneous operation giving compliance with the 0.4 second disconnection time of Regulation 413-02-11 and the 5 second disconnection time of Regulations 413-02-12 and 413-02-14

(e) Type B circuit-breakers to BS EN 60898 and RCBOs to BS EN 61009

Rating (amperes)	6	10	16	20	25	32	40	50	63	80	100	125	I_n
Z_s (ohms)	8.00		3.00		1.92		1.20		0.76		0.48		$48/I_n$
		4.80		2.40		1.50		0.96		0.60		0.38	

(f) Type C circuit-breakers to BS EN 60898 and RCBOs to BS EN 61009

Rating (amperes)	6	10	16	20	25	32	40	50	63	80	100	125	I_n
Z_s (ohms)	4.00		1.50		0.96		0.60		0.38		0.24		$24/I_n$
		2.40		1.20		0.75		0.48		0.30		0.19	

(g) Type D circuit-breakers to BS EN 60898 and RCBOs to BS EN 61009

Rating (amperes)	6	10	16	20	25	32	40	50	63	80	100	125	I_n
Z_s (ohms)	2.00		0.75		0.48		0.30		0.19		0.12		$12/I_n$
		1.20		0.60		0.38		0.24		0.15		0.10	

NOTE: The circuit loop impedances given in the table should not be exceeded when the conductors are at their normal operating temperature. If the conductors are at a different temperature when tested, the reading should be adjusted accordingly.

413-02-12 Irrespective of the value of U_0, for a final circuit which supplies a socket-outlet or portable equipment intended for manual movement during use, or hand-held Class I equipment, it shall be permissible to increase the disconnection time to a value not exceeding 5 s for the types and ratings of the overcurrent protective devices and associated maximum impedances of the circuit protective conductors shown in Table 41C. The impedance of the protective conductor shall be referred to the point of connection to the main equipotential bonding. Where additional equipotential bonding is installed in accordance with Regulation 413-02-13(ii) then the impedance of the circuit protective conductor specified in this paragraph applies to that portion of the circuit protective conductor between the point of additional bonding and the socket-outlet, or portable equipment.

TABLE 41C
Maximum impedance of circuit protective conductor related to the final circuit protective device
(see Regulation 413-02-12)

(a) General purpose (gG) fuses to BS 88-2.1 and BS 88-6

Rating (amperes)	6	10	16	20	25	32	40	50
Impedance (ohms)	2.48	1.48	0.83	0.55	0.43	0.34	0.26	0.19

(b) Fuses to BS 1361

Rating (amperes)	5	15	20	30	45
Impedance (ohms)	3.25	0.96	0.55	0.36	0.18

(c) Fuses to BS 3036

Rating (amperes)	5	15	20	30	45
Impedance (ohms)	3.25	0.96	0.63	0.43	0.24

(d) Fuses to BS 1362

Rating (amperes)	13
Impedance (ohms)	0.75

(e) Type B circuit-breakers to BS EN 60898 and RCBOs to BS EN 61009

Rating (amperes)	6	10	16	20	25	32	40	50	63	80	100	125	I_n
Impedance (ohms)	1.67	1.00	0.63	0.50	0.40	0.31	0.25	0.20	0.16	0.12	0.10	0.08	$10/I_n$

(f) Type C circuit-breakers to BS EN 60898 and RCBOs to BS EN 61009

Rating (amperes)	6	10	16	20	25	32	40	50	63	80	100	125	I_n
Impedance (ohms)	0.83	0.50	0.31	0.25	0.20	0.16	0.13	0.10	0.08	0.06	0.05	0.04	$5/I_n$

(g) Type D circuit-breakers to BS EN 60898 and RCBOs to BS EN 61009

Rating (amperes)	6	10	16	20	25	32	40	50	63	80	100	125	I_n
Impedance (ohms)	0.42	0.25	0.16	0.12	0.10	0.08	0.06	0.05	0.04	0.03	0.03	0.02	$2.5/I_n$

NOTE: The protective conductor impedances given in the table should not be exceeded when the conductors are at their normal operating temperature. If the conductors are at a different temperature when tested, the reading should be adjusted accordingly.

413-02-13 For a distribution circuit a disconnection time not exceeding 5 s is permitted.

For a final circuit supplying only stationary equipment and for a final circuit for which the requirement of Regulation 413-02-09 does not apply a disconnection time not exceeding 5 s is permitted. Where the disconnection time for such a final circuit exceeds that required by Table 41A and another final circuit requiring a disconnection time according to Table 41A is connected to the same distribution board or distribution circuit, one of the following conditions shall be fulfilled:

(i) the impedance of the protective conductor between the distribution board and the point at which the protective conductor is connected to the main equipotential bonding shall not exceed the value given in Table 41C for the appropriate protective device in the final circuit, or, for protective devices not included in Table 41C, 50 Z_s/U_o ohms (where Z_s is the earth fault loop impedance corresponding to a disconnection time of 5 s), or

(ii) there shall be equipotential bonding at the distribution board, which involves the same types of extraneous-conductive-parts as the main equipotential bonding according to Regulation 413-02-02 and is sized in accordance with Regulation 547-02-01.

413-02-14 Where a circuit-breaker is used to satisfy the requirements of Regulation 413-02-13, the maximum value of earth fault loop impedance (Z_s) shall be determined by the formula of Regulation 413-02-08. Alternatively, the values specified in Table 41B2 may be used instead of calculation for a nominal voltage to Earth (U_o) of 230 V for the types and ratings of circuit-breaker listed therein.

Where a fuse is used to satisfy the requirements of Regulation 413-02-13, maximum values of earth fault loop impedance (Z_s) corresponding to a disconnection time of 5 s are stated in Table 41D for a nominal voltage to Earth (U_o) of 230 V.

For types and rated currents of general purpose (gG) fuses other than those mentioned in Table 41D and for motor circuit fuses (gM) reference should be made to the appropriate British Standard to determine the value of I_a for compliance with Regulation 413-02-08.

TABLE 41D

Maximum earth fault loop impedance (Z_s) for 5 s disconnection time with U_o of 230 V
(see Regulations 413-02-13 and 413-02-14)

(a) General purpose (gG) fuses to BS 88-2.1 and BS 88-6

Rating (amperes)	6	10	16	20	25	32	40	50
Z_s (ohms)	14.1	7.74	4.36	3.04	2.40	1.92	1.41	1.09

	Rating (amperes)	63	80	100	125	160	200
	Z_s (ohms)	0.86	0.60	0.44	0.35	0.27	0.20

(b) Fuses to BS 1361

Rating (amperes)	5	15	20	30	45	60	80	100
Z_s (ohms)	17.1	5.22	2.93	1.92	1.00	0.73	0.52	0.38

(c) Fuses to BS 3036

Rating (amperes)	5	15	20	30	45	60	100
Z_s (ohms)	18.5	5.58	4.00	2.76	1.66	1.17	0.56

(d) Fuses to BS 1362

Rating (amperes)	13
Z_s (ohms)	4

NOTE: The circuit loop impedances given in the table should not be exceeded when the conductors are at their normal operating temperature. If the conductors are at a different temperature when tested, the reading should be adjusted accordingly.

413-02 15 *Deleted by BS 7671 : 1992, Amendment No 2.*

413-02-16 If protection is provided by a residual current device the following condition shall be fulfilled:

$$Z_s \, I_{\Delta n} \leq 50 \text{ V}$$

where:

Z_s is the earth fault loop impedance in ohms.

$I_{\Delta n}$ is the rated residual operating current of the protective device in amperes.

413-02-17 If a residual current device is used for automatic disconnection for a circuit which extends beyond the earthed equipotential zone, exposed-conductive-parts need not be connected to the TN system protective conductors provided that they are connected to an earth electrode affording a resistance appropriate to the operating current of the residual current device. The circuit thus protected is to be treated as a TT system and Regulations 413-02-18 to 413-02-20 apply.

TT system

413-02-18 Every exposed-conductive-part which is to be protected by a single protective device shall be connected, via the main earthing terminal, to a common earth electrode. However if several protective devices are in series, the exposed-conductive-parts may be connected to separate earth electrodes corresponding to each protective device.

413-02-19 One or more of the following types of protective device shall be used, the former being preferred:

(i) a residual current device

(ii) an overcurrent protective device.

413-02-20 The following condition shall be fulfilled for each circuit:

$$R_A \, I_a \leq 50 \text{ V}$$

where:

R_A is the sum of the resistances of the earth electrode and the protective conductor(s) connecting it to the exposed-conductive-part.

I_a is the current causing the automatic operation of the protective device within 5 s.

When the protective device is a residual current device, I_a is the rated residual operating current $I_{\Delta n}$.

IT system

413-02-21 No live conductor shall be directly connected with Earth. Where a connection with Earth is required it shall be through a high impedance such that in the event of a single fault to an exposed-conductive-part or to Earth the fault current is so low that it will not give rise to the risk of an electric shock. If a high impedance connection with Earth is made at the neutral point or at an artificial star point or to one of the live conductors, the relevant earth fault loop impedance shall satisfy that condition.

Where, to reduce overvoltage or to damp voltage oscillation, it is necessary to provide earthing through an impedance, its characteristics shall be appropriate to the requirements of the installation.

413-02-22 Disconnection in the event of a single fault to an exposed-conductive-part or to Earth is not imperative if the conditions of Regulation 413-02-21 are satisfied, but precautions shall be taken to guard against the risk of electric shock in the event of two faults existing simultaneously. Either or both of the following devices shall be used:

(i) an overcurrent protective device

(ii) a residual current protective device.

413-02-23 Every exposed-conductive-part shall be earthed such that the following condition shall be fulfilled for each circuit:

$$R_A \, I_d \leq 50 \text{ V}$$

where:

R_A is the sum of the resistances of the earth electrode and the protective conductor connecting it to the exposed-conductive-parts.

I_d is the fault current of the first fault of negligible impedance between a phase conductor and an exposed-conductive-part. The value of I_d takes account of protective conductor currents and the total earthing impedance of the electrical installation.

413-02-24 An insulation monitoring device shall be provided so as to indicate the occurrence of a first fault from a live part to an exposed-conductive-part or to Earth.

413-02-25 After the occurrence of a first fault, conditions for disconnection of supply in the event of a second fault depend on whether all exposed-conductive-parts are connected together by a protective conductor (collectively earthed) or are earthed in groups or individually:

(i) where exposed-conductive-parts are earthed collectively, the conditions for a TN system shall apply, subject to Regulation 413-02-26

(ii) where exposed-conductive-parts are earthed in groups or individually, conditions for protection shall comply with Regulation 413-02-20 as for TT systems.

Where in an IT system protection against indirect contact is provided by a residual current device, each final circuit shall be separately protected.

413-02-26 The following conditions shall be fulfilled where the neutral is not distributed (three-phase three-wire distribution):

$$Z_s \leq \frac{0.866\ U_o}{I_a}$$

or, where the neutral is distributed (three-phase four-wire distribution and single-phase distribution):

$$Z^1_s \leq \frac{0.5\ U_o}{I_a}$$

where:

Z_s is the impedance of the earth fault loop comprising the phase conductor and the protective conductor of the circuit.

Z^1_s is the impedance of the earth fault loop comprising the neutral conductor and the protective conductor of the circuit.

I_a is the current which disconnects the circuit within the time t specified in Table 41E when applicable (see Regulation 413-02-09), or within 5 s for all other circuits when this time is allowed (see Regulation 413-02-13).

TABLE 41E
Maximum disconnection time in IT systems (second fault)

Installation nominal voltage U_o/U (volts)	Maximum disconnection time t (seconds)	
	Neutral not distributed*	Neutral distributed
120/240	0.8	5.0
230/400	0.4	0.8
400/690	0.2	0.4
580/1000	0.1	0.2

where:

U_o is the nominal a.c. rms voltage between phase and neutral.

U is the nominal a.c. rms voltage between phases.

* phase to phase voltages only are available.

NOTES:

1. For voltages which are within the supply tolerance band (230/400 ±10 % V) the disconnection time appropriate to the nominal voltage applies.

2. For intermediate values of voltage, the next higher value of voltage in the table is to be used.

Supplementary equipotential bonding

413-02-27   Where supplementary equipotential bonding is necessary for compliance with Regulation 413-02-04 or Part 6, it shall connect together the exposed-conductive-parts of equipment in the circuits concerned including the earthing contacts of socket-outlets and extraneous-conductive-parts in accordance with Regulation 547-03.

413-02-28   The resistance (R) of the supplementary bonding conductor between simultaneously accessible exposed-conductive-parts and extraneous-conductive-parts shall fulfil the following condition:

$$R \leq \frac{50}{I_a}$$

where:

   I_a is the operating current of the protective device:

    (i)   for a residual current device, the rated residual operating current, $I_{\Delta n}$

    (ii)   for an overcurrent device, it is the minimum current which disconnects the circuit within 5 s.

413-03   **Protection by use of Class II equipment or by equivalent insulation** (see also Regulation 471-09)

413-03-01   Protection shall be provided by one or more of the following:

(i)   electrical equipment of the following types, type-tested and marked to the relevant standards:

    (a) electrical equipment having double or reinforced insulation (Class II equipment)

    (b) low voltage switchgear and controlgear assemblies having total insulation (see BS EN 60439)

(ii)   supplementary insulation applied to electrical equipment having basic insulation only, as a process in the erection of an electrical installation, providing a degree of safety equivalent to that of electrical equipment according to item (i) above and complying with Regulations 413-03-03 to 413-03-09

(iii)   reinforced insulation applied to uninsulated live parts, as a process in the erection of an electrical installation, providing a degree of safety equivalent to electrical equipment according to item (i) above and complying with Regulations 413-03-03 to 413-03-09, such insulation being recognised only where constructional features prevent the application of double insulation.

413-03-02   The installation of equipment described in item (i) of Regulation 413-03-01 shall be effected in such a way as not to impair the protection afforded in compliance with the equipment specification. Class II equipment shall be so installed that basic insulation is not the only protection between live parts of the installation and exposed metalwork of that equipment.

413-03-03   The enclosure provided for this measure shall not adversely affect the operation of the equipment protected.

413-03-04   The electrical equipment being ready for operation, all conductive parts separated from live parts only by basic insulation shall be contained in an insulating enclosure affording at least the degree of protection IP2X or IPXXB .

413-03-05   The insulating enclosure shall be capable of resisting mechanical, electrical and thermal stresses likely to be encountered.

A coating of paint, varnish or similar product is generally not considered to comply with these requirements. This requirement does not exclude, however, the use of a type-tested enclosure provided with such a coating if the relevant product standard admits its use and if the insulating coating has been tested according to the requirements of the relevant product standard.

413-03-06   If the insulating enclosure has not previously been tested, a suitable test shall be carried out (see Regulation 713-05-02).

413-03-07   The insulating enclosure shall not be pierced by conductive parts, other than circuit conductors, likely to transmit a potential. The insulating enclosure shall not contain any screws of insulating material, the replacement of which by metallic screws could impair the insulation provided by the enclosure.

Where the insulating enclosure has to be pierced by conductive parts (e.g. for operating handles of built-in equipment, and for screws) protection against indirect contact shall not be impaired.

413-03-08 Where a lid or door in an insulating enclosure can be opened without the use of a tool or key, every conductive part which is accessible if the lid or door is open shall be behind an insulating barrier which prevents a person from coming into contact with those parts; this insulating barrier shall provide a degree of protection of at least IP2X or IPXXB and be removable only by use of a tool.

413-03-09 No conductive part enclosed in an insulating enclosure shall be connected to a protective conductor.

Where provision is made within the enclosure for a protective conductor which necessarily runs through the enclosure in order to serve another item of electrical equipment whose supply circuit also runs through the enclosure, any such protective conductor and its terminals and joints shall be insulated as though they were live parts and its terminals shall be appropriately marked.

413-04 Protection by non-conducting location

413-04-01 This method of protection is not recognised for general application (see Regulation 471-10).

413-04-02 Exposed-conductive-parts which might attain different potentials through failure of the basic insulation of live parts shall be arranged so that a person will not come into simultaneous contact with:

(i) two exposed-conductive-parts, or

(ii) an exposed-conductive-part and any extraneous-conductive-part.

413-04-03 In a non-conducting location there shall be no protective conductors, and any socket-outlet shall not incorporate an earthing contact. A luminaire supporting coupler having a protective conductor contact shall not be installed.

413-04-04 The resistance of an insulating floor or wall at every point of measurement under the conditions specified in Regulation 713-08 shall be not less than:

(i) 50 kΩ where the voltage to earth does not exceed 500 V

(ii) 100 kΩ where the voltage to earth exceeds 500 V but does not exceed low voltage.

If at any point the resistance is less than the specified value, the floors and walls are deemed to be extraneous-conductive-parts for the purposes of protection against electric shock.

413-04-05 Permanent arrangements shall be made which shall afford protection where the use of mobile or portable equipment is envisaged.

413-04-06 Precautions shall be taken so that a potential on extraneous-conductive-parts in the location cannot be transmitted outside that location.

413-04-07 Regulation 413-04-02 shall be deemed to be fulfilled if the location has an insulating floor and insulating walls and one or more of the following arrangements applies:

(i) the distance between any separated exposed-conductive-parts and between exposed-conductive-parts and extraneous-conductive-parts is not less than 2.5 m or, for parts out of the zone of arm's reach, not less than 1.25 m

(ii) the interposition of effective obstacles between exposed-conductive-parts and extraneous-conductive-parts. Such obstacles are sufficiently effective if they extend the distances to be surmounted to the values stated in item (i) above. They shall not be connected to Earth or to exposed-conductive-parts; as far as possible they shall be of insulating material

(iii) the insulation or insulating arrangement of extraneous-conductive-parts. The insulation shall be of adequate electrical and mechanical strength.

413-05 Protection by earth-free local equipotential bonding (see also Regulation 471-11)

413-05-01 This method shall be used only in special circumstances.

413-05-02 An equipotential bonding conductor shall connect together every simultaneously accessible exposed-conductive-part and extraneous-conductive-part.

413-05-03 The local equipotential bonding conductors shall not be in electrical contact with Earth.

413-05-04 Precautions shall be taken so that persons entering or leaving the equipotential location cannot be exposed to dangerous potential difference, in particular, where a conductive floor insulated from Earth is connected to the earth-free equipotential bonding conductors.

413-06   Protection by electrical separation (see also Regulations 471-12 and 471-14-05)

413-06-01   Protection by electrical separation shall be afforded by compliance with Regulations 413-06-02 and 413-06-03 and with:

(i)   Regulation 413-06-04 for a supply to one item of equipment, or

(ii)   Regulation 413-06-05 for a supply to more than one item of equipment.

413-06-02   The source of supply to the circuit shall comply with the following requirements:

(i)   it shall be either:

    (a) an isolating transformer complying with BS 3535, in which there shall be no connection between the output winding and the body or the protective earthing circuit if any, or

    (b) a source of current such as a motor-generator with windings providing a degree of safety equivalent to that of the safety isolating transformer referred to above

(ii)   a mobile source of supply fed from a fixed installation shall be selected or installed in accordance with Regulation 413-03 (protection by use of Class II equipment or by equivalent insulation)

(iii)   equipment used as a fixed source of supply shall be either:

    (a) selected and installed in accordance with Regulation 413-03, or

    (b) such that the output is separated from the input and from the enclosure by insulation satisfying the conditions of Regulation 413-03. If such a source supplies several items of equipment, exposed-conductive-parts of that equipment shall not be connected to the exposed-conductive-parts of the source

(iv)   the voltage of the electrically separated circuit shall not exceed 500 V.

413-06-03   The separated circuit shall comply with the following requirements:

(i)   no live part of the separated circuit shall be connected at any point to another circuit or to Earth and to avoid the risk of a fault to Earth, particular attention shall be given to the insulation of such parts from Earth, especially for flexible cables and cords, and

(ii)   every part of a flexible cable or cord liable to mechanical damage shall be visible throughout its length, and

(iii)   a separate wiring system shall preferably be used for the separated circuit. Alternatively, multicore cables without metallic sheath, or insulated conductors in insulating conduit shall be used, their rated voltage being not less than the highest voltage likely to occur and each circuit shall be protected against overcurrent, and

(iv)   every live part of each separate circuit shall be electrically separated from all other circuits to a standard not less than that provided between the input and output windings of an isolating transformer to BS 3535. The same standard of electrical separation shall also be provided between live parts of relays, contactors etc. included in the separated circuit and between them and live parts of other circuits.

413-06-04   For a circuit supplying a single item of equipment, no exposed-conductive-part of the separated circuit shall be connected either to the protective conductor of the source or to any exposed-conductive-part of any other circuit.

413-06-05   If precautions are taken to protect the separated circuit from damage and insulation failure, a source of supply complying with Regulation 413-06-02 may supply more than one item of equipment provided that all the following requirements are fulfilled:

(i)   every exposed-conductive-part of the separated circuit shall be connected together by an insulated and non-earthed equipotential bonding conductor. Such a conductor shall not be connected to a protective conductor or exposed-conductive-part of any other circuit or to any extraneous-conductive-part, and

(ii)   every socket-outlet shall be provided with a protective conductor contact which shall be connected to the equipotential bonding conductor provided in accordance with item (i) above, and

(iii)   every flexible cable of equipment other than Class II equipment shall embody a protective conductor for use as an equipotential bonding conductor, and

(iv)   it shall be verified that, if two faults to exposed-conductive-parts occur and these are fed by conductors of different polarity, an associated protective device will meet the requirements of Regulation 413-02-04, and

(v)   no exposed-conductive-part of the source shall be simultaneously accessible with any exposed-conductive-part in the separated circuit.

CHAPTER 42

PROTECTION AGAINST THERMAL EFFECTS

CONTENTS

CHAPTER 42

421   GENERAL

421-01-01 Persons, fixed equipment and fixed materials adjacent to electrical equipment shall be protected against harmful effects of heat developed by electrical equipment, or thermal radiation, particularly the following effects:

   (i)   combustion, ignition or degradation of materials

   (ii)   risk of burns

   (iii)   impairment of the safe function of installed equipment.

Electrical equipment shall not present a fire hazard to adjacent materials.

422   PROTECTION AGAINST FIRE AND HARMFUL THERMAL EFFECTS

422-01-01 Fixed electrical equipment shall be selected and installed so that heat generated thereby does not cause danger or harmful effects to adjacent fixed material or to material which may foreseeably be in proximity to such equipment. In addition, any relevant installation instruction of the equipment manufacturer shall be observed.

422-01-02 Where fixed electrical equipment is installed having, in normal operation, a surface temperature sufficient to cause a risk of fire or harmful effects to adjacent materials, one or more of the following installation methods shall be adopted:

   (i)   mounting on a support or within an enclosure which will withstand, without risk of fire or harmful effect, such temperatures as may be generated. The support shall have a low thermal conductance

   (ii)   screening by material which can withstand without risk of fire or harmful effect the heat emitted by the electrical equipment

   (iii)   mounting so as to allow safe dissipation of heat and at a sufficient distance from adjacent material.

422-01-03 Where an arc or high temperature particles may be emitted by fixed equipment one or more of the following installation methods shall be adopted:

   (i)   total enclosure in arc-resistant material

   (ii)   screening by arc-resistant material from materials upon which the emissions could have harmful effects

   (iii)   mounting so as to allow safe extinction of the emissions at a sufficient distance from material upon which the emissions could have harmful effects.

Arc-resistant material used for this protective measure shall be non-ignitable, of low thermal conductivity and of adequate thickness to provide mechanical stability.

422-01-04 Every termination of live conductors or joint between them shall be contained within an enclosure selected in accordance with Regulation 526-03-02.

422-01-05 Where electrical equipment in a single location contains, in total, flammable liquid in excess of 25 litres, adequate precautions shall be taken to prevent the spread of burning liquid, flame and the products of combustion.

422-01-06 Fixed equipment causing a focusing or concentration of heat shall be at a sufficient distance from any fixed object or building element so that the fixed equipment cannot cause a dangerous temperature in the fixed object or building element.

422-01-07 Materials used for the construction of enclosures shall comply with the resistance to heat and fire requirements in an appropriate product standard.

Where no product standard exists, the materials of an enclosure constructed during erection shall withstand the highest temperature likely to be produced by the electrical equipment in normal use.

423 PROTECTION AGAINST BURNS

423-01-01 Excepting equipment for which a British Standard specifies a limiting temperature, an accessible part of fixed electrical equipment within arm's reach shall not attain a temperature in excess of the appropriate limit stated in Table 42A. Each such part of the fixed installation likely to attain under normal load conditions, even for a short period, a temperature exceeding the appropriate limit in Table 42A shall be guarded so as to prevent accidental contact.

TABLE 42A
The temperature limit under normal load conditions for an
accessible part of equipment within arm's reach

Part	Material of accessible surface	Maximum temperature (°C)
A hand-held means of operation	Metallic Non-metallic	55 65
A part intended to be touched but not hand-held	Metallic Non-metallic	70 80
A part which need not be touched for normal operation	Metallic Non-metallic	80 90

424 PROTECTION AGAINST OVERHEATING

424-01 Forced air heating systems

424-01-01 Forced air heating systems shall be such that their electric heating elements, other than those of central-storage heaters, cannot be activated until the prescribed air flow has been established and are deactivated when the air flow is reduced or stopped. In addition, they shall have two temperature limiting devices independent of each other which prevent permissible temperatures from being exceeded.

424-01-02 The frame and enclosure of electric heating elements shall be of non-ignitable material.

424-02 Appliances producing hot water or steam

424-02-01 All electric appliances producing hot water or steam shall be protected by design or method of erection against overheating in all service conditions.

CHAPTER 43

PROTECTION AGAINST OVERCURRENT

CONTENTS

CHAPTER 43

PROTECTION AGAINST OVERCURRENT

431   GENERAL

431-01-01   Except where the overcurrent is limited in accordance with Section 436, every live conductor shall be protected by one or more devices for automatic interruption of the supply in the event of overload current (Section 433) and fault current (Section 434), in accordance with Section 473.

431-01-02   The protection against overload current and the protection against fault current shall be co-ordinated in accordance with Section 435.

431-01-03   *Deleted by BS 7671 : 1992, Amendment No 1.*

432   NATURE OF PROTECTIVE DEVICES

432-01   **General**

432-01-01   A protective device shall be of the appropriate type indicated in Regulations 432-02 to 432-04.

432-02   **Protection against both overload current and fault current**

432-02-01   Except as permitted by Regulation 434-03-01, a device or devices providing protection against both overload current and fault current shall be capable of breaking and, for a circuit-breaker, making any overcurrent up to and including the prospective fault current at the point where the device is installed. In addition, all devices shall satisfy the requirements of Section 433 and Regulations 434-01-01, 434-03-01 and 434-03-02 and, for conductors in parallel, Regulations 473-01-06 to 473-01-08 and 473-02-05, as appropriate.

432-03   **Protection against overload current only**

432-03-01   A device providing protection against overload current shall satisfy the requirements of Section 433. Such a device may have a breaking capacity below the value of the prospective fault current at the point where the device is installed.

432-04   **Protection against fault current only**

432-04-01   Except as permitted by Regulation 434-03-01 a device providing protection against fault current shall satisfy the requirements of Section 434. Such a device shall be capable of breaking and, for a circuit-breaker, making any fault current up to and including the prospective fault current.

432-05   **Protection of conductors in parallel**

432-05-01   Conductors in parallel shall be protected against overcurrent in accordance with Chapter 47.

433   PROTECTION AGAINST OVERLOAD CURRENT

433-01   **General**

433-01-01   A protective device shall be provided to break any overload current flowing in the circuit conductors before such a current causes a temperature rise detrimental to insulation, joints, terminations or the surroundings of the conductors. Every circuit shall be designed so that a small overload of long duration is unlikely to occur.

433-02   **Co-ordination between conductor and protective device**

433-02-01   The characteristics of each protective device shall satisfy the following conditions:

  (i)   its nominal current or current setting (I_n) is not less than the design current (I_b) of the circuit, and

  (ii)   its nominal current or current setting (I_n) does not exceed the lowest of the current-carrying capacities (I_z) of any of the conductors of the circuit, and

  (iii)   the current (I_2) causing effective operation of the protective device does not exceed 1.45 times the lowest of the current-carrying capacities (I_z) of any of the conductors of the circuit.

433-02-02 Where the device is a general purpose type (gG) fuse to BS 88-2.1, a fuse to BS 88-6, a fuse to BS 1361, a circuit-breaker to BS EN 60898, a circuit-breaker to BS EN 60947-2 or a residual current circuit-breaker with integral overcurrent protection (RCBO) to BS EN 61009-1, compliance with condition (ii) also results in compliance with condition (iii).

433-02-03 Where the device is a semi-enclosed fuse to BS 3036 compliance with condition (iii) is afforded if its nominal current (I_n) does not exceed 0.725 times the current-carrying capacity (I_z) of the lowest rated conductor in the circuit protected.

433-02-04 For a ring final circuit protected by a 30 A or 32 A protective device complying with BS 88, BS 1361, BS 3036, BS EN 60898, BS EN 60947-2 or BS EN 61009-1 (RCBO) and supplying accessories to BS 1363 and wired with copper conductors, the minimum cross-sectional area of both phase and neutral conductors is 2.5 mm^2 except for two-core mineral insulated cables to BS 6207 or BS EN 60702-1 for which the minimum is 1.5 mm^2. Such ring final circuits are deemed to meet the requirements of Regulation 433-02-01 if the current-carrying capacity (I_z) of the cable is not less than 20 A, and if, under the intended conditions of use, the load current in any part of the ring is unlikely to exceed for long periods the current-carrying capacity (I_z) of the cable.

433-03 *Deleted by BS 7671 : 2001, for requirements see Regulations 473-01-06 to 08.*

434 PROTECTION AGAINST FAULT CURRENT

434-01 General

434-01-01 A protective device shall be provided in a circuit to break any fault current flowing in conductors of that same circuit before such current causes danger due to thermal or mechanical effects produced in those conductors or the associated connections.

The nominal current of such a protective device may be greater than the current-carrying capacity of the conductor being protected.

434-02 Determination of prospective fault current

434-02-01 The prospective fault current, under both short-circuit and earth fault conditions, at every relevant point of the complete installation shall be determined. This shall be done by calculation, ascertained by enquiry or by measurement.

434-03 Characteristics of a fault current protective device

434-03-01 Except where the following paragraph applies, the breaking capacity rating of each device shall be not less than the prospective short-circuit current or earth fault current at the point at which the device is installed.

A lower breaking capacity is permitted if another protective device or devices having the necessary breaking capacity is installed on the supply side. In this situation, the characteristics of the devices shall be co-ordinated so that the energy let-through of these devices does not exceed that which can be withstood, without damage, by the device or devices on the load side.

434-03-02 Except as required by Regulations 434-03-03 and 473-02-05, where an overload protective device complying with Section 433 is to provide fault current protection and has a rated breaking capacity not less than the value of the prospective fault current at its point of installation, it may be assumed that the Regulations are satisfied as regards fault current protection of the conductors on the load side of that point.

The validity of the assumption shall be checked, where there is doubt, for conductors in parallel and for certain types of circuit-breaker e.g. non-current-limiting types.

434-03-03 Where a protective device is provided for fault current protection only, the clearance time of the device under both short-circuit and earth fault conditions shall not result in the admissible limiting temperature of any live conductor being exceeded.

The time t, in which a given fault current will raise the live conductors from the highest permissible temperature in normal duty to the limiting temperature, can, as an approximation, be calculated from the formula:

$$t = \frac{k^2 S^2}{I^2}$$

where:

   t   is the duration in seconds

S   is the nominal cross-sectional area of conductor in mm^2

I   is the value of fault current in amperes, expressed for a.c. as the rms value, due account being taken of the current limiting effect of the circuit impedances

k   is a factor taking account of the resistivity, temperature coefficient and heat capacity of the conductor material, and the appropriate initial and final temperatures. For the common materials indicated in Table 43A, the k factor shall be as shown.

If greater accuracy is required, the calculation shall be made in accordance with the method given in BS 7454.

Other values of k may be used where the initial temperature is lower than the appropriate value stated in the table, i.e., where the conductor concerned is intended to carry a current less than its current-carrying capacity in normal service. For materials other than those mentioned in Table 43A, values of k shall be calculated by an appropriate method, and the values of temperature to be assumed shall be in accordance with the recommendations of the cable manufacturer.

For very short durations (less than 0.1 s) where asymmetry of the current is of importance and for current limiting devices, the value of $k^2 S^2$ for the cable shall be greater than the value of let-through energy ($I^2 t$) of the device as quoted by the manufacturer of the device.

TABLE 43A
Values of k for common materials, for calculation of the effects of fault current
These data are applicable only for disconnection times up to 5 seconds.
For longer times the cable manufacturer shall be consulted.

Conductor material	Insulation material	Assumed initial temperature (°C)	Limiting final temperature (°C)	k
Copper	70 °C thermoplastic (general purpose pvc)	70	160/140*	115/103*
	90 °C thermoplastic (pvc)	90	160/140*	100/86*
	60 °C thermosetting (rubber)	60	200	141
	85 °C thermosetting (rubber)	85	220	134
	90 °C thermosetting	90	250	143
	Impregnated paper	80	160	108
Copper	Mineral			
	- plastic covered or exposed to touch	70 (sheath)	160	115
	- bare and neither exposed to touch nor in contact with combustible materials	105 (sheath)	250	135
Aluminium	70 °C thermoplastic (general purpose pvc)	70	160/140*	76/68*
	90 °C thermoplastic (pvc)	90	160/140*	66/57*
	60 °C thermosetting (rubber)	60	200	93
	85 °C thermosetting (rubber)	85	220	89
	90 °C thermosetting	90	250	94
	Impregnated paper	80	160	71

* Where two values of limiting final temperature and of k are given, the lower value relates to cables having conductors of greater than 300 mm^2 cross-sectional area.

434-04   *Deleted by BS 7671 : 2001, for requirements see Regulation 473-02-05.*

435   CO-ORDINATION OF OVERLOAD CURRENT AND FAULT CURRENT PROTECTION

435-01-01   The characteristics of each device for overload current protection and for fault current protection shall be co-ordinated so that the energy let through by the fault current protective device does not exceed that which can be withstood without damage by the overload current protective device.

For a circuit incorporating a motor starter, this regulation does not preclude the type of co-ordination described in BS EN 60947-4-1, in respect of which the advice of the manufacturer of the starter shall be sought.

436   LIMITATION OF OVERCURRENT BY CHARACTERISTICS OF SUPPLY

436-01-01   A conductor shall be considered to be protected against overcurrent where its current-carrying capacity is greater than the current which can be supplied by the source.

CHAPTER 44

PROTECTION AGAINST OVERVOLTAGE

443 PROTECTION AGAINST OVERVOLTAGES OF ATMOSPHERIC ORIGIN OR DUE TO SWITCHING

443-01 Scope and object

443-01-01 This section deals with protection of electrical installations against transient overvoltages of atmospheric origin transmitted by the supply distribution system and against switching overvoltages generated by the equipment within the installation.

Protection according to this section can be expected if the relevant equipment product standards require at least the values of withstand voltage of Table 44A according to the overvoltage category of equipment in the installation. Examples of equipment with various impulse withstand categories are given in Table 44B.

Direct lightning strikes on the low voltage lines of the supply network or on electrical installations are not taken into account (conditions of external influence AQ3).

443-02 Arrangements for overvoltage control

443-02-01 Where an installation is supplied by a low voltage system containing no overhead lines, no additional protection against overvoltage of atmospheric origin is necessary if the impulse withstand voltage of equipment is in accordance with Table 44A.

A suspended cable having insulated conductors with earthed metallic covering is deemed to be an underground cable for the purposes of this section.

443-02-02 Where an installation is supplied by a low voltage network which includes overhead lines or where the installation includes an overhead line and the condition of external influences AQ1 ($\leq$ 25 thunderstorm days per year) exists, no additional protection against overvoltages of atmospheric origin is required if the impulse withstand voltage of equipment is in accordance with Table 44A.

443-02-03 Where an installation is supplied by or includes a low voltage overhead line, a measure of protection against overvoltages of atmospheric origin shall be provided according to Regulation 443-02-05 if the ceraunic level of the location corresponds to the condition of external influences AQ2 (> 25 thunderstorm days per year). The protection level of the surge protective device shall not be higher than the level of overvoltage Category II, given in Table 44A.

443-02-04 As an alternative to the AQ criteria in Regulations 443-02-02 and 443-02-03, the use of surge protection may be based on a risk assessment method.

443-02-05 In the conditions according to Regulation 443-02-03, protection against overvoltages of atmospheric origin shall be provided in the installation of the building by:

  (i) a surge protective device with a protection level not exceeding Category II, or

  (ii) other means providing at least an equivalent attenuation of overvoltages.

443-02-06 Where required or otherwise specified in accordance with this section, overvoltage protective devices shall be located as close as possible to the origin of the installation.

TABLE 44A
Required minimum impulse withstand voltage

Nominal voltage of the installation V	Required minimum impulse withstand voltage kV			
	Category IV (equipment with very high impulse voltage)	Category III (equipment with high impulse voltage)	Category II (equipment with normal impulse voltage)	Category I (equipment with reduced impulse voltage)
230/240 277/480	6	4	2.5	1.5
400/690	8	6	4	2.5
1000	Values to be determined by system engineer or, in the absence of information, the values for 400/690 can be chosen.			

TABLE 44B
Examples of various impulse category equipment

Category	Example
I	Equipment intended to be connected to the fixed electrical installation where protection against transient overvoltage is external to the equipment, either in the fixed installation or between the fixed installation and the equipment. Examples of equipment are household appliances, portable tools and similar loads intended to be connected to circuits in which measures have been taken to limit transient overvoltages.
II	Equipment intended to be connected to the fixed electrical installation e.g. household appliances, portable tools and similar loads, the protective means being either within or external to the equipment.
III	Equipment which is part of the fixed electrical installation and other equipment where a high degree of availability is expected, e.g. distribution boards, circuit-breakers, wiring systems, and equipment for industrial uses, stationary motors with permanent connection to the fixed installation.
IV	Equipment to be used at or in the proximity of the origin of the electrical installation upstream of the main distribution board, e.g. electricity meter, primary overcurrent device, ripple control unit.

CHAPTER 45

PROTECTION AGAINST UNDERVOLTAGE

451   GENERAL

451-01-01 Suitable precautions shall be taken where a reduction in voltage, or loss and subsequent restoration of voltage, could cause danger. Provisions for a circuit supplying a motor shall comply with Regulation 552-01-03.

451-01-02 Where current-using equipment or any other part of the installation may be damaged by a drop in voltage and it is verified that such damage is unlikely to cause danger, one of the following arrangements shall be adopted:

(i) suitable precautions against the damage foreseen shall be provided, or

(ii) it shall be verified, in consultation with the person or body responsible for the operation and maintenance of the installation, that the damage foreseen is an acceptable risk.

451-01-03 A suitable time delay may be incorporated in the operation of an undervoltage protective device if the operation of the equipment to which the protection relates allows without danger a brief reduction or loss of voltage.

451-01-04 Any delay in the opening or reclosing of a contactor shall not impede instantaneous disconnection by a control device or a protective device.

451-01-05 The characteristics of an undervoltage protective device shall be compatible with the requirements for starting and use of the equipment to which the protection relates, as stated in the appropriate British Standard.

451-01-06 Where the reclosure of a protective device is likely to cause danger, the reclosure shall not be automatic.

CHAPTER 46

ISOLATION AND SWITCHING

CONTENTS

CHAPTER 46

ISOLATION AND SWITCHING

460   GENERAL

460-01-01   A means shall be provided for non-automatic isolation and switching to prevent or remove hazards associated with the electrical installation or electrically powered equipment and machines. Such means shall comply with the appropriate requirements of this chapter and of Sections 476 and 537.

460-01-02   A main linked switch or linked circuit-breaker shall be provided as near as practicable to the origin of every installation as a means of switching the supply on load and as a means of isolation.

For a.c. systems, Regulation 460-01-04 applies. For d.c. systems, all poles shall be provided with a means of isolation.

Where an installation is supplied from more than one source, a main switch shall be provided for each source of supply and a durable warning notice shall be permanently fixed in such a position that any person seeking to operate any of these main switches will be warned of the need to operate all such switches to achieve isolation of the installation. Alternatively, a suitable interlock system shall be provided.

460-01-03   Except as provided by Regulation 460-01-05, neither an isolator (disconnector) nor a switch shall break a protective conductor or a PEN conductor.

460-01-04   Combined protective and neutral (PEN) conductors shall not be isolated or switched.

Except as required by Regulation 476-01-03, in TN-S or TN-C-S systems the neutral conductor need not be isolated or switched, where the neutral conductor can reliably be regarded as being at earth potential. For supplies which are provided in accordance with the Electricity Safety, Quality and Continuity Regulations 2002, the supply neutral conductor (PEN or N) is considered to be connected with earth by a suitably low resistance.

460-01-05   Where an installation is supplied from more than one source of energy, one of which requires a means of earthing independent of the means of earthing of other sources and it is necessary to ensure that not more than one means of earthing is applied at any time, a switch may be inserted in the connection between the neutral point and the means of earthing, provided that the switch is a linked switch arranged to disconnect and connect the earthing conductor for the appropriate source, at substantially the same time as the related live conductors.

460-01-06   Provision shall be made for disconnecting the neutral conductor. Where this is a joint it shall be such that it is in an accessible position, can only be disconnected by means of a tool, is mechanically strong and will reliably maintain electrical continuity.

461   ISOLATION

461-01-01   Every circuit shall be capable of being isolated from each of the live supply conductors, except as detailed in Regulation 460-01-04.

Provision may be made for isolation of a group of circuits by a common means, if the service conditions allow this.

461-01-02   Suitable provision shall be made so that precautions can be taken to prevent any equipment from being inadvertently or unintentionally energised.

461-01-03   Where an item of equipment or enclosure contains live parts that are not capable of being isolated by a single device, a durable warning notice shall be permanently fixed in such a position that any person before gaining access to live parts will be warned of the need to use the appropriate isolating devices, unless an interlocking arrangement is provided so that all the circuits concerned are isolated before access is gained.

461-01-04   Where necessary to prevent danger, adequate means shall be provided for the discharge of capacitive or inductive electrical energy.

461-01-05   Each device used for isolation shall be clearly identified by position or durable marking to indicate the installation or circuit which it isolates.

462 SWITCHING OFF FOR MECHANICAL MAINTENANCE

462-01-01 A means of switching off for mechanical maintenance shall be provided where mechanical maintenance may involve a risk of burns or a risk of injury from mechanical movement.

462-01-02 Each device for switching off for mechanical maintenance shall be suitably located, and identified by durable marking where necessary.

462-01-03 Except where the means of switching off is continuously under the control of any person performing such maintenance, suitable provision shall be made so that precautions can be taken to prevent any equipment from becoming unintentionally or inadvertently reactivated during mechanical maintenance.

463 EMERGENCY SWITCHING

463-01-01 A means of emergency switching shall be provided for every part of an installation which it may be necessary to cut off rapidly from the supply in order to prevent or remove danger.

Except as provided in Regulation 460-01-04, where a risk of electric shock is involved the means shall interrupt all live conductors.

463-01-02 A means of emergency switching shall act as directly as possible on the appropriate supply conductors, and shall be such that only a single initiative action is required.

463-01-03 The arrangement of emergency switching shall be such that its operation does not introduce a further hazard or interfere with the complete operation necessary to remove the hazard.

463-01-04 Each device for emergency switching shall be readily accessible and durably marked.

463-01-05 A means of emergency stopping shall be provided where mechanical movement of electrically actuated equipment may give rise to danger.

464 FUNCTIONAL SWITCHING (CONTROL)

464-01 General

464-01-01 A functional switching device shall be provided for each part of a circuit which may require to be controlled independently of other parts of the installation.

464-01-02 Functional switching devices need not necessarily control all live conductors of a circuit.

A switching device shall not be placed solely in the neutral conductor.

464-01-03 All current-using equipment requiring control shall be controlled by an appropriate functional switching device.

A single functional switching device may control several items of equipment intended to operate simultaneously.

464-01-04 Except for use on d.c. where this purpose is specifically excluded, a plug and socket-outlet of rating of not more than 16 A may be used for functional switching.

464-01-05 Functional switching devices enabling the change-over of supply from alternative sources shall switch all live conductors and shall not be capable of connecting the sources in parallel, unless the installation is specifically designed for this condition.

Where alternative sources of supply are provided, no provision is to be made for isolation of the PEN or protective conductors, unless the design specifically requires such isolation.

464-02 Control circuits (auxiliary circuits)

464-02-01 Control circuits shall be designed, arranged and protected to limit dangers resulting from a fault between the control circuit and other conductive parts liable to cause malfunction (e.g. inadvertent operation) of the controlled equipment.

CHAPTER 47

APPLICATION OF PROTECTIVE MEASURES FOR SAFETY

CONTENTS

473 PROTECTION AGAINST OVERCURRENT

473-01 **Protection against overload**

473-01-01 and 473-01-02 *Position of devices for overload protection*

473-01-03 and 473-01-04 *Omission of devices for protection against overload*

473-01-05 *Overload protective devices in IT systems*

473-01-06 *Overload protective of conductors in parallel*

473-01-07 *Equal current sharing between conductors in parallel*

473-01-08 *Unequal current sharing between conductors in parallel*

473-02 **Protection against fault current**

473-02-01 to 473-02-03 *Position of devices for fault current protection*

473-02-04 *Conditions for omission of devices for fault current protection*

473-02-05 *Fault current protection of conductors in parallel*

473-03 **Protection according to the nature of circuits and distribution systems**

473-03-01 to 473-03-03 *Phase conductors*

473-03-04 and 473-03-05 *Neutral conductor - TN or TT systems*

473-03-06 *Neutral conductor - IT systems*

473-03-07 *PEN conductor - TN-C-S systems*

474 *(Reserved for future use)*

475 *(Reserved for future use)*

476 ISOLATION AND SWITCHING

476-01 **General**

476-02 **Isolation**

476-03 **Emergency switching**

476-03-01 to 476-03-03 *Emergency switching*

476-03-04 to 476-03-07 *Other requirements for switching for safety*

CHAPTER 47

APPLICATION OF PROTECTIVE MEASURES FOR SAFETY

470 GENERAL

470-01-01 Protective measures shall be applied in every installation or part of an installation, or to equipment, as required by:

Section 471 - Protection against electric shock
Section 473 - Protection against overcurrent
Section 476 - Isolation and switching.

470-01-02 Precautions shall be taken so that no detrimental influence can occur between various protective measures in the same installation or part of an installation.

471 PROTECTION AGAINST ELECTRIC SHOCK

471-01 General

471-01-01 The application of the various protective measures described in Chapter 41 (relevant regulation numbers are indicated below in brackets) is qualified as follows.

Regulations 471-02 to 471-14 apply, except where otherwise stated, to normal dry conditions where a person can be assumed to have conventional normal body resistance and has no contact directly with earth potential.

Regulations 471-15 and 471-16 prescribe additional particular requirements for installations and locations where the risk of electric shock is increased by reduction in body resistance or by contact with earth potential.

Protection against both direct and indirect contact

471-02 Protection by SELV (Regulation 411-02)

471-02-01 This measure is generally applicable except that for some installations and locations of increased shock risk:

(i) it is the only measure against electric shock permitted, and

(ii) a reduction in the nominal voltage is prescribed, and

(iii) protection against direct contact, as prescribed in Regulation 411-02-09, shall be provided irrespective of the nominal voltage.

For some installations and locations, see the particular requirements of Part 6 of the Regulations.

471-03 Protection by limitation of discharge of energy (Regulation 411-04)

471-03-01 This measure shall be applied only to an individual item of current-using equipment complying with an appropriate British Standard, where the equipment incorporates means of limiting to a safe value the current that can flow from the equipment through the body of a person or livestock. The application of this measure may be extended to a part of an installation derived from such items of equipment, where the British Standard concerned provides specifically for this, e.g. to electric fences supplied from electric fence controllers complying with BS EN 61011 or BS EN 61011-1.

Protection against direct contact

471-04 Protection by insulation of live parts (Regulation 412-02)

471-04-01 This measure relates to basic insulation, and is intended to prevent contact with a live part. It is generally applicable for protection against direct contact, in conjunction with a measure for protection against indirect contact.

471-05 Protection by barriers or enclosures (Regulation 412-03)

471-05-01 This measure is intended to prevent or deter any contact with a live part. It is generally applicable for protection against direct contact, in conjunction with a measure for protection against indirect contact.

471-05-02 The exception in Regulation 412-03-01 allowing for an opening larger than IP2X or IPXXB in a barrier or an enclosure shall be applied only to an item of equipment or accessory complying with a British Standard where compliance with the generality of Regulation 412-03-01 is impracticable by reason of the function of the item, e.g. to a lampholder complying with BS EN 61184 or other appropriate Standard. Wherever that exception is used, the opening shall be as small as is consistent with the requirement for proper functioning and for replacement of a part.

471-06 Protection by obstacles (Regulation 412-04)

471-06-01 This measure is intended to prevent unintentional contact with a live part, but not intentional contact by deliberate circumvention of the obstacle. The application shall be limited to protection against direct contact and in an area accessible only to skilled persons, or to instructed persons under the direct supervision of a skilled person.

For some installations and locations of increased shock risk this protective measure shall not be used. See the particular requirements of Part 6 of the Regulations.

471-07 Protection by placing out of reach (Regulation 412-05)

471-07-01 This measure is intended to prevent unintentional contact with a live part and shall be applied for protection against direct contact. The application of the provisions of Regulations 412-05-02 to 412-05-04 shall be limited to each location accessible only to skilled persons, or instructed persons under the direct supervision of a skilled person.

For some installations and locations of increased shock risk this protective measure shall not be used. See the particular requirements of Part 6 of the Regulations.

Protection against indirect contact

471-08 Protection by earthed equipotential bonding and automatic disconnection of supply
(Regulation 413-02)

471-08-01 The requirement of Regulation 413-02 is generally applicable, and is intended to prevent the occurrence of a voltage of such magnitude and duration between simultaneously accessible conductive parts that danger could arise.

For installations and locations of increased shock risk, such as those in Part 6, additional measures may be required, such as:

   (i)   automatic disconnection of supply shall be by means of a residual current device having a rated residual operating current ($I_{\Delta n}$) not exceeding 30 mA

   (ii)   supplementary equipotential bonding

   (iii)   reduction of maximum fault clearance time.

471-08-02 For an installation which is part of a TN system, the limiting values of earth fault loop impedance and of circuit protective conductor impedance specified by Regulations 413-02-08 and 413-02-10 to 413-02-16 are applicable only where the exposed-conductive-parts of the equipment concerned and any extraneous-conductive-parts are situated within the earthed equipotential zone (see also Regulation 413-02-02).

Where the disconnection times specified by Regulation 413-02-08 cannot be met by the use of an overcurrent protective device, Regulation 413-02-04 shall be applied.

471-08-03 Where a circuit supplies fixed equipment outside the earthed equipotential zone and the equipment has exposed-conductive-parts which may be touched by a person in contact directly with the general mass of Earth, the earth fault loop impedance shall be such that disconnection occurs within the time stated in Table 41A.

471-08-04 *Deleted by BS 7671 : 2001, for requirements see Regulation 471-16-01.*

471-08-05 *Deleted by BS 7671 : 2001, for requirements see Regulation 471-16-02.*

471-08-06 Where the measure is used in an installation forming part of a TT system, every socket-outlet circuit shall be protected by a residual current device and shall comply with Regulation 413-02-16.

471-08-07 Automatic disconnection using a residual current device shall not be applied to a circuit incorporating a PEN conductor.

471-08-08 In every installation which provides for protection against indirect contact by automatic disconnection of supply, a circuit protective conductor shall be run to and terminated at each point in wiring and at each accessory except a lampholder having no exposed-conductive-parts and suspended from such a point.

471-09 Protection by the use of Class II equipment or equivalent insulation (Regulation 413-03)

471-09-01 This measure is intended to prevent the appearance of a dangerous voltage on the exposed metalwork of electrical equipment through a fault in the basic insulation. It is generally applicable to an item of equipment, either by the selection of equipment complying with an appropriate British Standard where that Standard provides for the use of Class II construction or total insulation, or by the application of suitable supplementary insulation during erection.

471-09-02 Where a circuit supplies items of Class II equipment, a circuit protective conductor shall be run to and terminated at each point in the wiring and at each accessory except a lampholder having no exposed-conductive-parts and suspended from such a point. This requirement need not be observed where Regulation 471-09-03 applies.

Exposed metalwork of Class II equipment shall be mounted so that it is not in electrical contact with any part of the installation connected to a protective conductor. Such a contact might impair the Class II protection provided by the equipment specification. In case of doubt the appropriate British Standard for the equipment, or the manufacturer, shall be consulted.

471-09-03 Where this measure is to be used as a sole means of protection against indirect contact (i.e. where a whole installation or circuit is intended to consist entirely of Class II equipment or the equivalent), it shall be verified that the installation or circuit concerned will be under effective supervision in normal use so that no change is made that would impair the effectiveness of the Class II or equivalent insulation. The measure shall not therefore be applied to any circuit which includes a socket-outlet or where a user may change items of equipment without authorisation.

471-09-04 Cable having a non-metallic sheath or a non-metallic enclosure shall not be described as being of Class II construction. However, the use of such cable installed in accordance with Chapter 52 shall be deemed to afford satisfactory protection against direct and indirect contact.

471-10 Protection by non-conducting location (Regulation 413-04)

471-10-01 This measure is intended to prevent simultaneous contact with parts which may be at different potentials through failure of the basic insulation of live parts.

This measure is not recognised in the Regulations for general use and shall be applied only in special situations which are under effective supervision.

This measure shall not be used in certain installations and locations of increased shock risk covered by Part 6 of the Regulations.

471-11 Protection by earth-free local equipotential bonding (Regulation 413-05)

471-11-01 This measure is intended to prevent the appearance of a dangerous voltage between simultaneously accessible parts in the event of failure of the basic insulation. It shall be applied under effective supervision only in special situations which are earth-free. Where this measure is applied, a warning notice complying with Regulation 514-13-02 shall be fixed in a prominent position adjacent to every point of access to the location concerned.

For some installations and locations of increased shock risk this measure shall not be used. See the particular requirements of Part 6 of the Regulations.

471-12 Protection by electrical separation (Regulation 413-06)

471-12-01 This measure is intended, in an individual circuit, to prevent shock current through contact with exposed-conductive-parts which might be energised by a fault in the basic insulation of that circuit. It may be applied to the supply of any individual item of equipment by means of a transformer complying with BS 3535 the secondary of which is not earthed, or a source affording equivalent safety. Its use to supply several items of equipment from a single separated source is recognised in the Regulations only for special situations under effective supervision, where specified by a suitably qualified electrical engineer. Where the measure is used to supply several items of equipment from a single source, a warning notice complying with Regulation 514-13-02 shall be fixed in a prominent position adjacent to every point of access to the location concerned.

471-13   Special provisions and exemptions

471-13-01 For an area to which only skilled persons, or instructed persons directly supervised by a skilled person, have access it is sufficient to provide against unintentional contact with live parts by the use of an obstacle in accordance with Regulations 412-04 and 471-06, or by placing each live part out of reach in accordance with Regulations 412-05 and 471-07, subject also to Regulations 471-13-02 and 471-13-03.

471-13-02 The dimensions of each passageway and working platform for an open type switchboard and other equipment having dangerous exposed live parts shall be adequate such as to allow persons, without hazard, to:

    (i)   operate and maintain the equipment, and

    (ii) pass one another as necessary with ease, and

    (iii) back away from the equipment.

471-13-03 Areas reserved for skilled or instructed persons shall be clearly and visibly indicated by suitable warning signs.

471-13-04 It is permissible to dispense with protective measures against indirect contact in the following instances:

    (i)   overhead line insulator brackets and metal parts connected to them if such parts are not situated within arm's reach

    (ii) steel reinforced concrete poles in which the steel reinforcement is not accessible

    (iii) exposed-conductive-parts which, owing to their reduced dimensions or their disposition cannot be gripped or cannot be contacted by a major surface of the human body, provided that connection of these parts to a protective conductor cannot readily be made or cannot be reliably maintained. This dispensation includes small isolated metal parts such as bolts, rivets, nameplates not exceeding 50 mm x 50 mm and cable clips

    (iv) fixing screws for non-metallic accessories provided that there is no appreciable risk of the screws coming into contact with live parts

    (v) inaccessible lengths of metal conduit not exceeding 150 mm

    (vi) metal enclosures mechanically protecting equipment complying with Regulations 413-03-01 to 413-03-09 and 471-09-01

    (vii) unearthed street furniture supplied from an overhead line and inaccessible in normal use.

471-14   Extra-low voltage systems other than SELV

471-14-01 Where extra-low voltage is used but not all the requirements of Regulation 411-02 regarding SELV are fulfilled, the appropriate measures described in Regulations 471-14-02 to 471-14-06 shall be taken in order to provide protection against electric shock. Systems employing these measures are:

    (i)   PELV systems (Regulation 471-14-02)

    (ii) functional extra-low voltage systems (Regulations 471-14-03 to 471-14-06).

471-14-02 If the extra-low voltage system complies with the requirements of Regulation 411-02 for SELV except for the requirements of Regulations 411-02-05(ii) and 411-02-07, protection against direct contact shall be provided by either:

    (i)   barriers or enclosures affording a degree of protection of at least IP2X or IPXXB, or

    (ii) insulation capable of withstanding a type-test voltage of 500 V a.c. rms for 60 seconds.

Protection against direct contact as provided above is not required if the equipment is within a building in which main equipotential bonding is applied in accordance with Regulation 413-02-02 and the voltage does not exceed:

    (a) 25 V a.c. rms or 60 V ripple-free d.c. when the equipment is normally used in dry locations only and large-area contact of live parts with the human body is not to be expected

    (b) 6 V a.c. rms or 15 V ripple-free d.c. in all other cases.

471-14-03 If the extra-low voltage system does not comply with the requirements of Section 411 for SELV in some respect other than that specified in Regulation 471-14-02, protection against direct contact shall be provided by one or more of the following:

    (i)   barriers or enclosures according to Regulation 412-03

    (ii) insulation corresponding to the minimum test voltage required for the primary circuit.

In addition, protection against indirect contact shall be provided in accordance with Regulations 471-14-04 or 471-14-05.

Where the extra-low voltage circuit is used to supply equipment whose insulation does not comply with the minimum test voltage required for the primary circuit, the accessible insulation of that equipment shall be reinforced during erection so that it is capable of withstanding a type-test voltage of 1500 V a.c. rms for 60 seconds.

471-14-04 If the primary circuit of the functional extra-low voltage source is protected by automatic disconnection, exposed-conductive-parts of equipment in the functional extra-low voltage system shall be connected to the protective conductor of the primary circuit. This shall not exclude the possibility of connecting a conductor of the functional extra-low voltage circuit to the protective conductor of the primary circuit.

471-14-05 If the primary circuit of the functional extra-low voltage source is protected by electrical separation (Regulation 413-06), the exposed-conductive-parts of equipment in the functional extra-low voltage circuit shall be connected to the non-earthed protective conductor of the primary circuit. This latter requirement shall be deemed not to contravene Regulations 413-06-04 and 413-06-05, the combination of the electrically separated circuit and the extra-low voltage circuit being regarded as one electrically separated circuit.

471-14-06 Every socket-outlet and luminaire supporting coupler in a functional extra-low voltage system shall require the use of a plug which is not dimensionally compatible with those used for any other system in use in the same premises.

471-15   Automatic disconnection and reduced low voltage systems

471-15-01 Where for functional reasons the use of extra-low voltage is impracticable and there is no requirement for the use of SELV, a reduced low voltage system may be used as specified in Regulations 471-15-02 to 471-15-07.

471-15-02 The nominal voltage of the reduced low voltage circuits shall not exceed 110 V a.c. rms between phases (three-phase 63.5 V to earthed neutral, single-phase 55 V to earthed midpoint).

471-15-03 The source of supply to a reduced low voltage circuit shall be one of the following:

  (i)   a double wound isolating transformer complying with BS 3535-2, or

  (ii)   a motor-generator having windings providing isolation equivalent to that provided by the windings of an isolating transformer, or

  (iii)   a source independent of other supplies, e.g. an engine driven generator.

471-15-04 The neutral (star) point of the secondary windings of three-phase transformers and generators, or the midpoint of the secondary windings of single-phase transformers and generators, shall be connected to Earth.

471-15-05 Protection against direct contact shall be provided by insulation in accordance with Regulations 412-02 and 471-04 or by a barrier or an enclosure in accordance with Regulations 412-03 and 471-05.

471-15-06 Protection against indirect contact by automatic disconnection shall be provided by means of an overcurrent protective device in each phase conductor or by a residual current device, and all exposed-conductive-parts of the reduced low voltage system shall be connected to Earth. The earth fault loop impedance at every point of utilisation, including socket-outlets, shall be such that the disconnection time does not exceed 5 s.

Where a circuit-breaker is used, the maximum value of earth fault loop impedance (Z_s) shall be determined by the formula of Regulation 413-02-08. Alternatively, the values specified in Table 471A may be used instead of calculation for the nominal voltages to Earth (U_o) and for the types and ratings of overcurrent device listed therein.

Where a fuse is used, maximum values of earth fault loop impedance (Z_s) corresponding to a disconnection time of 5 s are stated in Table 471A for nominal voltages to Earth (U_o) of 55 V and 63.5 V.

For types and rated currents of fuses other than those mentioned in Table 471A, reference should be made to the appropriate British Standard to determine the value of I_a for compliance with Regulation 413-02-08, according to the appropriate value of the nominal voltage to Earth (U_o).

Where a residual current device is used, the product of the rated residual operating current ($I_{\Delta n}$) in amperes and the earth fault loop impedance in ohms shall not exceed 50.

Maximum earth fault loop impedance (Z_S ohms) for a disconnection time 5 s and U_0 of 55 V (single-phase) and 63.5 V (three-phase) - see Regulations 471-15-02 and 471-15-06

	Circuit-breakers to BS EN 60898 and RCBOs to BS EN 61009 Type						General purpose (gG) fuses to BS 88-2.1 and BS 88-6	
	B		C		D			
U_0 (Volts)	55	63.5	55	63.5	55	63.5	55	63.5
Rating amperes								
6	1.83	2.12	0.92	1.07	0.47	0.53	3.20	3.70
10	1.10	1.27	0.55	0.64	0.28	0.32	1.77	2.05
16	0.69	0.79	0.34	0.40	0.18	0.20	1.00	1.15
20	0.55	0.64	0.28	0.32	0.14	0.16	0.69	0.80
25	0.44	0.51	0.22	0.26	0.11	0.13	0.55	0.63
32	0.34	0.40	0.17	0.20	0.09	0.10	0.44	0.51
40	0.28	0.32	0.14	0.16	0.07	0.08	0.32	0.37
50	0.22	0.25	0.11	0.13	0.06	0.06	0.25	0.29
63	0.17	0.20	0.09	0.10	0.04	0.05	0.20	0.23
80	0.14	0.16	0.07	0.08	0.04	0.04	0.14	0.16
100	0.11	0.13	0.05	0.06	0.03	0.03	0.10	0.12
125	0.09	0.10	0.04	0.05	0.02	0.03	0.08	0.09
I_n	$\dfrac{11}{I_n}$	$\dfrac{12.7}{I_n}$	$\dfrac{5.5}{I_n}$	$\dfrac{6.4}{I_n}$	$\dfrac{2.8}{I_n}$	$\dfrac{3.2}{I_n}$		

NOTE: The circuit loop impedances given in the table should not be exceeded when the conductors are at their normal operating temperature. If the conductors are at a different temperature when tested, the reading should be adjusted accordingly.

471-15-07 Every plug, socket-outlet and cable coupler of a reduced low voltage system shall have a protective conductor contact and shall not be dimensionally compatible with any plug, socket-outlet or cable coupler for use at any other voltage or frequency in the same installation.

471-16 Supplies for portable equipment outdoors

471-16-01 A socket-outlet rated at 32 A or less which may reasonably be expected to supply portable equipment for use outdoors shall be provided with supplementary protection to reduce the risk associated with direct contact by means of a residual current device having the characteristics specified in Regulation 412-06-02(ii).

This regulation does not apply to a socket-outlet supplied by a circuit incorporating one or more of the protective measures specified in items (i) to (iii) below and complying with the Regulations indicated:

 (i)   protection by SELV (see Regulations 411-02 and 471-02)

 (ii) protection by electrical separation (see Regulations 413-06 and 471-12)

 (iii) protection by automatic disconnection and reduced low voltage systems (see Regulation 471-15).

471-16-02 Except where one or more of the protective measures specified in items (i) to (iii) of Regulation 471-16-01 are applied in compliance with the corresponding regulations stated therein, a circuit supplying portable equipment for use outdoors, connected other than through a socket-outlet by means of flexible cable or cord having a current-carrying capacity of 32 A or less, shall be provided with supplementary protection to reduce the risk associated with direct contact, by means of a residual current device having the characteristics specified in Regulation 412-06-02(ii).

472   *(Reserved for future use)*

473 PROTECTION AGAINST OVERCURRENT

473-01 Protection against overload

Position of devices for overload protection

473-01-01 A device for protection against overload shall be placed at the point where a reduction occurs in the value of current-carrying capacity of the conductors of the installation due to a change in cross-sectional area, method of installation, type of cable or conductor, or in environmental conditions. This requirement does not apply where the arrangements mentioned in Regulation 473-01-02 are adopted, and no overload protective device need be provided where Regulation 473-01-04 applies.

473-01-02 A device protecting a conductor against overload may be placed along the run of that conductor, provided that the part of the run between the point where the value of current-carrying capacity is reduced and the position of the protective device has no branch circuit or outlet for the connection of current-using equipment and fulfils one of the following conditions:

(i) it is protected against fault current in accordance with the requirements stated in Section 434, or

(ii) it satisfies the requirements of Regulation 473-02-02.

This regulation shall not be applied to installations situated in locations presenting an abnormal fire risk or risk of explosion and where special requirements or recommendations apply (see Regulation 110-01-01 and Section 482).

Omission of devices for protection against overload

473-01-03 The omission of devices for protection against overload is permitted for circuits supplying current-using equipment where unexpected disconnection of the circuit could cause danger.

Examples of such cases are:

(i) exciter circuits of rotating machines

(ii) supply circuits of lifting magnets

(iii) secondary circuits of current transformers

(iv) circuits which supply fire extinguishing devices.

In such situations consideration shall be given to the provision of an overload alarm.

473-01-04 Devices for protection against overload need not be provided:

(i) for a conductor situated on the load side of the point where a reduction occurs in the value of current-carrying capacity, where the conductor is effectively protected against overload by a protective device placed on the supply side of that point

(ii) for a conductor which, because of the characteristics of the load or the supply, is not likely to carry overload current

(iii) *Deleted by BS 7671 : 1992, Amendment No 1.*

(iv) at the origin of an installation where the distributor provides an overload device and agrees that it affords protection to the part of the installation between the origin and the main distribution point of the installation where further overload protection is provided.

Overload protective devices in IT systems

473-01-05 The provisions of Regulations 473-01-02 and 473-01-04 are applicable to an installation forming part of an IT system only where the conductors concerned are protected by a residual current device, or all the equipment supplied by the circuit concerned (including the conductors) complies with the protective measure described in Regulations 413-03-01 to 413-03-09 (i.e. protection by use of Class II equipment or by equivalent insulation) or by use of an insulation monitoring device.

Overload protection of conductors in parallel

473-01-06 Except for a ring final circuit where spurs are allowed, where a single protective device protects conductors in parallel there shall be no branch circuits or devices for isolation or switching in any of the parallel conductors.

Equal current sharing between conductors in parallel

473-01-07 Where a single device protects conductors in parallel sharing currents equally, the value of I_z to be used in Regulation 433-02 is the sum of the current-carrying capacities of the various conductors.

It is deemed that current sharing is equal if the requirements of the second paragraph of Regulation 523-02-01 are satisfied.

Unequal current sharing between conductors in parallel

473-01-08 Where the use of a single conductor per phase is impractical and the currents in the parallel conductors are unequal, the design current and requirements for overload protection for each conductor shall be considered individually.

473-02   Protection against fault current

Position of devices for fault current protection

473-02-01 A device for protection against fault current shall be placed at the point where a reduction occurs in the value of current-carrying capacity of the conductors of the installation such as may be due to a change in cross-sectional area, method of installation, type of cable or conductor, or in environmental conditions. This requirement does not apply where the arrangements mentioned in Regulations 473-02-02 or 473-02-03 are adopted, and no fault current protective device need be provided where Regulation 473-02-04 applies.

473-02-02 The fault current protective device may be placed at a point on the load side of that specified by Regulation 473-02-01 under the following conditions:

Between the point where the value of current-carrying capacity is reduced and the position of the protective device, each conductor shall:

   (i)   not exceed 3 m in length, and

  (ii)   be erected in such a manner as to reduce to a minimum the risk of fault current, and

 (iii)   be erected in such a manner as to reduce to a minimum the risk of fire or danger to persons.

473-02-03 The fault current protective device may be positioned other than as required by Regulation 473-02-01, where a protective device on the supply side of that position protects the load side conductors against fault current, in accordance with Regulation 434-03-03.

This regulation shall not be applied to installations situated in locations presenting an abnormal fire risk or risk of explosion and where special requirements or recommendations apply (see Regulation 110-01-01 and Section 482).

Conditions for omission of devices for fault current protection

473-02-04 A device for protection against fault current may be omitted in the following circumstances provided that the conductor thus not protected against fault current complies with conditions (ii) and (iii) of Regulation 473-02-02:

   (i)   for a conductor connecting a generator, transformer, rectifier or battery with its control panel

  (ii)   in a measuring circuit where disconnection could cause danger, e.g. secondary circuit of a current transformer

 (iii)   in a circuit supplying equipment where unexpected opening of the circuit causes a greater danger than a fault current condition

 (iv)   at the origin of an installation where the distributor provides a fault current device and agrees that device affords protection to the parts of the installation between the origin and the main distribution point of the installation where the next step for fault current protection is provided.

Fault current protection of conductors in parallel

473-02-05 A single protective device may protect conductors in parallel against the effects of fault currents provided that the operating characteristic of that device results in its effective operation should a fault occur at the most onerous position in one parallel conductor. Account shall be taken of the sharing of the fault currents between the parallel conductors. A fault can be fed from both ends of a parallel conductor.

If operation of a single protective device may not be effective then one or more of the following measures shall be taken:

   (i)   the wiring is carried out in such a way as to reduce the risk of a fault in any parallel conductor to a minimum, for example, by protection against mechanical damage, and conductors are not placed close to combustible material, or

   (ii)   for two conductors in parallel a fault current protective device is provided at the supply end of each parallel conductor, or

   (iii)   for more than two conductors in parallel fault current protective devices are provided at the supply and load ends of each parallel conductor.

473-03   Protection according to the nature of circuits and distribution systems

Phase conductors

473-03-01 A means of detection of overcurrent shall be provided for each phase conductor, and shall cause the disconnection of the conductor in which the overcurrent is detected, but not necessarily the disconnection of other live conductors except where the disconnection of one phase could cause danger or damage.

473-03-02 In a TT system, for a circuit supplied between phases and in which the neutral conductor is not distributed, overcurrent protection need not be provided for one of the phase conductors, provided that both the following conditions are fulfilled:

   (i)   there exists, in the same circuit or on the supply side, differential protection intended to cause disconnection of all the phase conductors, and

   (ii)   the neutral conductor is not distributed from an artificial neutral point of the circuit situated on the load side of that differential protective device.

473-03-03 In an IT system without a neutral conductor the overload protective device may be omitted in one of the phase conductors if a residual current protective device is installed in each circuit.

Neutral conductor - TN or TT systems

473-03-04 In an installation forming part of a TN or TT system, where the cross-sectional area of the neutral conductor is at least equal or equivalent to that of the phase conductors, it is not usually necessary to provide overcurrent detection and the associated disconnecting device for the neutral conductor.

Overcurrent detection shall, however, be provided for the neutral conductor in a polyphase circuit where the harmonic content of the phase currents is such that the current in the neutral conductor is reasonably expected to exceed that in the phase conductors. This detection shall cause disconnection of the phase conductors but not necessarily of the neutral conductor.

473-03-05 In an installation forming part of a TN or TT system, where the cross-sectional area of the neutral conductor is less than that of the phase conductors, overcurrent detection shall be provided for the neutral conductor, appropriate to the cross-sectional area of the conductor. This detection shall cause the disconnection of the phase conductors but not necessarily of the neutral conductor.

Overcurrent detection need not be provided for the neutral conductor where all the following conditions are fulfilled:

   (i)   the neutral conductor is protected against fault current by the protective device for the phase conductors of the circuit, and

   (ii)   the maximum current, including harmonics, likely to be carried by the neutral conductor in normal service, is significantly less than the value of the current-carrying capacity of that conductor, and

   (iii)   the neutral conductor has been selected in accordance with Section 524-02.

Neutral conductor - IT systems

473-03-06 Where the neutral conductor is distributed then, except where the conditions described in (i) or (ii) below apply, overcurrent detection shall be provided for the neutral conductor of every circuit. Such overcurrent detection shall cause disconnection of all live conductors (including the neutral) of the circuit with which it is associated. The exceptional conditions are:

(i) where the particular neutral conductor is effectively protected against fault current by a protective device placed on the supply side, for example, at the origin of the installation, in accordance with Regulation 434-03-01

(ii) where the particular circuit is protected by a residual current operated protective device with a rated residual operating current ($I_{\Delta n}$) not exceeding 0.15 times the current-carrying capacity of the corresponding neutral conductor. This device shall disconnect all the live conductors of the corresponding circuit, including the neutral conductor.

PEN conductor - TN-C-S systems

473-03-07 The requirements of Regulations 473-03-04 and 473-03-05 for the neutral conductor also apply to PEN conductors. The overcurrent device shall not disconnect the PEN conductor and Regulations 460-01-03 and 460-01-04 apply.

474 *(Reserved for future use)*

475 *(Reserved for future use)*

476 ISOLATION AND SWITCHING

476-01 General

476-01-01 Every installation shall be provided with means of isolation and switching complying with Chapter 46, and with the other means of switching for safety required by Regulation 476-01-02. This requirement is satisfied where the distributor provides switchgear complying with Chapter 46 at the origin of the installation and agrees that it may be used as the means of isolation for that part of the installation between the origin and the main distribution point of the installation where the next step for isolation is provided.

Means of electrical switching off for mechanical maintenance, or means of emergency switching, or both, shall be provided for any parts of the installation to which Section 462 or 463 respectively applies.

Where more than one of these functions are to be performed by a common device, the arrangement and characteristics of the device shall satisfy all the requirements of the Regulations for the various functions concerned. Devices for functional switching may serve also for the purposes described above where they satisfy the relevant requirements.

476-01-02 Every circuit and final circuit shall be provided with a means of switching for interrupting the supply on load. A group of circuits may be switched by a common device. Additionally, such means shall be provided for every circuit or other part of the installation which it may be necessary for safety reasons to switch independently of other circuits or other parts of the installation. This regulation does not apply to short connections between the origin of the installation and the consumer's main switchgear.

476-01-03 A main switch intended for operation by unskilled persons e.g. of a household or similar installation, shall interrupt both live conductors of a single-phase supply.

476-02 Isolation

476-02-01 Where an isolator (disconnector) is to be used in conjunction with a circuit-breaker as a means of isolating main switchgear for maintenance, it shall be interlocked with the circuit-breaker; alternatively, it shall be so placed and/or guarded that it can be operated only by skilled persons.

476-02-02 Where an isolating device for a particular circuit is placed remotely from the equipment to be isolated, provision shall be made so that the means of isolation can be secured in the open position. Where this provision takes the form of a lock or removable handle, the key or handle shall be non-interchangeable with any others used for a similar purpose within the premises.

476-02-03 Every motor circuit shall be provided with a disconnector which shall disconnect the motor and all equipment, including any automatic circuit-breaker, used therewith.

476-02-04 For every electric discharge lighting installation having an open circuit voltage exceeding low voltage, one or more of the following means shall be provided for the isolation of every self-contained luminaire, or of every circuit supplying luminaires at a voltage exceeding low voltage:

  (i) an interlock on a self-contained luminaire, so arranged that before access can be had to live parts the supply is automatically disconnected, such means being additional to the switch normally used for controlling the circuit

 (ii) an effective local means for the isolation of the circuit from the supply, such means being additional to the switch normally used for controlling the circuit

(iii) a switch having a lock or removable handle, or a distribution board which can be locked, in either case complying with Regulation 476-02-02.

476-03   Emergency switching

476-03-01 For every emergency switching device, account shall be taken of the intended use of the premises so that access to the device is not likely to be impeded in the conditions of emergency foreseen.

476-03-02 A means of emergency stopping shall be provided in every place where an electrically driven machine may give rise to danger. This means shall be readily accessible and easily operated. Where more than one means of starting the machine is provided and danger might be caused by unexpected restarting, means shall be provided to prevent such restarting.

476-03-03 Where additional danger could arise from inappropriate operation of an emergency switching device, the switching device shall be arranged so as to be available for operation by skilled and instructed persons only.

Other requirements for switching for safety

476-03-04 Every fixed or stationary appliance which may give rise to a hazard in normal use and is connected to the supply other than by means of a plug and socket-outlet complying with Regulation 537-05-04 shall be provided with a means of interrupting the supply on load. The operation of the means of interrupting the supply on load shall be so placed as not to put the operator in danger. This means may be incorporated in the appliance or, if separate from the appliance, shall be in a readily accessible position. Where two or more such appliances are installed in the same room, one interrupting means may be used to control all the appliances.

476-03-05 A fireman's switch shall be provided in the low voltage circuit supplying :

  (i) exterior electrical installations operating at a voltage exceeding low voltage, and

 (ii) interior discharge lighting installations operating at a voltage exceeding low voltage.

For the purpose of this regulation, an installation in a covered market, arcade or shopping mall is considered to be an exterior installation. A temporary installation in a permanent building used for exhibitions is considered not to be an exterior installation.

This requirement does not apply to a portable discharge lighting luminaire or to a sign of rating not exceeding 100 W and fed from a readily accessible socket-outlet.

476-03-06 Every exterior installation covered by Regulation 476-03-05 on each single premises shall wherever practicable be controlled by a single fireman's switch. Similarly, every internal installation covered by Regulation 476-03-05 in each single premises shall be controlled by a single fireman's switch independent of the switch for any exterior installation.

476-03-07 Every fireman's switch provided for compliance with Regulation 476-03-05 shall comply with all the relevant requirements of the following items (i) to (iv) and any requirements of the local fire authority:

  (i) for an exterior installation, the switch shall be outside the building and adjacent to the equipment, or alternatively a notice indicating the position of the switch shall be placed adjacent to the equipment and a notice shall be fixed near the switch so as to render it clearly distinguishable

 (ii) for an interior installation, the switch shall be in the main entrance to the building or in another position to be agreed with the local fire authority

(iii) the switch shall be placed in a conspicuous position, reasonably accessible to firemen and, except where otherwise agreed with the local fire authority, at not more than 2.75 m from the ground or the standing beneath the switch

(iv) where more than one switch is installed on any one building, each switch shall be clearly marked to indicate the installation or part of the installation which it controls.

CHAPTER 48

CHOICE OF PROTECTIVE MEASURES AS A FUNCTION OF EXTERNAL INFLUENCES

CONTENTS

CHAPTER 48

CHOICE OF PROTECTIVE MEASURES AS A FUNCTION OF EXTERNAL INFLUENCES

482   PRECAUTIONS WHERE PARTICULAR RISKS OF DANGER OF FIRE EXIST

482-01   General

482-01-01 The requirements of this section are additional to those of Chapter 42 and Section 527.

This section applies to:

(i) installations in locations with risks of fire due to the nature of processed or stored materials e.g. the manufacturing, processing or storage of combustible materials, the accumulation of materials such as dust and fibres as in barns, woodworking factories, paper mills, textile factories or similar

(ii) installations in locations constructed of combustible materials.

Electrical equipment shall be selected and erected such that its temperature in normal operation, and foreseeable temperature rise in the event of a fault, is unlikely to cause a fire, taking due account of external influences. This shall be achieved by the construction of the equipment or by additional protective measures taken during erection.

This section does not apply to:

(iii) selection and erection of installations in locations with explosion risks, see BS EN 50014 : Electrical apparatus for potentially explosive atmospheres: General requirements

(iv) installations in escape routes, see, for example, BS 5266.

482-02   Locations with risks of fire due to the nature of processed or stored materials

482-02-01 Electrical equipment shall be restricted, so far as is reasonably practicable, to that necessary for use in the location. The equipment shall fulfil the requirements of Regulations 482-02-02 to 482-02-18.

482-02-02 Where materials such as dust or fibres, sufficient to cause a fire hazard, could accumulate on enclosures of electrical equipment, adequate measures shall be taken to prevent the enclosures from exceeding the temperatures given in Regulation 482-02-18.

482-02-03 Electrical equipment shall be suitable for the location and its enclosure shall provide a degree of protection of at least IP5X.

482-02-04 A cable not completely embedded in non-combustible material such as plaster or concrete or otherwise protected from fire, shall meet the flame propagation characteristics as specified in BS EN 50265-2-1 or 2-2.

Where the risk of flame propagation is high, e.g. in long vertical runs or bunched cables, the cable shall meet the flame propagation characteristics as specified in BS 4066-3.

482-02-05 A wiring system which passes through but is not intended for electrical supply within the location shall:

(i) meet the requirements of Regulations 482-02-03 or 482-02-04 as applicable, and

(ii) have no joint within the location, unless the joint is placed in an enclosure that does not adversely affect the flame propagation characteristics of the wiring system.

482-02-06 Except for mineral insulated cables and busbar trunking systems, wiring systems shall be protected against insulation faults to earth as follows:

(i) in TN and TT systems, by residual current devices having a rated residual operating current ($I_{\Delta n}$) not exceeding 300 mA in accordance with Regulation 531-02-04;

(ii) in IT systems, by insulation monitoring devices with audible and visible signals. Adequate supervision is required to facilitate manual disconnection as soon as appropriate. In the event of a second fault, the disconnection time of the overcurrent protective device shall not exceed 5 s.

482-02-07 A PEN conductor shall not be used. This regulation does not apply to wiring systems which pass through the location.

482-02-08 Every circuit shall be capable of being isolated from all live supply conductors by a linked switch or linked circuit-breaker.

Provision may be made for isolation of a group of circuits by a common means, if the service conditions allow this.

482-02-09 Exposed bare and live conductors shall not be used.

482-02-10 Flexible cables and flexible cords shall be of the following construction:

(i) heavy duty type having a voltage rating of not less than 450/750 V, or

(ii) suitably protected against mechanical damage.

482-02-11 Motors which are automatically or remotely controlled or which are not continuously supervised, shall be protected against excessive temperature by a protective device with manual reset. Motors with star-delta starting shall be protected against excessive temperature in both the star and delta connections.

482-02-12 In locations where there may be fire hazards due to presence of materials such as dust and fibres, only luminaires with limited surface temperature in accordance with BS EN 60598-2-24 shall be used.

482-02-13 Except as otherwise recommended by the manufacturer, spotlights and projectors shall be installed at the following minimum distances from combustible materials:

(i) rating up to 100 W – 0.5 m

(ii) rating over 100 up to 300 W – 0.8 m

(iii) rating over 300 up to 500 W – 1.0 m

482-02-14 The luminaire shall be of a type that prevents lamp components from falling from the luminaire.

482-02-15 Where heating and ventilation systems containing heating elements are installed, the dust or fibre content and the temperature of the air shall not present a fire hazard. Temperature limiting devices according to Regulation 424-01 shall have manual reset.

482-02-16 Heating appliances shall be fixed. Where a heating appliance is mounted close to combustible materials, barriers shall be provided to prevent the ignition of such materials.

482-02-17 Heat storage appliances shall be of a type which prevent the ignition of combustible dust and/or fibres by the heat storing core.

482-02-18 Enclosures of equipment such as heaters and resistors shall not attain higher surface temperatures than:

(i) 90 °C under normal conditions, and

(ii) 115 °C under fault conditions.

482-03 Locations with combustible constructional materials

482-03-01 Electrical equipment, e.g. installation boxes and distribution boards, installed on or in a combustible wall shall comply with the relevant standard for enclosure temperature rise.

482-03-02 Electrical equipment that does not comply with Regulation 482-03-01 shall be enclosed with a suitable thickness of non-flammable material. The effect of the material on the heat dissipation from electrical equipment shall be taken into account.

482-03-03 Cables and cords shall comply with the requirements of BS EN 50265-2-1 or 2-2.

482-03-04 Conduit and trunking systems shall be in accordance with BS EN 50086-1 and BS EN 50085-1 respectively and shall meet the fire resistance tests within these standards.

PART 5

SELECTION AND ERECTION OF EQUIPMENT

CONTENTS

CHAPTER 51

COMMON RULES

CONTENTS

PART 5

SELECTION AND ERECTION OF EQUIPMENT

CHAPTER 51

COMMON RULES

510   GENERAL

510-01-01   This chapter deals with the selection of equipment and its erection to provide compliance with the measures of protection for safety, the requirements for proper functioning for intended use of the installation, and the requirements appropriate to the external influences foreseen. Every item of equipment shall be selected and erected so as to allow compliance with the requirements of this Chapter and other relevant chapters of these Regulations.

511   COMPLIANCE WITH STANDARDS

511-01-01   Every item of equipment shall comply with the relevant requirements of the applicable British Standard, or Harmonized Standard appropriate to the intended use of the equipment. The edition of the Standard shall be the current edition, with those amendments pertaining at a date to be agreed by the parties to the contract concerned (see Appendix 1).

Alternatively, if equipment complying with a foreign national standard based on an IEC Standard is to be used, the designer or other person responsible for specifying the installation shall verify that any differences between that standard and the corresponding British Standard or Harmonized Standard will not result in a lesser degree of safety than that afforded by compliance with the British Standard.

511-01-02   Where equipment to be used is not covered by a British Standard or Harmonized Standard or is used outside the scope of its standard, the designer or other person responsible for specifying the installation shall confirm that the equipment provides the same degree of safety as that afforded by compliance with the Regulations.

512   OPERATIONAL CONDITIONS AND EXTERNAL INFLUENCES

512-01   **Voltage**

512-01-01   Every item of equipment shall be suitable for the nominal voltage (U_o) of the installation or the part of the installation concerned, where necessary taking account of the highest and/or lowest voltage likely to occur in normal service. In an IT system, equipment shall be insulated for the nominal voltage between phases.

512-02   **Current**

512-02-01   Every item of equipment shall be suitable for:

  (i) the design current, taking into account any capacitive and inductive effects, and

 (ii) the current likely to flow in abnormal conditions for such periods of time as are determined by the characteristics of the protective devices concerned.

Switchgear, protective devices, accessories and other types of equipment shall not be connected to conductors intended to operate at a temperature exceeding 70 °C at the equipment in normal service, unless the equipment manufacturer has confirmed that the equipment is suitable for such conditions.

512-03   **Frequency**

512-03-01   If frequency has an influence on the characteristics of the equipment, the rated frequency of the equipment shall correspond to the nominal frequency of the supply to the circuit concerned.

512-04   **Power**

512-04-01   Every item of equipment selected on the basis of its power characteristics shall be suitable for the duty demanded of the equipment.

512-05   Compatibility

512-05-01   Every item of equipment shall be selected and erected so that it will neither cause harmful effects to other equipment nor impair the supply during normal service including switching operations.

512-06   External influences

512-06-01   Every item of equipment shall be of a design appropriate to the situation in which it is to be used or its mode of installation shall take account of the conditions likely to be encountered, including the test requirements of Part 7.

If the equipment does not, by its construction, have the characteristics relevant to the external influences of its location, it shall be provided with appropriate additional protection in the erection of the installation. Such protection shall not adversely affect the operation of the equipment thus protected.

512-06-02   Where different external influences occur simultaneously the degree of protection provided shall take account of any mutual effect.

513   ACCESSIBILITY

513-01-01   Except for a joint in cables where Section 526 allows such a joint to be inaccessible, every item of equipment shall be arranged so as to facilitate its operation, inspection and maintenance and access to each connection. Such facility shall not be significantly impaired by mounting equipment in an enclosure or a compartment.

514   IDENTIFICATION AND NOTICES

514-01   General

514-01-01   Except where there is no possibility of confusion, a label or other suitable means of identification shall be provided to indicate the purpose of each item of switchgear and controlgear.

Where the operator cannot observe the operation of switchgear and controlgear and where this might lead to danger, a suitable indicator shall be fixed in a position visible to the operator.

514-01-02   As far as is reasonably practicable, wiring shall be so arranged or marked that it can be identified for inspection, testing, repair or alteration of the installation.

514-01-03   Except where there is no possibility of confusion, unambiguous marking shall be provided at the interface between conductors identified in accordance with these Regulations and conductors identified to previous versions of the Regulations. Appendix 7 gives guidance on how this can be achieved.

514-02   Conduit

514-02-01   Where an electrical conduit is required to be distinguished from a pipeline or another service, orange shall be used as the basic identification colour.

514-03   Identification of conductors

514-03-01   Except where identification is not required by Regulation 514-06, cores of cables shall be identified by:
  (i)   colour as required by Regulation 514-04 and /or
  (ii) lettering and/or numbering as required by Regulation 514-05.

514-03-02   Every core of a cable shall be identifiable at its terminations and preferably throughout its length.

Binding and sleeves for identification purposes shall comply with BS 3858 where appropriate.

Switchboards

514-03-03   Any identification of a switchboard busbar or conductor shall comply with the requirements of Table 51 so far as these are applicable.

514-04   Identification of conductors by colour

Neutral or mid-point conductor

514-04-01   Where a circuit includes a neutral or mid-point conductor identified by colour, the colour used shall be blue.

Protective conductor

514-04-02   The bi-colour combination green-and-yellow shall be used exclusively for identification of a protective conductor and this combination shall not be used for any other purpose.

Single-core cables that are coloured green-and-yellow throughout their length shall only be used as a protective conductor and shall not be over-marked at their terminations, except as permitted by Regulation 514-04-03.

In this combination one of the colours shall cover at least 30 % and at most 70 % of the surface being coloured, while the other colour shall cover the remainder of the surface.

A bare conductor or busbar used as a protective conductor shall be identified, where necessary, by equal green-and-yellow stripes, each not less than 15 mm and not more than 100 mm wide, close together, either throughout the length of the conductor or in each compartment and unit and at each accessible position. If adhesive tape is used, it shall be bi-coloured.

PEN conductor

514-04-03   A PEN conductor shall, when insulated, be marked by one of the following methods:
  (i)   green-and-yellow throughout its length with, in addition, blue markings at the terminations, or
  (ii)   blue throughout its length with, in addition, green-and-yellow markings at the terminations.

Other conductors

514-04-04   Other conductors shall be identified by colour in accordance with Table 51.

514-04-05   The single colour green shall not be used.

Bare conductors

514-04-06   A bare conductor shall be identified, where necessary, by the application of tape, sleeve or disc of the appropriate colour prescribed in Table 51 or by painting with such a colour.

514-05   Identification of conductors by letters and/or numbers

514-05-01   The lettering or numbering system applies to identification of individual conductors and of conductors in a group. The identification shall be clearly legible and durable. All numerals shall be in strong contrast to the colour of the insulation. The identification shall be given in letters or Arabic numerals. In order to avoid confusion, unattached numerals 6 and 9 shall be underlined.

Protective conductor

514-05-02   Conductors with green-and-yellow colour identification shall not be numbered other than for the purpose of circuit identification.

Alphanumeric

514-05-03   The preferred alphanumeric system is described in Table 51.

Numeric

514-05-04   Conductors may be identified by numbers, the number 0 being reserved for the neutral or mid-point conductor.

514-06   Omission of identification by colour or marking

514-06-01   Identification by colour or marking is not required for:
  (i)   concentric conductors of cables
  (ii)   metal sheath or armour of cables when used as a protective conductor
  (iii)   bare conductors where permanent identification is not practicable
  (iv)   extraneous-conductive-parts used as a protective conductor
  (v)   exposed-conductive-parts used as a protective conductor.

TABLE 51
Identification of conductors

Function	Alphanumeric	Colour
Protective conductors		Green-and-yellow
Functional earthing conductor		Cream
..a.c. power circuit[1]		
Phase of single-phase circuit	L	Brown
Neutral of single- or three-phase circuit	N	Blue
Phase 1 of three-phase a.c. circuit	L1	Brown
Phase 2 of three-phase a.c. circuit	L2	Black
Phase 3 of three-phase a.c. circuit	L3	Grey
Two-wire unearthed d.c. power circuit		
Positive of two-wire circuit	L+	Brown
Negative of two-wire circuit	L-	Grey
Two-wire earthed d.c. power circuit		
Positive (of negative earthed) circuit	L+	Brown
Negative (of negative earthed) circuit[2]	M	Blue
Positive (of positive earthed) circuit[2]	M	Blue
Negative (of positive earthed) circuit	L-	Grey
Three-wire d.c. power circuit		
Outer positive of two-wire circuit derived from three-wire system	L+	Brown
Outer negative of two-wire circuit derived from three-wire system	L-	Grey
Positive of three-wire circuit	L+	Brown
Mid-wire of three-wire circuit[2][3]	M	Blue
Negative of three-wire circuit	L-	Grey
Control circuits, ELV and other applications		
Phase conductor	L	Brown, Black, Red, Orange, Yellow, Violet, Grey, White, Pink or Turquoise
Neutral or mid-wire[4]	N or M	Blue

NOTES:

[1]   Power circuits include lighting circuits.

[2]   M identifies either the mid-wire of a three-wire d.c. circuit, or the earthed conductor of a two-wire earthed d.c. circuit.

[3]   Only the middle wire of three-wire circuits may be earthed.

[4]   An earthed PELV conductor is blue.

514-07   *Deleted by BS 7671 : 2001, Amendment No 2, 2004.*

514-08   **Identification of a protective device**

514-08-01   A protective device shall be arranged and identified so that the circuit protected may be easily recognised.

514-09   Diagrams

514-09-01   A legible diagram, chart or table or equivalent form of information shall be provided indicating in particular:

(i)   the type and composition of each circuit (points of utilisation served, number and size of conductors, type of wiring), and

(ii)   the method used for compliance with Regulation 413-01-01 and where appropriate the data required by Regulation 413-02-04, and

(iii)   the information necessary for the identification of each device performing the functions of protection, isolation and switching, and its location, and

(iv)   any circuit or equipment vulnerable to a typical test.

For simple installations the foregoing information may be given in a schedule. A durable copy of the schedule relating to a distribution board shall be provided within or adjacent to each distribution board.

Any symbol used shall comply with BS EN 60617.

514-10   Warning notice - voltage

514-10-01   Every item of equipment or enclosure within which a nominal voltage (U_o) exceeding 230 volts exists, and where the presence of such a voltage would not normally be expected, shall be so arranged that before access is gained to a live part, a warning of the maximum voltage present is clearly visible.

Where terminals or other fixed live parts between which a nominal voltage (U_o) exceeding 230 volts exists are housed in separate enclosures or items of equipment which, although separated, can be reached simultaneously by a person, a notice shall be secured in a position such that anyone, before gaining access to such live parts, is warned of the maximum voltage which exists between those parts.

Means of access to all live parts of switchgear and other fixed live parts where different nominal voltages exist shall be marked to indicate the voltages present.

514-11   Warning notice - isolation

514-11-01   A notice of durable material in accordance with Regulation 461-01-03, shall be fixed in each position where there are live parts which are not capable of being isolated by a single device. The location of each isolator (disconnector) shall be indicated unless there is no possibility of confusion.

514-12   Notice - periodic inspection and testing

514-12-01   A notice of such durable material as to be likely to remain easily legible throughout the life of the installation, shall be fixed in a prominent position at or near the origin of every installation upon completion of the work carried out in accordance with Chapters 71 or 73.

The notice shall be inscribed in indelible characters not smaller than those here illustrated and shall read as follows:

IMPORTANT

This installation should be periodically inspected and tested and a report on its condition obtained, as prescribed in the IEE Wiring Regulations BS 7671 Requirements for Electrical Installations.

Date of last inspection......................

Recommended date of next inspection..................

514-12-02 Where an installation incorporates a residual current device a notice shall be fixed in a prominent position at or near the origin of the installation. The notice shall be in indelible characters not smaller than those here illustrated and shall read as follows:

> This installation, or part of it, is protected by a device which automatically switches off the supply if an earth fault develops. Test quarterly by pressing the button marked 'T' or 'Test'. The device should switch off the supply and should then be switched on to restore the supply. If the device does not switch off the supply when the button is pressed, seek expert advice.

514-13   Warning notice - earthing and bonding connections

514-13-01 A permanent label to BS 951 with the words "Safety Electrical Connection - Do Not Remove" shall be permanently fixed in a visible position at or near:

  (i)   the point of connection of every earthing conductor to an earth electrode, and

  (ii)   the point of connection of every bonding conductor to an extraneous-conductive-part, and

  (iii) the main earth terminal, where separate from main switchgear.

514-13-02 Where Regulations 471-11 or 471-12 apply, the warning notice specified shall be durably marked in legible type not smaller than that illustrated here and shall read as follows:

> The equipotential protective bonding conductors associated with the electrical installation in this location MUST NOT BE CONNECTED TO EARTH.
>
> Equipment having exposed-conductive-parts connected to earth must not be brought into this location.

514-14   Warning notice - non-standard colours

514-14-01 If wiring alterations or additions are made to an installation such that some of the wiring complies with Regulation 514-04 but there is also wiring to previous versions of these Regulations, a warning notice shall be affixed at or near the appropriate distribution board with the following wording:

> CAUTION
>
> This installation has wiring colours to two versions of BS 7671. Great care should be taken before undertaking extension, alteration or repair that all conductors are correctly identified.

515   MUTUAL DETRIMENTAL INFLUENCE

515-01   Prevention of mutual detrimental influence

515-01-01 Electrical equipment shall be selected and erected so as to avoid any harmful influence between the electrical installation and any non-electrical installations envisaged.

515-01-02 Where equipment carrying current of different types or at different voltages is grouped in a common assembly (such as a switchboard, a cubicle or a control desk or box), all the equipment belonging to any one type of current or any one voltage shall be effectively segregated wherever necessary to avoid mutual detrimental influence.

515-02 Electromagnetic compatibility

515-02-01 The immunity levels of equipment shall be chosen taking into account the electromagnetic influences that can occur when connected and erected as for normal use, and taking into account the intended level of continuity of service necessary for the application. See the specific standard or BS EN 50082.

515-02-02 Equipment shall be chosen with sufficiently low emission levels so that it cannot cause unacceptable electromagnetic interference with other electrical equipment by electrical conduction or propagation in the air. If necessary, measures shall be taken to minimise the effects of the emission. See the specific standard or BS EN 50081.

CHAPTER 52

SELECTION AND ERECTION OF WIRING SYSTEMS

CONTENTS

CHAPTER 52

SELECTION AND ERECTION OF WIRING SYSTEMS

521   SELECTION OF TYPE OF WIRING SYSTEM

521-01   Cables and conductors for low voltage

521-01-01   Every non-flexible or flexible cable or flexible cord for use at low voltage shall comply with the appropriate British or Harmonized Standard.

For aerial use or suspension any non-flexible cable sheathed with lead, pvc or an elastomeric material may incorporate a catenary wire or include hard-drawn copper conductors.

This regulation does not apply to a flexible cord forming part of a portable appliance or luminaire where the appliance or luminaire as a whole is the subject of and complies with a British or Harmonized Standard, or to special flexible cables and flexible cords for combined power and telecommunication wiring (see Regulation 528-01-02).

Insulated flexible cable and flexible cord may incorporate a flexible metallic armour, braid or screen.

521-01-02   A busbar trunking system shall comply with BS EN 60439-2.

521-01-03   Every conductor, other than a cable, for use as an overhead line operating at low voltage shall comply with an appropriate British Standard for overhead conductors.

521-01-04   A flexible cable or flexible cord shall be used for fixed wiring only where the relevant provisions of the Regulations are met.

521-02   Cables for a.c. circuits - electromagnetic effects

521-02-01   Single-core cables armoured with steel wire or tape shall not be used for a.c. circuits. Conductors of a.c. circuits installed in ferromagnetic enclosures shall be arranged so that the conductors of all phases and the neutral conductor (if any) and the appropriate protective conductor of each circuit are contained in the same enclosure.

Where such conductors enter a ferrous enclosure they shall be arranged so that the conductors are not individually surrounded by a ferrous material, or other provision shall be made to prevent eddy (induced) currents.

521-03   Electromechanical stresses

521-03-01   Every conductor or cable shall have adequate strength and be so installed as to withstand the electromechanical forces that may be caused by any current, including fault current, it may have to carry in service.

521-04   Conduits and conduit fittings

521-04-01   A conduit or conduit fitting shall comply with the appropriate British Standard referred to below:

  (i)   steel conduit and fittings - BS 31, BS EN 60423, BS EN 50086-1

  (ii)   flexible steel conduit - BS 731-1, BS EN 60423, BS EN 50086-1

  (iii)   steel conduit fittings with metric threads - BS 4568, BS EN 60423, BS EN 50086-1

  (iv)   non-metallic conduits and fittings - BS 4607, BS EN 60423, BS EN 50086-2-1

521-05   Trunking, ducting and fittings

521-05-01   Where applicable, trunking, ducting and their fittings shall comply with BS 4678 or BS EN 50085-1. Where BS 4678 does not apply, non-metallic trunking, ducting and their fittings shall be of insulating material complying with the ignitability characteristic 'P' of BS 476 Part 5.

521-06   Lighting track systems

521-06-01   A lighting track system shall comply with BS EN 60570.

521-07 Methods of installation of cables and conductors

521-07-01 The methods of installation of a wiring system for which the Regulations specifically provide are shown in Appendix 4 Table 4A1.

The use of another method is not precluded provided that compliance with the Regulations is maintained.

521-07-02 A bare live conductor shall be installed on insulators.

521-07-03 Non-sheathed cables for fixed wiring shall be enclosed in conduit, ducting or trunking. This regulation does not apply to a protective conductor complying with Section 543 of the Regulations.

Where cables having different temperature ratings are installed in the same enclosure, all the cables shall be deemed to have the lowest temperature rating.

522 SELECTION AND ERECTION IN RELATION TO EXTERNAL INFLUENCES
(see Chapter 32 and Appendix 5)

522-01 Ambient temperature (AA)

522-01-01 A wiring system shall be selected and erected so as to be suitable for the highest and lowest local ambient temperature likely to be encountered.

522-01-02 The components of a wiring system, including cables and wiring enclosures, shall be installed or handled only at temperatures within the limits stated in the relevant product specification or as recommended by the manufacturer.

522-02 External heat sources

522-02-01 To avoid the effects of heat from external sources including solar gain one or more of the following methods, or an equally effective method, shall be used to protect the wiring system:

  (i) shielding

 (ii) placing sufficiently far from the source of heat

(iii) selecting a system with due regard for the additional temperature rise which may occur

 (iv) *Deleted by BS 7671 : 1992, Amendment No 2.*

  (v) local reinforcement or substitution of insulating material.

522-02-02 Parts of a cable or flexible cord within an accessory, appliance or luminaire shall be suitable for the temperatures likely to be encountered, as determined in accordance with Regulation 522-01-01, or shall be provided with additional insulation suitable for those temperatures.

522-03 Presence of water (AD) or high humidity (AB)

522-03-01 A wiring system shall be selected and erected so that no damage is caused by condensation or ingress of water during installation, use and maintenance.

522-03-02 Where water may collect or condensation may form in a wiring system provision shall be made for its harmless escape through suitably located drainage points.

522-03-03 Where a wiring system may be subjected to waves (AD6), protection against mechanical damage shall be afforded by one or more of the methods given in Regulations 522-06 to 522-08.

522-04 Presence of solid foreign bodies (AE)

522-04-01 A wiring system shall be selected and erected to minimize the ingress of solid foreign bodies during installation, use and maintenance.

522-04-02 In a location where dust or other substance in significant quantity may be present (AE4, AE5 or AE6) additional precautions shall be taken to prevent its accumulation in quantities which could adversely affect the heat dissipation from the wiring system.

522-05 Presence of corrosive or polluting substances (AF)

522-05-01 Where the presence of corrosive or polluting substances is likely to give rise to corrosion or deterioration, parts of the wiring system likely to be affected shall be suitably protected or manufactured from materials resistant to such substances.

522-05-02 Metals liable to initiate electrolytic action shall not be placed in contact with each other.

522-05-03 Materials liable to cause mutual or individual deterioration or hazardous degradation shall not be placed in contact with each other.

522-06 Impact (AG)

522-06-01 Wiring systems shall be selected and erected so as to minimize mechanical damage e.g. damage due to impact, abrasion, penetration, compression or tension, during installation, use and maintenance.

522-06-02 In a fixed installation where an impact of medium severity (AG2) or high severity (AG3) can occur, protection shall be afforded by:

   (i)   the mechanical characteristics of the wiring system, or

   (ii)   the location selected, or

   (iii)   the provision of additional local or general mechanical protection,

or by any combination of the above.

522-06-03 Except where installed in a conduit or duct which provides equivalent protection against mechanical damage, a cable buried in the ground shall incorporate an earthed armour or metal sheath or both, suitable for use as a protective conductor, or be of insulated concentric construction. Buried cables shall be marked by cable covers or a suitable marking tape. Buried conduits and ducts shall be suitably identified. Buried cables, conduits and ducts shall be at a sufficient depth to avoid being damaged by any reasonably foreseeable disturbance of the ground.

522-06-04 A wiring system buried in a floor shall be sufficiently protected to prevent damage caused by the intended use of the floor.

522-06-05 A cable installed under a floor or above a ceiling shall be run in such a position that it is not liable to be damaged by contact with the floor or the ceiling or their fixings. A cable passing through a timber joist within a floor or ceiling construction or through a ceiling support (e.g. under floorboards), shall:

   (i)   be at least 50 mm measured vertically from the top, or bottom as appropriate, of the joist or batten, or

   (ii)   incorporate an earthed armour or metal sheath suitable for use as a protective conductor, or shall be of insulated concentric construction, or shall be protected by enclosure in earthed steel conduit securely supported, or by equivalent mechanical protection sufficient to prevent penetration of the cable by nails, screws and the like (see also Regulation 471-13-04(v)).

522-06-06 A cable concealed in a wall or partition at a depth of less than 50 mm from the surfaces of the wall or partition shall:

   (i)   incorporate an earthed metallic covering which complies with the requirements of these Regulations for a protective conductor of the circuit concerned, the cable complying with BS 5467, BS 6346, BS 6724, BS 7846, BS EN 60702-1 or BS 8436, or

   (ii)   be of insulated concentric construction complying with BS 4553-1, BS 4553-2 or BS 4553-3, or

   (iii)   be enclosed in earthed conduit, trunking or ducting satisfying the requirements of these Regulations for a protective conductor, or be mechanically protected sufficient to prevent penetration of the cable by nails, screws and the like, or

   (iv)   be installed in a zone within 150 mm from the top of the wall or partition or within 150 mm of an angle formed by two adjoining walls or partitions. Where the cable is connected to a point, accessory or switchgear on any surface of the wall or partition, the cable may be installed in a zone either horizontally or vertically, to the point, accessory or switchgear. Where the location of the accessory, point or switchgear can be determined from the reverse side, a zone formed on one side of a wall of 100 mm thickness or less or partition of 100 mm thickness or less extends to the reverse side.

522-06-07 *Deleted by BS 7671 : 2001, Amendment No 2, 2004. For requirements see Regulation 522-06-06.*

522-07 Vibration (AH)

522-07-01 A wiring system supported by, or fixed to, a structure or equipment subject to vibration of medium severity (AH2) or high severity (AH3) shall be suitable for the conditions and in particular shall employ cable with fixings and connections suitable for such a situation.

522-08 Other mechanical stresses (AJ)

522-08-01 A wiring system shall be selected and erected so as to minimize during installation, use and maintenance, damage to the sheath and insulation of cables and insulated conductors and their terminations.

522-08-02 Where the wiring system is designed to be withdrawable, there shall be adequate means of access for drawing cable in or out and, if buried in the structure, a conduit or cable ducting system for each circuit shall be completely erected before cable is drawn in.

522-08-03 The radius of every bend in a wiring system shall be such that conductors and cables shall not suffer damage.

522-08-04 Where a conductor or a cable is not continuously supported it shall be supported by suitable means at appropriate intervals in such a manner that the conductor or cable does not suffer damage by its own weight.

522-08-05 Every cable or conductor used as fixed wiring shall be supported in such a way that it is not exposed to undue mechanical strain and so that there is no appreciable mechanical strain on the terminations of the conductors, account being taken of mechanical strain imposed by the supported weight of the cable or conductor itself.

522-08-06 A flexible wiring system shall be installed so that excessive tensile and torsional stresses to the conductors and connections are avoided.

522-09 Presence of flora and/or mould growth (AK)

522-09-01 Where expected conditions constitute a hazard (AK2), the wiring system shall be selected accordingly or special protective measures shall be adopted.

522-10 Presence of fauna (AL)

522-10-01 Where expected conditions constitute a hazard (AL2), the wiring system shall be selected accordingly or special protective measures shall be adopted.

522-11 Solar radiation (AN) and ultra-violet radiation

522-11-01 Where significant solar radiation (AN2) or ultra-violet radiation is experienced or expected, a wiring system suitable for the conditions shall be selected and erected or adequate shielding shall be provided. Special precautions may need to be taken for equipment subject to ionising radiation.

522-12 Building design (CB)

522-12-01 Where structural movement (CB3) is experienced or expected, the cable support and protection system employed shall be capable of permitting relative movement so that conductors are not subjected to excessive mechanical stress.

522-12-02 For flexible or unstable structures (CB4) flexible wiring systems shall be used.

522-12-03 No wiring system shall penetrate an element of building construction which is intended to be load bearing unless the integrity of the load bearing element can be assured after such penetration.

523 CURRENT-CARRYING CAPACITY OF CONDUCTORS

523-01 Conductor operating temperature

523-01-01 The current to be carried by any conductor for sustained periods during normal operation shall be such that the conductor operating temperature given in the appropriate table of current-carrying capacity in Appendix 4 is not exceeded (see Table 52B).

Where a conductor operates at a temperature exceeding 70 °C it shall be ascertained that the equipment connected to the conductor is suitable for the conductor operating temperature (see Regulation 512-02).

523-02   Conductors in parallel

523-02-01   Except for ring final circuits, where two or more conductors are connected in parallel in the same phase or pole of a system, measures shall be taken to ensure that the load current is shared equally between them.

This requirement is considered to be fulfilled if the conductors are of the same construction, material and cross-sectional area, are approximately the same length, have no branch circuits along the length and have appropriate phase disposition.

Where the parallel cables are non-twisted single-core cables installed in trefoil or flat formation and have cross-sectional areas greater than 50 mm^2 in copper or 70 mm^2 in aluminium, the arrangement of the different phases shall be such as to ensure optimum equalization of load current between them.

This regulation shall be applied unless the suitability of another particular arrangement is verified.

523-03   Cables connected to bare conductors or busbars

523-03-01   Where a cable is to be connected to a bare conductor or busbar its type of insulation and/or sheath shall be suitable for the maximum operating temperature of the bare conductor or busbar.

523-04   Cables in thermal insulation

523-04-01   Where a cable is to be run in a space to which thermal insulation is likely to be applied, the cable shall wherever practicable be fixed in a position such that it will not be covered by the thermal insulation. Where fixing in such a position is impracticable the cross-sectional area of the cable shall be increased appropriately.

For a cable installed in a thermally insulated wall or above a thermally insulated ceiling, the cable being in contact with a thermally conductive surface on one side, current-carrying capacities are tabulated in Appendix 4, the appropriate Reference Method being Reference Method 4.

For a single cable likely to be totally surrounded by thermally insulating material over a length of more than 0.5 m, the current-carrying capacity shall be taken, in the absence of more precise information, as 0.5 times the current-carrying capacity for that cable clipped direct to a surface and open (Reference Method 1).

Where a cable is to be totally surrounded by thermal insulation for less than 0.5 m the current-carrying capacity of the cable shall be reduced appropriately depending on the size of cable, length in insulation and thermal properties of the insulation. The derating factors in Table 52A are appropriate to conductor sizes up to 10 mm^2 in thermal insulation having a thermal conductivity (λ) greater than 0.0625 Wm^{-1}K^{-1}.

TABLE 52A
Cable surrounded by thermal insulation

Length in insulation (mm)	Derating factor
50	0.89
100	0.81
200	0.68
400	0.55

TABLE 52B (Regulation 523-01)
Maximum conductor operating temperatures

Conductor material	Insulation material	Conductor operating temperature (°C)	Limiting final temperature (°C)	See Appendix 4 Table
Copper	70 °C thermoplastic (general purpose pvc)	70	160/140*	4D1 to 4
	90 °C thermoplastic (pvc)	90	160/140*	
	60 °C thermosetting (rubber)	60	200	4H1
	85 °C thermosetting (rubber)	85	220	4F1 & 4F2
	90 °C thermosetting	90	250	4E1 to 4
	Impregnated paper	80	160	
Copper	Mineral - plastic covered or exposed to touch	70 (sheath)	160	4J1
	- bare and neither exposed to touch nor in contact with combustible materials	105 (sheath)	250	4J2
Aluminium	70 °C thermoplastic (general purpose pvc)	70	160/140*	4K1 to 4
	90 °C thermoplastic (pvc)	90	160/140*	
	60 °C thermosetting (rubber)	60	200	
	85 °C thermosetting (rubber)	85	220	
	90 °C thermosetting	90	250	
	Impregnated paper	80	160	4L1 to 4

* above 300 mm^2

TABLE 52C (Regulation 524-01)
Minimum nominal cross-sectional area of conductor

Type of wiring system	Use of circuit	Conductor		
		Material	Minimum permissible nominal cross-sectional area (mm²)	
Cables and insulated conductors	Power and lighting circuits	Copper Aluminium	1.0 16.0 (see NOTE 1)	
	Signalling and control circuits	Copper	0.5 (see NOTE 2)	
Bare conductors	Power circuits	Copper Aluminium	10 16	
	Signalling and control circuits	Copper	4	
Flexible connections with insulated conductors and cables	For a specific appliance		As specified in the relevant British Standard	
	For any other application	Copper	0.5 (see NOTE 2)	
	Extra-low voltage circuits for special applications		0.5	

NOTES:

(1) Connectors used to terminate aluminium conductors shall be tested and approved for this specific use.

(2) For cables containing 7 or more cores in signalling and control circuits intended for electronic equipment, a minimum nominal cross-sectional area of 0.1 mm² is permitted.

523-05 Metallic sheaths and/or non-magnetic armour of single-core cables

523-05-01 The metallic sheaths and/or non-magnetic armour of single-core cables in the same circuit shall normally be bonded together at both ends of their run (solid bonding). Alternatively, the sheaths or armour of such cables having conductors of cross-sectional area exceeding 50 mm^2 and a non-conducting outer sheath may be bonded together at one point in their run (single point bonding) with suitable insulation at the un-bonded ends, in which case the length of the cables from the bonding point shall be limited so that, at full load, voltages from sheaths and/or armour to Earth:

    (i)   do not exceed 25 volts, and

    (ii)   do not cause corrosion when the cables are carrying their full load current, and

    (iii)   do not cause danger or damage to property when the cables are carrying short-circuit current.

524 CROSS-SECTIONAL AREAS OF CONDUCTORS

524-01 Phase conductors in a.c. circuits and live conductors in d.c. circuits

524-01-01 The nominal cross-sectional area of phase conductors in a.c. circuits and of live conductors in d.c. circuits shall be not less than the values specified in Table 52C.

524-02 Neutral conductors

524-02-01 In a single-phase circuit the neutral conductor shall have a cross-sectional area not less than that of the phase conductor.

524-02-02 In a polyphase circuit the neutral conductor shall have a current-carrying capacity adequate to afford compliance with Regulation 523-01-01 for the maximum current likely to flow in it under normal operating conditions. (See Section 473 for overcurrent protection of neutral conductors).

When assessing the maximum likely neutral current account shall be taken of:

    (i)   inequality of phase loading,

    (ii)   inequality of power factor in each phase, and

    (iii)   harmonic currents in the neutral conductor.

524-02-03 In a discharge lighting circuit and polyphase circuits where the harmonic content of the phase currents is greater than 10% of the fundamental current, the neutral conductor shall have a cross-sectional area not less than that of the phase conductor(s).

525 VOLTAGE DROP IN CONSUMERS' INSTALLATIONS

525-01 Voltage drop in consumers' installations

525-01-01 Under normal service conditions the voltage at the terminals of any fixed current-using equipment shall be greater than the lower limit corresponding to the British Standard relevant to the equipment.

Where the fixed current-using equipment concerned is not the subject of a British Standard the voltage at the terminals shall be such as not to impair the safe functioning of that equipment.

525-01-02 The requirements of Regulation 525-01-01 are deemed to be satisfied for a supply given in accordance with the Electricity Safety, Quality and Continuity Regulations 2002 if the voltage drop between the origin of the installation (usually the supply terminals) and a socket-outlet or the terminals of the fixed current-using equipment does not exceed 4 % of the nominal voltage of the supply.

A greater voltage drop may be accepted for a motor during starting periods and for other equipment with high inrush currents provided that it is verified that the voltage variations are within the limits specified in the relevant British Standards for the equipment or, in the absence of a British Standard, in accordance with the manufacturer's recommendations.

526 ELECTRICAL CONNECTIONS

526-01 Connections between conductors and between a conductor and equipment

526-01-01 Every connection between conductors and between a conductor and equipment shall provide durable electrical continuity and adequate mechanical strength (see Other mechanical stresses, Regulation 522-08).

526-02 Selection of means of connection

526-02-01 The selection of the means of connection shall take account, as appropriate, of the following:

(i) the material of the conductor and its insulation

(ii) the number and shape of the wires forming the conductor

(iii) the cross-sectional area of the conductor

(iv) the number of conductors to be connected together

(v) the temperature attained by the terminals in normal service such that the effectiveness of the insulation of the conductors connected to them is not impaired

(vi) where a soldered connection is used the design shall take account of creep, mechanical stress and temperature rise under fault current conditions

(vii) the provision of adequate locking arrangements in situations subject to vibration or thermal cycling.

526-03 Enclosed connections

526-03-01 Where a connection is made in an enclosure the enclosure shall provide adequate mechanical protection and protection against relevant external influences.

526-03-02 Every termination and joint in a live conductor or a PEN conductor shall be made within one of the following or a combination thereof:

(i) a suitable accessory complying with the appropriate British Standard

(ii) an equipment enclosure complying with the appropriate British Standard

(iii) a suitable enclosure of material complying with the relevant glow-wire test requirements of BS 6458-2.1

(iv) an enclosure formed or completed with building material considered to be non-combustible when tested to BS 476-4

(v) an enclosure formed or completed by part of the building structure, having the ignitability characteristic 'P' as specified in BS 476 Part 5.

526-03-03 Cores of sheathed cables from which the sheath has been removed and non-sheathed cables at the termination of conduit, ducting or trunking shall be enclosed as required by Regulation 526-03-02.

526-04 Accessibility of connections

526-04-01 Except for the following, every connection and joint shall be accessible for inspection, testing and maintenance:

(i) a compound-filled or encapsulated joint

(ii) a connection between a cold tail and a heating element (e.g. a ceiling and floor heating system, a pipe trace-heating system)

(iii) a joint made by welding, soldering, brazing or compression tool

(iv) a joint forming part of the equipment complying with the appropriate product standard.

527 SELECTION AND ERECTION TO MINIMIZE THE SPREAD OF FIRE

527-01 General

527-01-01 The risk of spread of fire shall be minimized by selection of an appropriate material and erection in accordance with Section 527.

527-01-02 The wiring system shall be installed so that the general building structural performance and fire safety are not materially reduced.

527-01-03 Cables complying with the requirements for flame propagation when assessed in accordance with BS EN 50265-1 may be installed without special precautions. Where the risk of fire is high special precautions shall be taken.

527-01-04 Cables not complying with the flame propagation requirements of BS EN 50265-1 shall be limited to short lengths for connection of appliances to the permanent wiring system and shall not pass from one fire-segregated compartment to another.

527-01-05 Conduit and trunking complying with the resistance to flame propagation requirements of BS EN 50085 or BS EN 50086 may be installed without special precautions. Other products complying with standards having similar requirements for resistance to flame propagation may be installed without special precautions.

527-01-06 A part of a wiring system which complies with the requirements of the relevant British Standard, which Standard has no requirement for testing for resistance to the propagation of flame, shall be completely enclosed in non-combustible building material having the ignitability characteristic 'P' as specified in BS 476 Part 5.

527-02 Sealing of wiring system penetrations

527-02-01 Where a wiring system passes through elements of building construction such as floors, walls, roofs, ceilings, partitions or cavity barriers, the openings remaining after passage of the wiring system shall be sealed according to the degree of fire resistance required of the element concerned (if any).

527-02-02 Where a wiring system such as conduit, cable ducting, cable trunking, busbar or busbar trunking penetrates elements of building construction having specified fire resistance it shall be internally sealed so as to maintain the degree of fire resistance of the respective element as well as being externally sealed to maintain the required fire resistance. A non flame propagating wiring system having a maximum internal cross-sectional area of 710 mm^2 need not be internally sealed.

Except for fire resistance over one hour, this regulation is satisfied if the sealing of the wiring system concerned has been type-tested by the method specified in BS 476-23.

527-02-03 Each sealing arrangement used in accordance with Regulations 527-02-01 and 527-02-02 shall comply with the following requirements and Regulation 527-04:

   (i)   it shall be compatible with the material of the wiring system with which it is in contact, and

   (ii) it shall permit thermal movement of the wiring system without reduction of the sealing quality, and

   (iii) it shall be removable without damage to existing cable where space permits future extension to be made, and

   (iv) it shall resist relevant external influences to the same degree as the wiring system with which it is used.

527-03 Erection conditions

527-03-01 During the erection of a wiring system temporary sealing arrangements shall be provided as appropriate.

527-03-02 During alteration work sealing which has been disturbed shall be reinstated as soon as practicable.

527-04 Verification

527-04-01 Each sealing arrangement shall be visually inspected at an appropriate time during erection to verify that it conforms to the manufacturer's erection instructions and the details shall be recorded.

528-01 Proximity to electrical services

528-01-01 Neither a band I nor a band II circuit shall be contained within the same wiring system as a circuit of nominal voltage exceeding that of low voltage unless every cable is insulated for the highest voltage present or one of the following methods is adopted:

 (i) each conductor in a multicore cable is insulated for the highest voltage present in the cable, or is enclosed within an earthed metallic screen of current-carrying capacity equivalent to that of the largest conductor enclosed within the screen, or

 (ii) the cables are insulated for their respective system voltages and installed in a separate compartment of a cable ducting or cable trunking system, or have an earthed metallic covering.

528-01-02 A band I circuit shall not be contained in the same wiring system as band II voltage circuits unless one of the following methods is adopted:

 (i) every cable is insulated for the highest voltage present

 (ii) for a multicore cable or cord, the cores of the band I circuit shall be insulated individually or collectively for the highest voltage present in the band II circuit

 (iii) for a multicore cable or cord, the cores of the band I circuit shall be separated from the cores of the band II circuit by an earthed metal screen of equivalent current-carrying capacity to that of the largest core of the band II circuit

 (iv) the cables are insulated for their system voltage and installed in a separate compartment of a cable ducting or trunking system

 (v) the cables are installed on a tray or ladder where physical separation is provided by a partition

 (vi) a separate conduit, trunking or ducting system is employed.

For SELV and PELV circuits the requirements of Regulations 411-02-05, 411-02-06 and 411-02-07 shall apply as appropriate.

For telecommunication circuits, data transfer circuits and similar, consideration shall be given to electrical interference, both electromagnetic and electrostatic. See BS EN 50081 and BS EN 50082.

528-01-03 *Deleted by BS 7671 : 1992, Amendment No 2.*

528-01-04 Fire alarm and emergency lighting circuits shall be segregated from all other cables and from each other in accordance with BS 5839 and BS 5266. Telecommunication circuits shall be segregated in accordance with BS 6701 as appropriate.

528-01-05 *Deleted by BS 7671 : 1992, Amendment No 2.*

528-01-06 *Deleted by BS 7671 : 1992, Amendment No 2.*

528-01-07 In conduit, duct, ducting, trunking or wiring systems, where controls or outlets for band I and band II voltage circuits are mounted in or on a common box, switchplate or block, the cables and connections of circuits of different voltage bands shall be segregated by an effective partition which, if of metal, shall be earthed.

528-01-08 *Deleted by BS 7671 : 1992, Amendment No 2.*

528-02 Proximity to non-electrical services

528-02-01 Where a wiring system is located in close proximity to a non-electrical service both the following conditions shall be met:

 (i) the wiring system shall be suitably protected against the hazards likely to arise from the presence of the other service in normal use, and

 (ii) protection against indirect contact shall be afforded in accordance with the requirements of Section 413.

528-02-02 A wiring system shall not be installed in the vicinity of a service which produces heat, smoke or fume likely to be detrimental to the wiring, unless protected from harmful effects by shielding arranged so as not to affect the dissipation of heat from the wiring.

528-02-03 Where a wiring system is routed near a service liable to cause condensation (such as water, steam or gas services) precautions shall be taken to protect the wiring system from deleterious effects.

528-02-04 Where a wiring system is to be installed in proximity to a non-electrical service it shall be so arranged that any foreseeable operation carried out on either service will not cause damage to the other.

528-02-05 *Deleted by BS 7671 : 1992, Amendment No 2.*

528-02-06 No cable shall be run in a lift (or hoist) shaft unless it forms part of the lift installation as defined in BS 5655.

529   SELECTION AND ERECTION IN RELATION TO MAINTAINABILITY, INCLUDING CLEANING

529-01-01 Where any protective measure must be removed in order to carry out maintenance, reinstatement of the protective measure shall be practicable without reducing the original degree of protection.

529-01-02 Provision shall be made for safe and adequate access to all parts of the wiring system which may require maintenance.

CHAPTER 53

SWITCHGEAR
(For protection, isolation and switching)

CONTENTS

CHAPTER 53

SWITCHGEAR
(For protection, isolation and switching)

530   COMMON REQUIREMENTS

530-01-01 Where an item of switchgear is required by the Regulations to disconnect all live conductors of a circuit, it shall be of a type such that the neutral conductor cannot be disconnected before the phase conductors and is reconnected before, or at the same time as, the phase conductors.

530-01-02 No fuse or, excepting where linked, switch or circuit-breaker shall be inserted in the neutral conductor of TN or TT systems.

530-01-03 A device embodying more than one function shall comply with all the requirements of this Chapter appropriate to each separate function.

531   DEVICES FOR PROTECTION AGAINST ELECTRIC SHOCK

531-01   **Overcurrent protective devices**

531-01-01 For a TN or a TT system, every overcurrent protective device which is to be used also for protection against electric shock (indirect contact) shall be selected so that its operating time is:

  (i)   appropriate to the value of fault current that would flow in the event of a fault of negligible impedance between a phase conductor and exposed-conductive-parts, so that the permissible final temperature of the phase conductor and the associated protective conductor is not exceeded (see also Regulation 543-01-01), and

  (ii) appropriate for compliance with the requirements of Regulation 413-02-04.

531-01-02 For an IT system, where exposed-conductive-parts are connected together and an overcurrent protective device is to be used to provide protection against electric shock in the event of a second fault, the requirements for the protective device are the same as those for a TN system, as specified in Regulation 531-01-01.

531-02   **Residual current devices**

531-02-01 A residual current device shall be capable of disconnecting all the phase conductors of the circuit at substantially the same time.

531-02-02 The magnetic circuit of the transformer of a residual current device shall enclose all the live conductors of the protected circuit. The associated protective conductor shall be outside the magnetic circuit.

531-02-03 The residual operating current of the protective device shall comply with the requirements of Section 413 as appropriate to the type of system earthing.

531-02-04 A residual current device shall be so selected and the electrical circuits so subdivided that any protective conductor current which may be expected to occur during normal operation of the connected load(s) will be unlikely to cause unnecessary tripping of the device.

531-02-05 The use of a residual current device associated with a circuit normally expected to have a protective conductor, shall not be considered sufficient for protection against indirect contact if there is no such conductor, even if the rated residual operating current ($I_{\Delta n}$) of the device does not exceed 30 mA.

531-02-06 A residual current device which is powered from an auxiliary source and which does not operate automatically in the case of failure of the auxiliary source shall be used only if one of the two following conditions is fulfilled:

  (i)   protection against indirect contact is maintained even in the case of failure of the auxiliary source, or

  (ii) the device is incorporated in an installation intended to be supervised, tested and inspected by an instructed person or a skilled person.

531-02-07 A residual current device shall be located so that its operation will not be impaired by magnetic fields caused by other equipment.

531-02-08 Where a residual current device for protection against indirect contact is used with, but separately from, an overcurrent protective device, it shall be verified that the residual current operated device is capable of withstanding, without damage, the thermal and mechanical stresses to which it is likely to be subjected in the case of a fault occurring on the load side of the point at which it is installed.

531-02-09 Where, for compliance with the requirements of the Regulations for protection against indirect contact or otherwise to prevent danger, two or more residual current devices are in series, and where discrimination in their operation is necessary to prevent danger, the characteristics of the devices shall be such that the intended discrimination is achieved.

531-02-10 Where a residual current device may be operated by a person other than a skilled or instructed person, it shall be designed or installed so that it is not possible to modify or adjust the setting or the calibration of its rated residual operating current ($I_{\Delta n}$) or time delay mechanism without a deliberate act involving the use of either a key or tool and resulting in a visible indication of its setting or calibration.

531-03 Residual current devices in a TN system

531-03-01 In a TN system, where, for certain equipment in a certain part of the installation, one or more of the conditions in Regulation 413-02-08 cannot be satisfied, that part may be protected by a residual current device.

The exposed-conductive-parts of that part of the installation shall be connected to the TN earthing system protective conductor or to a separate earth electrode which affords an impedance appropriate to the operating current of the residual current device.

In this latter case the circuit shall be treated as a TT system and Regulation 413-02-17 applies.

531-04 Residual current devices in a TT system

531-04-01 If an installation which is part of a TT system is protected by a single residual current device, this shall be placed at the origin of the installation unless the part of the installation between the origin and the device complies with the requirements for protection by the use of Class II equipment or equivalent insulation (Regulations 413-03 and 471-09). Where there is more than one origin this requirement applies to each origin.

531-05 Residual current devices in an IT system

531-05-01 Where protection is provided by a residual current device and disconnection following a first fault is not envisaged, the non-operating residual current of the device shall be at least equal to the current which circulates on the first fault to earth of negligible impedance affecting a phase conductor.

531-06 Insulation monitoring devices

531-06-01 An insulation monitoring device shall be so designed or installed that it shall be possible to modify the setting only by the use of a key or a tool.

532 *(Reserved for future use)*

533 OVERCURRENT PROTECTIVE DEVICES

533-01 Overcurrent protective devices

533-01-01 For every fuse and circuit-breaker there shall be provided on or adjacent to it an indication of its intended nominal current as appropriate to the circuit it protects. For a semi-enclosed fuse the intended nominal current to be indicated is the value to be selected in accordance with Regulation 533-01-04.

A fuse having a fuse link likely to be replaced by a person other than a skilled person or an instructed person shall preferably be of a type such that it cannot be replaced inadvertently by one having a higher nominal current.

533-01-02 A fuse link likely to be replaced by a person other than a skilled person or an instructed person shall either:

(i) have marked on or adjacent to it an indication of the type of fuse link intended to be used, or

(ii) be of a type such that there is no possibility of inadvertent replacement by a fuse link having the intended nominal current but a higher fusing factor than that intended.

533-01-03 A fuse which is likely to be removed or replaced whilst the supply is connected shall be of a type such that it can be removed or replaced without danger.

533-01-04 A fuse shall preferably be of the cartridge type. Where a semi-enclosed fuse is selected, it shall be fitted with an element in accordance with the manufacturer's instructions if any. In the absence of such instructions, it shall be fitted with a single element of tinned copper wire of the appropriate diameter specified in Table 53A.

TABLE 53A
Sizes of tinned copper wire for use in semi-enclosed fuses

Nominal current of fuse element (A)	Nominal diameter of wire (mm)
3	0.15
5	0.2
10	0.35
15	0.5
20	0.6
25	0.75
30	0.85
45	1.25
60	1.53
80	1.8
100	2.0

533-01-05 Where a circuit-breaker may be operated by a person other than a skilled or instructed person, it shall be designed or installed so that it is not possible to modify the setting or the calibration of its overcurrent release without a deliberate act involving the use of either a key or a tool and resulting in a visible indication of its setting or calibration.

533-01-06 Where necessary to prevent danger, the characteristics and setting of a device for overcurrent protection shall be such that any intended discrimination in its operation is achieved.

533-02 Selection of a device for the protection of a wiring system against overload

533-02-01 The nominal current (or current setting) of the protective device shall be chosen in accordance with Regulation 433-02. In certain cases, to avoid unintentional operation, the peak current values of the loads may have to be taken into consideration.

In the case of a cyclic load, the values of I_n and I_2 shall be chosen on the basis of values of I_b and I_z for the thermally equivalent constant load,

where the relevant symbols are defined as:

I_b the current for which the circuit is designed i.e. the current intended to be carried in normal service

I_z the current-carrying capacity of the cable for continuous service under the particular installation conditions concerned

I_n the nominal current of the overcurrent protective device

I_2 the current giving effective operation of the overload protective device.

533-03 Selection of a device for the protection of a wiring system against fault current

533-03-01 The application of the rules of Chapter 43 shall take into account minimum and maximum fault current conditions.

534   *(Reserved for future use)*

535   DEVICES FOR PROTECTION AGAINST UNDERVOLTAGE

535-01-01 A device for protection against undervoltage shall be selected and erected so as to allow compliance with the requirements of Chapter 45.

536   *(Reserved for future use)*

537   ISOLATING AND SWITCHING DEVICES

537-01   General

537-01-01   Isolating and switching devices installed in accordance with Sections 461 to 464 shall comply with the appropriate requirements of Regulations 537-02 to 537-05. A common device may be used for more than one of these functions if the appropriate requirements for each function are met.

537-02   Devices for isolation

537-02-01   Except as detailed by Regulation 460-01-04, the devices for isolation shall effectively isolate all live supply conductors from the circuit concerned. Equipment used for isolation shall comply with Regulations 537-02-02 to 537-02-10.

537-02-02   The isolating distance between contacts or other means of isolation when in the open position shall be not less than that determined for an isolator (disconnector) in accordance with the requirement of BS 1363-4, BS 3676, BS EN 60669-2-4, BS EN 60898, BS EN 60947-2, BS EN 60947-3, BS EN 61008-1 or BS EN 61009-1.

537-02-03   A semiconductor device shall not be used as an isolating device.

537-02-04   The position of the contacts or other means of isolation shall be either externally visible or clearly and reliably indicated. An indication of the isolated position shall occur only when the specified isolation has been obtained in each pole.

537-02-05   Where a link is inserted in the neutral conductor, the link shall comply with either or both of the following requirements:

    (i)   it cannot be removed without the use of tools

    (ii)   it is accessible to skilled persons only.

537-02-06   A device for isolation shall be selected and/or installed in such a way as to prevent unintentional closure, such as that which may be caused by mechanical shock or vibration.

537-02-07   Provision shall be made for securing an off-load isolation device against inadvertent and unauthorised operation.

537-02-08   Means of isolation shall preferably be provided by a multipole switching device which disconnects all poles of the relevant supply but single-pole devices situated adjacent to each other are not excluded.

537-02-09   Each device used for isolation shall be clearly identified by position or durable marking, to indicate the installation or circuit it isolates.

537-02-10   A plug and socket-outlet or similar device may be used as a means of isolation.

537-03   Devices for switching off for mechanical maintenance

537-03-01   A device for switching off for mechanical maintenance shall be inserted where practicable in the main supply circuit. Alternatively, such a device may be inserted in the control circuit, provided that supplementary precautions are taken to provide a degree of safety equivalent to that of interruption of the main supply, e.g. where such an arrangement is specified in the appropriate British Standard.

537-03-02   A device for switching off for mechanical maintenance, or a control switch for such a device, shall be manually initiated and shall have an externally visible contact gap or a clearly and reliably indicated OFF or OPEN position. Indication of that position shall occur only when the OFF or OPEN position on each pole has been fully attained.

537-03-03   A device for switching off for mechanical maintenance shall be selected and/or installed in such a way as to prevent unintentional reclosure, such as that which may be caused by mechanical shock or vibration.

537-03-04   Where a switch is used as a device for switching off for mechanical maintenance, it shall be capable of cutting off the full load current of the relevant part of the installation.

537-03-05   A plug and socket-outlet or similar device of rating not exceeding 16 A may be used as a device for switching off for mechanical maintenance.

537-04   Devices for emergency switching

537-04-01   A means of interrupting the supply for the purpose of emergency switching shall be capable of cutting off the full load current of the relevant part of the installation. Where appropriate, due account shall be taken of stalled motor conditions.

537-04-02   Means for emergency switching shall consist of:

(i)   a single switching device directly cutting off the incoming supply, or

(ii)   a combination of several items of equipment operated by a single action and resulting in the removal of the hazard by cutting off the appropriate supply; emergency stopping may include the retention of supply for electric braking facilities.

A plug and socket-outlet or similar device shall not be selected as a device for emergency switching.

537-04-03   Where practicable a device for emergency switching shall be manually operated directly interrupting the main circuit. A device such as a circuit-breaker or a contactor operated by remote control shall open on de-energisation of the coil, or another technique of suitable reliability shall be employed.

537-04-04   The operating means (such as a handle or pushbutton) for a device for emergency switching shall be clearly identifiable and preferably coloured red. It shall be installed in a readily accessible position where the hazard might occur and, where appropriate, further devices shall be provided where additional emergency switching may be needed.

537-04-05   The operating means of the device for emergency switching shall be of the latching type or capable of being restrained in the OFF or STOP position. The resetting of the emergency switching device shall not re-energise the equipment concerned. A device in which the operating means automatically resets is permitted where both that operating means and the means of re-energising are under the control of one and the same person.

Other requirements for switching for safety

537-04-06   A fireman's switch provided for compliance with Regulations 476-03-05 to 476-03-07 shall:

(i)   be coloured red and have fixed on or near it a permanent durable nameplate marked with the words 'FIREMAN'S SWITCH' the plate being the minimum size 150 mm by 100 mm, in lettering easily legible from a distance appropriate to the site conditions but not less than 36 point, and

(ii)   have its ON and OFF positions clearly indicated by lettering legible to a person standing on the ground at the intended site, with the OFF position at the top, and

(iii)   be provided with a device to prevent the switch being inadvertently returned to the ON position, and

(iv)   be arranged to facilitate operation by a fireman.

537-05   Devices for functional switching

537-05-01   Functional switching devices shall be suitable for the most onerous duty intended.

537-05-02   Functional switching devices such as semiconductor switching devices may control the current without necessarily opening the corresponding poles.

537-05-03   Off-load isolators (disconnectors), fuses and links shall not be used for functional switching.

537-05-04   A plug and socket-outlet of rating not exceeding 16 A may be used as a switching device.

537-05-05   Excepting for use on d.c. where this purpose is specifically excluded, a plug and socket-outlet of rating exceeding 16 A may be used as a switching device where the plug and socket-outlet has a breaking capacity appropriate to the use intended (see also Regulation 537-04-02 regarding emergency switching).

CHAPTER 54

EARTHING ARRANGEMENTS AND PROTECTIVE CONDUCTORS

CONTENTS

CHAPTER 54

EARTHING ARRANGEMENTS AND PROTECTIVE CONDUCTORS

541 GENERAL

541-01-01 Every means of earthing and every protective conductor shall be selected and erected so as to satisfy the requirements of the Regulations.

541-01-02 The earthing system of the installation may be subdivided, in which case each part thus divided shall comply with the requirements of this Chapter.

541-01-03 Where there is also a lightning protection system, reference shall be made to BS 6651.

542 CONNECTIONS TO EARTH

542-01 Earthing arrangements

542-01-01 The main earthing terminal shall be connected with Earth by one of the methods described in Regulations 542-01-02 to 542-01-05, as appropriate to the type of system of which the installation is to form a part (see Section 312 and definition of a 'system') and in compliance with Regulations 542-01-06 to 542-01-08.

542-01-02 For a TN-S system, means shall be provided for the main earthing terminal of the installation to be connected to the earthed point of the source of energy. Part of the connection may be formed by the distributor's lines and equipment.

542-01-03 For a TN-C-S system, where protective multiple earthing is provided, means shall be provided for the main earthing terminal of the installation to be connected by the distributor to the neutral of the source of energy.

542-01-04 For a TT or IT system, the main earthing terminal shall be connected via an earthing conductor to an earth electrode complying with Regulation 542-02.

542-01-05 *Deleted by BS 7671 : 2001, Amendment No 2, 2004.*

542-01-06 The earthing arrangements may be used jointly or separately for protective and functional purposes, according to the requirements of the installation.

542-01-07 The earthing arrangements shall be such that:

   (i)   the value of impedance from the consumer's main earthing terminal to the earthed point of the supply for TN systems, or to Earth for TT and IT systems, is in accordance with the protective and functional requirements of the installation, and considered to be continuously effective, and

  (ii) earth fault currents and protective conductor currents which may occur are carried without danger, particularly from thermal, thermomechanical and electromechanical stresses, and

 (iii) they are adequately robust or have additional mechanical protection appropriate to the assessed conditions of external influence.

542-01-08 Precautions shall be taken against the risk of damage to other metallic parts through electrolysis.

542-01-09 Where a number of installations have separate earthing arrangements, any protective conductors common to any of these installations shall either be capable of carrying the maximum fault current likely to flow through them or be earthed within one installation only and insulated from the earthing arrangements of any other installation. In the latter circumstances, if the protective conductor forms part of a cable, the protective conductor shall be earthed only in the installation containing the associated protective device.

542-02   Earth electrodes

542-02-01   The following types of earth electrode are recognised for the purposes of the Regulations:

(i)   earth rods or pipes

(ii)   earth tapes or wires

(iii)   earth plates

(iv)   underground structural metalwork embedded in foundations

(v)   welded metal reinforcement of concrete (except pre-stressed concrete) embedded in the earth

(vi)   lead sheaths and other metal coverings of cables, where not precluded by Regulation 542-02-05

(vii)   other suitable underground metalwork.

542-02-02   The type and embedded depth of an earth electrode shall be such that soil drying and freezing will not increase its resistance above the required value.

542-02-03   The design used, and the construction of, an earth electrode shall be such as to withstand damage and to take account of possible increase in resistance due to corrosion.

542-02-04   The metalwork of a gas, water or other service shall not be used as a protective earth electrode. This requirement does not preclude the bonding of such metalwork as required by Regulation 413-02.

542-02-05   The use, as an earth electrode, of the lead sheath or other metal covering of a cable shall be subject to all of the following conditions:

(i)   adequate precautions to prevent excessive deterioration by corrosion, and

(ii)   the sheath or covering shall be in effective contact with earth, and

(iii)   the consent of the owner of the cable shall be obtained, and

(iv)   arrangements shall exist for the owner of the electrical installation to be warned of any proposed change to the cable which might affect its suitability as an earth electrode.

542-03   Earthing conductors

542-03-01   Every earthing conductor shall comply with Section 543 and, where PME conditions apply, shall meet the requirements of Regulation 547-02-01 for the cross-sectional area of a main equipotential bonding conductor. In addition, where buried in the ground, the earthing conductor shall have a cross-sectional area not less than that stated in Table 54A. For a tape or strip conductor, the thickness shall be such as to withstand mechanical damage and corrosion (see BS 7430).

TABLE 54A
Minimum cross-sectional areas of a buried earthing conductor

	Protected against mechanical damage	Not protected against mechanical damage
Protected against corrosion by a sheath	as required by Regulation 543-01	16 mm^2 copper 16 mm^2 coated steel
Not protected against corrosion	25 mm^2 copper 50 mm^2 steel	25 mm^2 copper 50 mm^2 steel

542-03-02   *Deleted by BS 7671 : 1992, Amendment No 1.*

542-03-03   The connection of an earthing conductor to an earth electrode or other means of earthing shall be soundly made and be electrically and mechanically satisfactory, and labelled in accordance with Regulation 514-13-01. It shall be suitably protected against corrosion.

542-04   Main earthing terminals or bars

542-04-01   In every installation a main earthing terminal shall be provided to connect the following to the earthing conductor:

(i)   the circuit protective conductors, and

(ii)   the main bonding conductors, and

(iii)   functional earthing conductors (if required), and

(iv)   lightning protection system bonding conductor (if any).

542-04-02 To facilitate measurement of the resistance of the earthing arrangements, means shall be provided in an accessible position for disconnecting the earthing conductor. Such means may conveniently be combined with the main earthing terminal or bar. Any joint shall be capable of disconnection only by means of a tool, shall be mechanically strong, and shall ensure the maintenance of electrical continuity.

543　　PROTECTIVE CONDUCTORS

543-01　　Cross-sectional areas

543-01-01 The cross-sectional area of every protective conductor, other than an equipotential bonding conductor, shall be:

(i)　calculated in accordance with Regulation 543-01-03, or

(ii)　selected in accordance with Regulation 543-01-04.

Calculation in accordance with Regulation 543-01-03 is necessary if the choice of cross-sectional areas of phase conductors has been determined by considerations of short-circuit current and if the earth fault current is expected to be less than the short-circuit current.

If the protective conductor:

(iii)　is not an integral part of a cable, or

(iv)　is not formed by conduit, ducting or trunking, or

(v)　is not contained in an enclosure formed by a wiring system;

the cross-sectional area shall be not less than 2.5 mm^2 copper equivalent if protection against mechanical damage is provided, and 4 mm^2 copper equivalent if mechanical protection is not provided (see also Regulation 543-03-01).

For a protective conductor buried in the ground Regulation 542-03-01 for earthing conductors also applies. The cross-sectional area of an equipotential bonding conductor shall comply with Section 547.

543-01-02 Where a protective conductor is common to several circuits, the cross-sectional area of the protective conductor shall be:

(i)　calculated in accordance with Regulation 543-01-03 for the most onerous of the values of fault current and operating time encountered in each of the various circuits, or

(ii)　selected in accordance with Regulation 543-01-04 so as to correspond to the cross-sectional area of the largest phase conductor of the circuits.

543-01-03 The cross-sectional area, where calculated, shall be not less than the value determined by the following formula or shall be obtained by reference to BS 7454:

$$S = \frac{\sqrt{I^2 t}}{k}$$

where:

S　is the nominal cross-sectional area of the conductor in mm^2.

I　is the value in amperes (rms for a.c.) of fault current for a fault of negligible impedance, which can flow through the associated protective device, due account being taken of the current limiting effect of the circuit impedances and the limiting capability ($I^2 t$) of that protective device.

　　Account shall be taken of the effect, on the resistance of circuit conductors, of their temperature rise as a result of overcurrent - see Regulation 413-02-05.

t　is the operating time of the disconnecting device in seconds corresponding to the fault current I amperes.

k　is a factor taking account of the resistivity, temperature coefficient and heat capacity of the conductor material, and the appropriate initial and final temperatures.

Values of k for protective conductors in various use or service are as given in Tables 54B, 54C, 54D, 54E and 54F. The values are based on the initial and final temperatures indicated below each table.

Where the application of the formula produces a non-standard size, a conductor having the nearest larger standard cross-sectional area shall be used.

TABLE 54B
Values of k for insulated protective conductor not incorporated in a cable and not bunched with cables, or for separate bare protective conductor in contact with cable covering but not bunched with cables where the assumed initial temperature is 30 °C

Material of conductor	Insulation of protective conductor or cable covering			
	70 °C thermoplastic (general purpose pvc)	90 °C thermoplastic (pvc)	85 °C thermosetting (rubber)	90 °C thermosetting
Copper	143/133*	143/133*	166	176
Aluminium	95/88*	95/88*	110	116
Steel	52	52	60	64
Assumed initial temperature	30 °C	30 °C	30 °C	30 °C
Final temperature	160 °C/140 °C*	160 °C/140 °C*	220 °C	250 °C

* Above 300 mm^2

TABLE 54C
Values of k for protective conductor incorporated in a cable or bunched with cables, where the assumed initial temperature is 70 °C or greater

Material of conductor	Insulation material			
	70 °C thermoplastic (general purpose pvc)	90 °C thermoplastic (pvc)	85 °C thermosetting (rubber)	90 °C thermosetting
Copper	115/103*	100/86*	134	143
Aluminium	76/68*	66/57*	89	94
Assumed initial temperature	70 °C	90 °C	85 °C	90 °C
Final temperature	160 °C/140 °C*	160 °C/140 °C*	220 °C	250 °C

* Above 300 mm^2

TABLE 54D
Values of k for protective conductor as a sheath or armour of a cable

Material of conductor	Insulation material			
	70 °C thermoplastic (general purpose pvc)	90 °C thermoplastic (pvc)	85 °C thermosetting (rubber)	90 °C thermosetting
Aluminium	93	85	93	85
Steel	51	46	51	46
Lead	26	23	26	23
Assumed initial temperature	60 °C	80 °C	75 °C	80 °C
Final temperature	200 °C	200 °C	220 °C	200 °C

TABLE 54E
Values of k for steel conduit, ducting and trunking as the protective conductor

Material of protective conductor conduit	Insulation material			
	70 °C thermoplastic (general purpose pvc)	90 °C thermoplastic (pvc)	85 °C thermosetting (rubber)	90 °C thermosetting
Steel conduit, ducting and trunking	47	44	54	58
Assumed initial temperature	50 °C	60 °C	58 °C	60 °C
Final temperature	160 °C	160 °C	220 °C	250 °C

TABLE 54F
Values of k for bare conductor where there is no risk of damage to any neighbouring material by the temperatures indicated
The temperatures indicated are valid only where they do not impair the quality of the connections

Material of conductor	Conditions		
	Visible and in restricted areas	Normal conditions	Fire risk
Copper	228	159	138
Aluminium	125	105	91
Steel	82	58	50
Assumed initial temperature	30 °C	30 °C	30 °C
Final temperature			
Copper conductors	500 °C	200 °C	150 °C
Aluminium conductors	300 °C	200 °C	150 °C
Steel conductors	500 °C	200 °C	150 °C

543-01-04 Where it is desired not to calculate the minimum cross-sectional area of a protective conductor in accordance with Regulation 543-01-03, the cross-sectional area may be determined in accordance with Table 54G.

Where the application of Table 54G produces a non-standard size, a conductor having the nearest larger standard cross-sectional area shall be used.

TABLE 54G
Minimum cross-sectional area of protective conductor in relation to the cross-sectional area of associated phase conductor

Cross-sectional area of phase conductor S	Minimum cross-sectional area of the corresponding protective conductor	
	If the protective conductor is of the same material as the phase conductor	If the protective conductor is not the same material as the phase conductor
(mm^2)	(mm^2)	(mm^2)
$S \leq 16$	S	$\dfrac{k_1}{k_2} \times S$
$16 < S \leq 35$	16	$\dfrac{k_1}{k_2} \times 16$
$S > 35$	$\dfrac{S}{2}$	$\dfrac{k_1}{k_2} \times \dfrac{S}{2}$

where:

k_1 is the value of k for the phase conductor, selected from Table 43A in Chapter 43 according to the materials of both conductor and insulation.

k_2 is the value of k for the protective conductor, selected from Tables 54B, 54C, 54D, 54E or 54F, as applicable.

543-02　Types of protective conductor

543-02-01　Flexible or pliable conduit shall not be selected as a protective conductor. Neither a gas pipe nor an oil pipe shall be selected as a protective conductor.

543-02-02　A protective conductor may consist of one or more of the following:

   (i)　a single-core cable

   (ii)　a conductor in a cable

   (iii)　an insulated or bare conductor in a common enclosure with insulated live conductors

   (iv)　a fixed bare or insulated conductor

   (v)　a metal covering, for example, the sheath, screen or armouring of a cable

   (vi)　a metal conduit or other enclosure or electrically continuous support system for conductors

   (vii)　an extraneous-conductive-part complying with Regulation 543-02-06.

543-02-03　A protective conductor of the types described in items (i) to (iv) of Regulation 543-02-02 and of cross-sectional area 10 mm^2 or less, shall be of copper.

543-02-04　Where a metal enclosure or frame of a low voltage switchgear or controlgear assembly or busbar trunking system is used as a protective conductor, it shall satisfy the following three requirements:

   (i)　its electrical continuity shall be assured, either by construction or by suitable connection, in such a way as to be protected against mechanical, chemical or electrochemical deterioration, and

   (ii)　its cross-sectional area shall be at least equal to that resulting from the application of Regulation 543-01, or verified by test in accordance with BS EN 60439-1, and

   (iii)　it shall permit the connection of other protective conductors at every predetermined tap-off point.

543-02-05　The metal covering including the sheath (bare or insulated) of a cable, in particular the sheath of a mineral insulated cable, trunking and ducting for electrical purposes and metal conduit, may be used as a protective conductor for the associated circuit, if it satisfies both requirements of items (i) and (ii) of Regulation 543-02-04.

543-02-06　Except as prohibited in Regulation 543-02-01, an extraneous-conductive-part may be used as a protective conductor if it satisfies all the following requirements:

   (i)　electrical continuity shall be assured, either by construction or by suitable connection, in such a way as to be protected against mechanical, chemical or electrochemical deterioration, and

   (ii)　the cross-sectional area shall be at least equal to that resulting from the application of Regulation 543-01-01, and

   (iii)　unless compensatory measures are provided, precautions shall be taken against its removal, and

   (iv)　it has been considered for such a use and, if necessary, suitably adapted.

543-02-07　Where the protective conductor is formed by conduit, trunking, ducting or the metal sheath and/or armour of a cable, the earthing terminal of each accessory shall be connected by a separate protective conductor to an earthing terminal incorporated in the associated box or other enclosure.

543-02-08　An exposed-conductive-part of equipment shall not be used to form a protective conductor for other equipment except as provided by Regulations 543-02-02, 543-02-04 and 543-02-05.

543-02-09　Except where the circuit protective conductor is formed by a metal covering or enclosure containing all of the conductors of the ring, the circuit protective conductor of every ring final circuit shall also be run in the form of a ring having both ends connected to the earthing terminal at the origin of the circuit.

543-02-10　A separate metal enclosure for cable shall not be used as a PEN conductor.

543-03 Preservation of electrical continuity of protective conductors

543-03-01 A protective conductor shall be suitably protected against mechanical and chemical deterioration and electrodynamic effects.

543-03-02 Excepting items (i) and (ii) below, a protective conductor having a cross-sectional area up to and including 6 mm^2 shall be protected throughout by a covering at least equivalent to that provided by the insulation of a single-core non-sheathed cable of appropriate size having a voltage rating of at least 450/750 V:

(i) a protective conductor forming part of a multicore cable

(ii) cable trunking or conduit used as a protective conductor.

Where the sheath of a cable incorporating an uninsulated protective conductor of cross-sectional area up to and including 6 mm^2 is removed adjacent to joints and terminations, the protective conductor shall be protected by insulating sleeving complying with BS 2848.

543-03-03 Except for a joint in metal conduit, ducting, trunking or support systems, the connection of a protective conductor shall comply with the requirements for accessibility of Regulation 526-04.

543-03-04 No switching device shall be inserted in a protective conductor except for the following:

(i) as permitted by Regulation 460-01-05

(ii) multipole linked switching or plug-in devices in which the protective conductor circuit shall not be interrupted before the live conductors and shall be re-established not later than when the live conductors are re-connected.

Joints which can be disconnected for test purposes are permitted in a protective conductor circuit.

543-03-05 Where electrical earth monitoring is used, the operating coil shall be connected in the pilot conductor and not in the protective earthing conductor (see BS 4444).

543-03-06 Every joint in metallic conduit shall be mechanically and electrically continuous by screwing or by substantial mechanical clamps. Plain slip or pin-grip sockets shall not be used.

544 EARTHING ARRANGEMENTS FOR PROTECTIVE PURPOSES

544-01-01 When overcurrent protective devices are used for protection against electric shock, the protective conductor shall be incorporated in the same wiring system as the live conductors or in their immediate proximity.

545 EARTHING ARRANGEMENTS FOR FUNCTIONAL PURPOSES

545-01-01 *Deleted by BS 7671 : 2001 see BS EN 50310 : 2000*

546 EARTHING ARRANGEMENTS FOR COMBINED PROTECTIVE AND FUNCTIONAL PURPOSES

546-01 General

546-01-01 Where earthing for combined protective and functional purposes is required, the requirements for protective measures shall take precedence.

546-02 Combined protective and neutral (PEN) conductors

546-02-01 The provisions of Regulations 546-02-02 to 546-02-08 may be applied only:

(i) where any necessary authorisation for use of a PEN conductor has been obtained by the distributor and where the installation complies with the conditions for that authorisation, or

(ii) where the installation is supplied by a privately owned transformer or convertor in such a way that there is no metallic connection (except for the earthing connection) with the distributor's network, or

(iii) where the supply is obtained from a private generating plant.

546-02-02 A conductor of the following types may serve as a PEN conductor provided that the part of the installation concerned is not supplied through a residual current device:

(i) for a fixed installation, a conductor of a cable not subject to flexing and having a cross-sectional area not less than 10 mm^2 for copper or 16 mm^2 for aluminium

(ii) the outer conductor of a concentric cable where that conductor has a cross-sectional area not less than 4 mm^2 in a cable complying with an appropriate British Standard and selected and erected in accordance with Regulations 546-02-03 to 546-02-08.

546-02-03 The outer conductor of a concentric cable shall not be common to more than one circuit. This requirement does not preclude the use of a twin or multicore cable to serve a number of points contained within one final circuit.

546-02-04 The conductance of the outer conductor of a concentric cable (measured at a temperature of 20 °C) shall:

(i) for a single-core cable, be not less than that of the internal conductor

(ii) excepting for a cable complying with BS 5593, for a multicore cable in a multiphase or multipole circuit, be not less than that of one internal conductor

(iii) for a multicore cable serving a number of points contained within one final circuit or having the internal conductors connected in parallel, be not less than that of the internal conductors connected in parallel.

546-02-05 At every joint in the outer conductor of a concentric cable and at a termination, the continuity of that joint shall be supplemented by a conductor additional to any means used for sealing and clamping the outer conductor. The conductance of the additional conductor shall be not less than that specified in Regulation 546-02-04 for the outer conductor.

546-02-06 No means of isolation or switching shall be inserted in the outer conductor of a concentric cable.

546-02-07 Excepting a cable to BS 6207 or BS EN 60207-1 installed in accordance with manufacturers' instructions, the PEN conductor of every cable shall be insulated or have an insulating covering suitable for the highest voltage to which it may be subjected.

546-02-08 If from any point of the installation the neutral and protective functions are provided by separate conductors, those conductors shall not then be re-connected together beyond that point. At the point of separation, separate terminals or bars shall be provided for the protective and neutral conductors. The PEN conductor shall be connected to the terminals or bar intended for the protective earthing conductor and the neutral conductor. The conductance of the terminal link or bar shall not be less than that specified in Regulation 546-02-04.

547   PROTECTIVE BONDING CONDUCTORS

547-01   General

547-01-01 *Deleted by BS 7671 : 1992, Amendment No 1.*

547-02   Main equipotential bonding conductors

547-02-01 Except where PME conditions apply, a main equipotential bonding conductor shall have a cross-sectional area not less than half the cross-sectional area required for the earthing conductor of the installation and not less than 6 mm^2. The cross-sectional area need not exceed 25 mm^2 if the bonding conductor is of copper or a cross-sectional area affording equivalent conductance in other metals.

Where PME conditions apply, the main equipotential bonding conductor shall be selected in accordance with the neutral conductor of the supply and Table 54H.

TABLE 54H

Minimum cross-sectional area of the main equipotential bonding conductor in relation to the neutral of the supply

NOTE: Local distributor's network conditions may require a larger conductor.

Copper equivalent cross-sectional area of the supply neutral conductor	Minimum copper equivalent[*] cross-sectional area of the main equipotential bonding conductor
35 mm^2 or less	10 mm^2
over 35 mm^2 up to 50 mm^2	16 mm^2
over 50 mm^2 up to 95 mm^2	25 mm^2
over 95 mm^2 up to 150 mm^2	35 mm^2
over 150 mm^2	50 mm^2

[*] The minimum copper equivalent cross-sectional area is given by a copper bonding conductor of the tabulated cross-sectional area or a bonding conductor of another metal affording equivalent conductance.

547-02-02 The main equipotential bonding connection to any gas, water or other service shall be made as near as practicable to the point of entry of that service into the premises. Where there is an insulating section or insert at that point, or there is a meter, the connection shall be made to the consumer's hard metal pipework and before any branch pipework. Where practicable the connection shall be made within 600 mm of the meter outlet union or at the point of entry to the building if the meter is external.

547-03 Supplementary bonding conductors

547-03-01 A supplementary bonding conductor connecting two exposed-conductive-parts shall have a conductance, if sheathed or otherwise provided with mechanical protection, not less than that of the smaller protective conductor connected to the exposed-conductive-parts. If mechanical protection is not provided, its cross-sectional area shall be not less than 4 mm^2.

547-03-02 A supplementary bonding conductor connecting an exposed-conductive-part to an extraneous-conductive-part shall have a conductance, if sheathed or otherwise provided with mechanical protection, not less than half that of the protective conductor connected to the exposed-conductive-part. If mechanical protection is not provided, its cross-sectional area shall be not less than 4 mm^2.

547-03-03 A supplementary bonding conductor connecting two extraneous-conductive-parts shall have a cross-sectional area not less than 2.5 mm^2 if sheathed or otherwise provided with mechanical protection or 4 mm^2 if mechanical protection is not provided, except that where one of the extraneous-conductive-parts is connected to an exposed-conductive-part in compliance with Regulation 547-03-02, that regulation shall apply also to the conductor connecting the two extraneous-conductive-parts.

547-03-04 Except where Regulation 547-03-05 applies, supplementary bonding shall be provided by a supplementary conductor, a conductive part of a permanent and reliable nature, or by a combination of these.

547-03-05 Where supplementary bonding is to be applied to a fixed appliance which is supplied via a short length of flexible cord from an adjacent connection unit or other accessory, incorporating a flex outlet, the circuit protective conductor within the flexible cord shall be deemed to provide the supplementary bonding connection to the exposed-conductive-parts of the appliance, from the earthing terminal in the connection unit or other accessory.

CHAPTER 55

OTHER EQUIPMENT

CONTENTS

CHAPTER 55

OTHER EQUIPMENT

551   GENERATING SETS

551-01   **Scope**

551-01-01   This section applies to low voltage and extra-low voltage installations which incorporate generating sets intended to supply, either continuously or occasionally, all or part of the installation. Requirements are included for:

(i)   supply to an installation which is not connected to the distributor's network

(ii)   supply to an installation as an alternative to the distributor's network

(iii) supply to an installation in parallel with the distributor's network

(iv)   appropriate combinations of the above.

This section does not apply to self-contained items of extra-low voltage electrical equipment which incorporate both the source of energy and the energy-using load and for which a specific product standard exists that includes the requirements for electrical safety.

Requirements of the distributor shall be ascertained before a generating set is installed in an installation which is connected to the distributor's network.

551-01-02   Generating sets with the following power sources are considered :

(i)   combustion engines

(ii)   turbines

(iii) electric motors

(iv)   photovoltaic cells

(v)   electrochemical sources

(vi)   other suitable sources.

551-01-03   Generating sets with the following electrical characteristics are considered :

(i)   mains-excited and separately-excited synchronous generators

(ii)   mains-excited and self-excited asynchronous generators

(iii) mains-commutated and self-commutated static inverters with or without bypass facilities.

551-01-04   The use of generating sets for the following purposes is considered:

(i)   supply to permanent installations

(ii)   supply to temporary installations

(iii) supply to portable equipment which is not connected to a permanent fixed installation.

551-02   **General**

551-02-01   The means of excitation and commutation shall be appropriate for the intended use of the generating set and the safety and proper functioning of other sources of supply shall not be impaired by the generating set.

551-02-02   The prospective short-circuit current and prospective earth fault current shall be assessed for each source of supply or combination of sources which can operate independently of other sources or combinations. The short-circuit rating of protective devices within the installation and, where appropriate, connected to the distributor's network, shall not be exceeded for any of the intended methods of operation of the sources.

551-02-03   Where the generating set is intended to provide a supply to an installation which is not connected to the distributor's network or to provide a supply as a switched alternative to the distributor's network, the capacity and operating characteristics of the generating set shall be such that danger or damage to equipment does not arise after the connection or disconnection of any intended load as a result of the deviation of the voltage or frequency from the intended operating range. Means shall be provided to automatically disconnect such parts of the installation as may be necessary if the capacity of the generating set is exceeded.

551-03   Extra-low voltage systems supplied from more than one source

551-03-01 Where a SELV or PELV system may be supplied by more than one source, the requirements of Regulation 411-02-02 shall apply to each source. Where one or more of the sources is earthed, the requirements of Regulation 471-14-01 for PELV systems shall apply.

If one or more of the sources does not meet the requirements of Regulations 411-02-01 to 411-02-04 inclusive the system shall be treated as a FELV system and the requirements of Regulation 411-03 shall apply.

551-03-02 Where it is necessary to maintain the supply to an extra-low voltage system following the loss of one or more sources of supply, each source of supply or combination of sources of supply which can operate independently of other sources or combinations shall be capable of supplying the intended load of the extra-low voltage system. Provisions shall be made so that the loss of low voltage supply to an extra-low voltage source does not lead to danger or damage for other extra-low voltage equipment.

551-04   Protection against indirect contact

551-04-01 Protection against indirect contact shall be provided for the installation in respect of each source of supply or combination of sources of supply which can operate independently of other sources or combinations of sources.

Protection by automatic disconnection of supply

551-04-02 Protection by automatic disconnection of supply shall be provided in accordance with Regulation 413-02, except as modified for particular circumstances by Regulations 551-04-03, 551-04-04 or 551-04-06.

Additional requirements for installations where the generating set provides a switched alternative supply to the distributor's network (standby systems).

551-04-03 Protection by automatic disconnection of supply shall not rely upon the connection to the earthed point of the distributor's network when the generator is operating as a switched alternative to a TN system. A suitable earth electrode shall be provided.

Additional requirements for installations incorporating static inverters

551-04-04 Where the conditions for automatic disconnection of Regulation 413-02 cannot be achieved for parts of the installation on the load side of the static inverter, supplementary equipotential bonding shall be provided on that side in accordance with Regulations 413-02-27 and 413-02-28.

The resistance (R) of the supplementary equipotential bonding conductor between simultaneously accessible exposed-conductive-parts and extraneous-conductive-parts shall fulfil the following condition :

$$R \leq \frac{50}{I}$$

where:

    I is the maximum fault current which can be supplied by the static inverter alone for a period of up to 5 s.

Where a static inverter is intended to operate in parallel with a distributor's network the requirements of Regulation 551-07 also apply.

551-04-05 Precautions shall be taken or equipment shall be selected so that the correct operation of protective devices is not impaired by direct current generated by a static inverter or by the presence of filters.

Additional requirements for protection by automatic disconnection where the installation and generating set are not permanently fixed.

551-04-06 For portable generating sets and generating sets which are intended to be moved to unspecified locations for temporary or short-term use, the following requirements apply to installations which are not permanently fixed:

   (i)   between separate items of equipment, protective conductors shall be provided which are part of a suitable cord or cable and which comply with Table 54G. All protective conductors shall comply with Chapter 54

  (ii)   in TN, TT and IT systems a residual current device with a rated residual operating current ($I_{\Delta n}$) not exceeding 30 mA shall be installed in accordance with the requirements for automatic disconnection of Regulation 413-02.

For construction site installations, see Section 604.

551-05 Protection against overcurrent

551-05-01 Where means of detecting overcurrent of the generating set is provided, this shall be located as near as practicable to the generator terminals.

551-05-02 Where a generating set is intended to operate in parallel with a distributor's network, or where two or more generating sets may operate in parallel, circulating harmonic currents shall be limited so that the thermal rating of conductors is not exceeded.

The effects of circulating harmonic currents shall be limited by one or more of the following:

- (i) the selection of generating sets with compensated windings
- (ii) the provision of a suitable impedance in the connection to generator star points
- (iii) the provision of switches which interrupt the circulatory circuit but which are interlocked so that at all times protection against indirect contact is not impaired
- (iv) the provision of filtering equipment
- (v) other suitable means.

551-06 Additional requirements for installations where the generating set provides a supply as a switched alternative to the distributor's network (standby systems)

551-06-01 Precautions complying with the relevant requirements of Chapter 46 for isolation shall be taken, so that the generator cannot operate in parallel with the distributor's network. Suitable precautions shall include one or more of the following:

- (i) an electrical, mechanical or electromechanical interlock between the operating mechanisms or control circuits of the changeover switching devices
- (ii) a system of locks with a single transferable key
- (iii) a three-position break-before-make changeover switch
- (iv) an automatic changeover switching device with a suitable interlock
- (v) other means providing equivalent security of operation.

551-06-02 For TN-S systems where the neutral is not isolated, any residual current device shall be positioned to avoid incorrect operation due to the existence of any parallel neutral earth path.

551-07 Additional requirements for installations where the generating set may operate in parallel with the distributor's network

551-07-01 In selecting and using a generating set to run in parallel with a distributor's network, care shall be taken to avoid adverse effects to the supply network and to other installations in respect of power factor, voltage changes, harmonic distortion, unbalance, starting, synchronising or voltage fluctuation effects. The distributor shall be consulted in respect of particular requirements. Where parallel operation is required, the use of automatic synchronising systems which consider frequency, phase and voltage is preferred.

551-07-02 Protection shall be provided to disconnect the generating set from the distributor's network in the event of loss of that supply or deviation of the voltage or frequency at the supply terminals from values declared for normal supply.

The type of protection and the sensitivity and operating times depend upon the protection of the distributor's network and shall be in accordance with the distributor's requirements.

551-07-03 Means shall be provided to prevent the connection of a generating set to the distributor's network if the voltage and frequency of the distributor's network are outside the limits of operation of the protection required by Regulation 551-07-02.

551-07-04 Means shall be provided to enable the generating set to be isolated from the distributor's network. The means of isolation shall be accessible to the distributor at all times, so far as is reasonably practicable.

551-07-05 Where a generating set may also operate as a switched alternative to the distributor's network, the installation shall also comply with Regulation 551-06.

552-01   Rotating machines

552-01-01 All equipment, including cable, of every circuit carrying the starting, accelerating and load currents of a motor shall be suitable for a current at least equal to the full-load current rating of the motor when rated in accordance with the appropriate British Standard. Where the motor is intended for intermittent duty and for frequent starting and stopping, account shall be taken of any cumulative effects of the starting or braking currents upon the temperature rise of the equipment of the circuit.

552-01-02 Every electric motor having a rating exceeding 0.37 kW shall be provided with control equipment incorporating means of protection against overload of the motor. This requirement does not apply to a motor incorporated in an item of current-using equipment complying as a whole with an appropriate British Standard.

552-01-03 Except where failure to start after a brief interruption would be likely to cause greater danger, every motor shall be provided with means to prevent automatic restarting after a stoppage due to a drop in voltage or failure of supply, where unexpected restarting of the motor might cause danger. These requirements do not preclude arrangements for starting a motor at intervals by an automatic control device, where other adequate precautions are taken against danger from unexpected restarting.

552-01-04 Where reverse-current braking of a motor is provided, provision shall be made for the avoidance of reversal of the direction of rotation at the end of braking if such reversal may cause danger.

552-01-05 Where safety depends on the direction of rotation of a motor, provision shall be made for the prevention of reverse operation due, for example, to the loss of one phase.

553   ACCESSORIES

553-01   Plugs and socket-outlets

553-01-01 Every plug and socket-outlet shall comply with all the requirements of items (i) and (ii) below, and in addition shall comply with the appropriate requirements of Regulations 553-01-02 to 553-02-02:

(i)   except for SELV circuits, it shall not be possible for any pin of a plug to make contact with any live contact of its associated socket-outlet while any other pin of the plug is completely exposed, and

(ii)   it shall not be possible for any pin of a plug to make contact with any live contact of any socket-outlet within the same installation other than the type of socket-outlet for which the plug is designed.

553-01-02 Except for SELV or a special circuit from Regulation 553-01-05, every plug and socket-outlet shall be of the non-reversible type, with provision for the connection of a protective conductor.

553-01-03 Except where Regulation 553-01-05 applies, in a low voltage circuit every plug and socket-outlet shall conform with the applicable British Standard listed in Table 55A.

TABLE 55A
Plugs and socket-outlets for low voltage circuits

Type of plug and socket-outlet	Rating (amperes)	Applicable British Standard
Fused plugs and shuttered socket-outlets, 2-pole and earth, for a.c.	13	BS 1363 (fuses to BS 1362)
Plugs, fused or non-fused, and socket-outlets, 2-pole and earth	2, 5, 15, 30	BS 546 (fuses, if any, to BS 646)
Plugs, fused or non-fused, and socket-outlets, protected-type, 2-pole with earthing contact	5, 15, 30	BS 196
Plugs and socket-outlets (industrial type)	16, 32, 63, 125	BS EN 60309-2

553-01-04 Every socket-outlet for household and similar use shall be of the shuttered type and, for an a.c. installation, shall preferably be of a type complying with BS 1363.

553-01-05 A plug and socket-outlet not complying with BS 1363, BS 546, BS 196 or BS EN 60309-2, may be used in single-phase a.c. or two-wire d.c. circuits operating at a nominal voltage not exceeding 250 volts for:

    (i) the connection of an electric clock, provided that the plug and socket-outlet are designed specifically for that purpose, and that each plug incorporates a fuse of rating not exceeding 3 amperes complying with BS 646 or BS 1362 as appropriate

    (ii) the connection of an electric shaver, provided that the socket-outlet is either incorporated in a shaver supply unit complying with BS 3535 or, in a room other than a bathroom, is a type complying with BS 4573

    (iii) a circuit having special characteristics such that danger would otherwise arise or it is necessary to distinguish the function of the circuit.

553-01-06 A socket-outlet on a wall or similar structure shall be mounted at a height above the floor or any working surface to minimize the risk of mechanical damage to the socket-outlet or to an associated plug and its flexible cord which might be caused during insertion, use or withdrawal of the plug.

553-01-07 Where portable equipment is likely to be used, provision shall be made so that the equipment can be fed from an adjacent and conveniently accessible socket-outlet, taking account of the length of flexible cord normally fitted to portable appliances and luminaires.

553-02 Cable couplers

553-02-01 Except for a SELV or a Class II circuit, a cable coupler shall comply where appropriate with BS 196, BS EN 60309-2, BS 4491 or BS 6991, shall be non-reversible and shall have provision for the connection of a protective conductor.

553-02-02 A cable coupler shall be arranged so that the connector of the coupler is fitted at the end of the cable remote from the supply.

553-03 Lampholders

553-03-01 Except where the lampholder and its wiring are enclosed in earthed metal or insulating material having the ignitability characteristic 'P' as specified in BS 476 Part 5 or where separate overcurrent protection is provided, a lampholder shall not be connected to any circuit where the rated current of the overcurrent protective device exceeds the appropriate value stated in Table 55B.

TABLE 55B
Overcurrent protection of lampholders

Type of lampholder			Maximum rating (amperes) of overcurrent protective device protecting the circuit
Bayonet (BS EN 61184) :	B15	SBC	6
	B22	BC	16
Edison screw (BS EN 60238) :	E14	SES	6
	E27	ES	16
	E40	GES	16

553-03-02 A lampholder for a filament lamp shall not be installed in a circuit operating at a voltage exceeding 250 volts.

553-03-03 Bayonet lampholders B15 and B22 shall comply with BS EN 61184 and shall have the temperature rating T2 described in that British Standard.

553-03-04 In circuits of a TN or a TT system, except for E14 and E27 lampholders complying with BS EN 60238, the outer contact of every Edison screw or single centre bayonet cap type lampholder shall be connected to the neutral conductor. This regulation also applies to track mounted systems.

553-04   Lighting points

553-04-01   At each fixed lighting point one of the following accessories shall be used:

(i)   a ceiling rose to BS 67

(ii) a luminaire supporting coupler to BS 6972 or BS 7001

(iii) a batten lampholder to BS 7895, BS EN 60238 or BS EN 61184

(iv) a luminaire designed to be connected directly to the circuit wiring

(v)   a suitable socket-outlet

(vi) a connection unit to BS 5733 or BS 1363-4.

A lighting installation shall be appropriately controlled, e.g. by a switch or combination of switches to BS 3676 and/or BS 5518, or by a suitable automatic control system, which where necessary shall be suitable for discharge lighting circuits.

553-04-02   A ceiling rose shall not be installed in any circuit operating at a voltage normally exceeding 250 volts.

553-04-03   A ceiling rose shall not be used for the attachment of more than one outgoing flexible cord unless it is specially designed for multiple pendants.

553-04-04   Luminaire supporting couplers are designed specifically for the mechanical support and electrical connection of luminaires and shall not be used for the connection of any other equipment.

554   CURRENT-USING EQUIPMENT

554-01   Luminaires

554-01-01   Where a pendant luminaire is installed, the associated accessory shall be suitable for the mass suspended (see also Regulation 522-08-06).

554-01-02   An extra-low voltage luminaire without provision for the connection of a protective conductor shall be installed only as part of a SELV system.

554-02   High voltage discharge lighting installations

554-02-01   Every high voltage electric sign and high voltage luminous discharge tube installation shall be constructed, selected and erected in accordance with the requirements of BS 559.

554-03   Electrode water heaters and boilers

554-03-01   Every electrode boiler and electrode water heater shall be connected to an a.c. system only, and shall be selected and erected in accordance with the appropriate requirements of this section.

554-03-02   The supply to the heater or boiler shall be controlled by a linked circuit-breaker arranged to disconnect the supply from all electrodes simultaneously and provided with an overcurrent protective device in each conductor feeding an electrode.

554-03-03   The earthing of the heater or boiler shall comply with the requirements of Chapter 54 and, in addition, the shell of the heater or boiler shall be bonded to the metallic sheath and armour, if any, of the incoming supply cable. The protective conductor shall be connected to the shell of the heater or boiler and shall comply with Regulation 543-01-01.

554-03-04   Where an electrode water heater or electrode boiler is directly connected to a supply at a voltage exceeding low voltage, the installation shall include a residual current device arranged to disconnect the supply from the electrodes on the occurrence of a sustained protective conductor current in excess of 10 % of the rated current of the heater or boiler under normal conditions of operation, except that if in any instance a higher value is essential to ensure stability of operation of the heater or boiler, the value may be increased to a maximum of 15 %. A time delay may be incorporated in the device to prevent unnecessary operation in the event of imbalance of short duration.

554-03-05   Where an electrode water heater or electrode boiler is connected to a three-phase low voltage supply, the shell of the heater or boiler shall be connected to the neutral of the supply as well as to the earthing conductor. The current-carrying capacity of the neutral conductor shall be not less than that of the largest phase conductor connected to the equipment.

554-03-06 Except as provided by Regulation 554-03-07, where the supply to an electrode water heater or electrode boiler is single-phase and one electrode is connected to a neutral conductor earthed by the distributor, the shell of the water heater or boiler shall be connected to the neutral of the supply as well as to the earthing conductor.

554-03-07 Where the heater or boiler is not piped to a water supply or in physical contact with any earthed metal, and where the electrodes and the water in contact with the electrodes are so shielded in insulating material that they cannot be touched while the electrodes are live, a fuse in the phase conductor may be substituted for the circuit-breaker required under Regulation 554-03-02 and the shell of the heater or boiler need not be connected to the neutral of the supply.

554-04   Heaters for liquids or other substances having immersed heating elements

554-04-01 Every heater for liquid or other substance shall incorporate or be provided with an automatic device to prevent a dangerous rise in temperature.

554-05   Water heaters having immersed and uninsulated heating elements

554-05-01 Every single-phase water heater or boiler having an uninsulated heating element immersed in the water shall comply with the requirements of Regulations 554-05-02 and 554-05-03. This type of water heater or boiler is deemed not to be an electrode water heater or boiler.

554-05-02 All metal parts of the heater or boiler which are in contact with the water (other than current-carrying parts) shall be solidly and metallically connected to a metal water pipe through which the water supply to the heater or boiler is provided, and that water pipe shall be connected to the main earthing terminal by means independent of the circuit protective conductor.

554-05-03 The heater or boiler shall be permanently connected to the electricity supply through a double-pole linked switch which is either separate from and within easy reach of the heater or boiler or is incorporated therein and the wiring from the heater or boiler shall be directly connected to that switch without use of a plug and socket-outlet; and, where the heater or boiler is installed in a room containing a fixed bath, the switch shall comply in addition with Section 601.

554-05-04 Before a heater or boiler of the type referred to in Regulation 554-05 is connected, the installer shall confirm that no single-pole switch, non-linked circuit-breaker or fuse is fitted in the neutral conductor in any part of the circuit between the heater or boiler and the origin of the installation.

554-06   Heating conductors and cables

554-06-01 Where a heating cable is required to pass through, or be in close proximity to, material which presents a fire hazard, the cable shall be enclosed in material having the ignitability characteristic 'P' as specified in BS 476 Part 5 and shall be adequately protected from any mechanical damage reasonably foreseeable during installation and use.

554-06-02 A heating cable intended for laying directly in soil, concrete, cement screed or other material used for road and building construction shall be:

(i)   capable of withstanding mechanical damage under the conditions that can reasonably be expected to prevail during its installation, and

(ii) constructed of material that will be resistant to damage from dampness and/or corrosion under normal conditions of service.

554-06-03 A heating cable laid directly in soil, a road or the structure of a building shall be installed so that it:

(i)   is completely embedded in the substance it is intended to heat, and

(ii) does not suffer damage in the event of movement normally to be expected in it or the substance in which it is embedded, and

(iii) complies in all respects with the makers instructions and recommendations.

554-06-04 The loading of every floor-warming cable under operating conditions shall be limited to a value such that the appropriate conductor temperature specified in Table 55C is not exceeded.

TABLE 55C
Maximum conductor operating temperatures for a floor-warming cable

Type of cable	Maximum conductor operating temperature (°C)
General-purpose pvc over conductor	70
Enamelled conductor, polychlorophene over enamel, pvc overall	70
Enamelled conductor pvc overall	70
Enamelled conductor, pvc over enamel, lead-alloy 'E' sheath overall	70
Heat-resisting pvc over conductor	85
Nylon over conductor, heat-resisting pvc overall	85
Synthetic rubber or equivalent elastomeric insulation over conductor	85
Mineral insulation over conductor, copper sheath overall	*
Silicone-treated woven-glass sleeve over conductor	180

NOTE: * The temperature depends upon many factors including the following:

    (i)   the type of seal employed,

    (ii)   whether the heating section is connected to a cold lead-in section or not,

    (iii)   the outer covering material, if any, and

    (iv)   the material in contact with the heating section.

554-07 Electric surface heating systems

554-07-01 The equipment, system design, installation and testing of an electric surface heating system shall be in accordance with BS 6351.

555 TRANSFORMERS

555-01 Autotransformers and step-up transformers

555-01-01 Where an autotransformer is connected to a circuit having a neutral conductor, the common terminal of the winding shall be connected to the neutral conductor.

555-01-02 A step-up autotransformer shall not be connected to an IT system.

555-01-03 Where a step-up transformer is used, a linked switch shall be provided for disconnecting the transformer from all live conductors of the supply.

CHAPTER 56

SUPPLIES FOR SAFETY SERVICES

CONTENTS

CHAPTER 56

SUPPLIES FOR SAFETY SERVICES

561   GENERAL

561-01-01 For a safety service, a source of supply shall be selected which will maintain a supply of adequate duration.

561-01-02 For a safety service required to operate in fire conditions, all equipment shall be provided, either by construction or by erection, with protection providing fire resistance of adequate duration.

561-01-03 A protective measure against indirect contact without automatic disconnection at the first fault is preferred. In an IT system, continuous insulation monitoring shall be provided to give audible and visible indications of a first fault.

561-01-04 Equipment shall be arranged to facilitate periodic inspection, testing and maintenance.

562   SOURCES

562-01-01 A source for safety services shall be one of the following:

(i) a primary cell or cells

(ii) a storage battery

(iii) a generating set capable of independent operation

(iv) a separate feeder effectively independent of the normal feeder (provided that an assessment is made that the two supplies are unlikely to fail concurrently).

562-01-02 A source for a safety service shall be installed as fixed equipment and in such a manner that it cannot be adversely affected by failure of the normal source.

562-01-03 A source for a safety service shall be placed in a suitable location and be accessible only to skilled or instructed persons

562-01-04 A single source for a safety service shall not be used for another purpose. However, where more than one source is available, such sources may supply standby systems provided that, in the event of failure of one source, the energy remaining available will be sufficient for the starting and operation of all safety services; this generally necessitates the automatic off-loading of equipment not providing safety services.

562-01-05 Regulations 562-01-03 and 562-01-04 do not apply to equipment individually supplied by a self-contained battery.

562-01-06 The location of the source shall be properly and adequately ventilated so that any exhaust gases, smoke or fumes from the source cannot penetrate, to a hazardous extent, areas occupied by persons.

563   CIRCUITS

563-01-01 The circuit of a safety service shall be independent of any other circuit and an electrical fault or any intervention or modification in one system shall not affect the correct functioning of the other.

563-01-02 The circuit of a safety service shall have adequate fire resistance for the locations through which it passes.

563-01-03 The protection against overload prescribed in Regulation 473-01-01 or Regulation 552-01-02 may be omitted.

563-01-04 Every overcurrent protective device shall be selected and erected so as to avoid an overcurrent in one circuit impairing the correct operation of any other safety services circuit.

563-01-05 Switchgear and controlgear shall be clearly identified and grouped in locations accessible only to skilled or instructed persons.

563-01-06 Every alarm, indication and control device shall be clearly identified.

564   UTILISATION EQUIPMENT

564-01-01 In equipment supplied by two different circuits, a fault occurring in one circuit shall not impair the protection against electric shock nor the correct operation of the other circuit.

565   SPECIAL REQUIREMENTS FOR SAFETY SERVICES HAVING SOURCES NOT CAPABLE OF OPERATION IN PARALLEL

565-01-01 Precautions shall be taken by mechanical or electrical interlocking or both to avoid the paralleling of sources.

565-01-02 The requirements of the Regulations for protection against fault current and against electric shock shall be met for each source.

566   SPECIAL REQUIREMENTS FOR SAFETY SERVICES HAVING SOURCES CAPABLE OF OPERATION IN PARALLEL

566-01-01 The requirements of the Regulations for protection against short-circuit and against electric shock shall be met whether the installation is supplied by either of the two sources or by both in parallel.

566-01-02 Precautions shall be taken, where necessary, to limit current circulation, particularly that of third harmonics or multiples thereof, in the connection between the neutral points of sources.

PART 6

SPECIAL INSTALLATIONS OR LOCATIONS

PARTICULAR REQUIREMENTS

CONTENTS

PART 6

SPECIAL INSTALLATIONS OR LOCATIONS

600   GENERAL

600-01   The particular requirements for each special installation or location in Part 6 supplement or modify the general requirements contained in other parts of the Regulations.

600-02   The absence of reference to the exclusion of a Chapter, a Section or a Clause means that the corresponding general regulations are applicable.

SECTION 601

LOCATIONS CONTAINING A BATH OR SHOWER

601-01   **Scope**

601-01-01   The particular requirements of this section apply to locations containing baths, showers and cabinets containing a shower and/or bath, and the surrounding zones. They do not apply to emergency facilities in industrial areas and laboratories. For locations containing baths or showers for medical treatment, or for disabled persons, special requirements may be necessary.

601-02   **Classification of zones**

601-02-01   These requirements are based on the dimensions of four zones: zone 0, zone 1, zone 2 and zone 3. The zones are determined taking account of walls, doors, fixed partitions, ceilings and floors, where these effectively limit the extent of a zone. Figures 601A and 601B are examples of the zones.

Zone 0 is the interior of the bath tub or shower basin.

In a location containing a shower without a basin, zone 0 is limited by the floor and by the plane 0.05 m above the floor. In this case:

(i)   where the shower head is demountable and able to be moved around in use, zone 0 is limited by the vertical plane(s) at a radius of 1.2 m horizontally from the water outlet at the wall, or

(ii)   where the shower head is not demountable, zone 0 is limited by the vertical plane(s) at a radius of 0.60 m from the shower head.

Zone 1 is limited by:

(i)   the upper plane of zone 0 and the horizontal plane 2.25 m above the floor, and

(ii)   (a) by the vertical plane(s) circumscribing the bath tub or shower basin and includes the space below the bath tub or shower basin where that space is accessible without the use of a tool, or

        (b) for a shower without a basin and with a demountable shower head able to be moved around in use, the vertical plane(s) at a radius of 1.2 m from the water outlet at the wall, or

        (c) for a shower without a basin and with a shower head which is not demountable, the vertical plane(s) at a radius 0.60 m from the shower head.

Zone 2 is limited by:

(i)   the vertical plane(s) external to zone 1 and parallel vertical plane(s) 0.60 m external to zone 1, and

(ii)   the floor and the horizontal plane 2.25 m above the floor.

In addition, where the ceiling height exceeds 2.25 m above the floor, the space above zone 1 up to the ceiling or a height of 3.0 m above the floor, whichever is lower, is zone 2.

Zone 3 is limited by:

(i)   the vertical plane(s) external to zone 2 and the parallel vertical plane(s) 2.40 m external to zone 2, and

(ii)   the floor and the horizontal plane 2.25 m above the floor.

In addition, where the ceiling height exceeds 2.25 m above the floor, the space above zone 2 up to the ceiling or a height of 3.0 m above the floor, whichever is lower, is zone 3.

Protection for safety

601-03   Protection against electric shock

601-03-01 *Deleted by BS 7671 : 2001*

601-03-02 Where SELV or PELV is used, whatever the nominal voltage, protection against direct contact shall be provided by:

(i) barriers or enclosures affording at least the degree of protection IP2X or IPXXB, or

(ii) insulation capable of withstanding a type-test voltage of 500 V a.c. rms for 1 minute

601-04   Supplementary equipotential bonding

601-04-01 Local supplementary equipotential bonding complying with Regulation 547-03 shall be provided connecting together the terminal of the protective conductor of each circuit supplying Class I and Class II equipment in zones 1, 2 or 3, and extraneous-conductive-parts in these zones including the following:

(i) metallic pipes supplying services and metallic waste pipes (e.g. water, gas)

(ii) metallic central heating pipes and air conditioning systems

(iii) accessible metallic structural parts of the building; (metallic door architraves, window frames and similar parts are not considered to be extraneous-conductive-parts unless they are connected to metallic structural parts of the building)

(iv) metallic baths and metallic shower basins.

The supplementary equipotential bonding may be provided in close proximity to the location.

601-04-02 The requirements of Regulation 601-04-01 do not apply to zone 3 where a cabinet containing a shower is installed in a room other than a bathroom or shower room, e.g. in a bedroom.

601-05   Application of protective measures against electric shock

601-05-01 In zone 0, only protection by SELV at a nominal voltage (U_0) not exceeding 12 V a.c. rms or 30 V ripple-free d.c. is permitted, the safety source being installed outside zones 0, 1 and 2.

601-05-02 The measures of protection by obstacles (Regulation 412-04) and by placing out of reach (Regulation 412-05) are not permitted.

601-05-03 The measures of protection by non-conducting location (Regulation 413-04) and by earth-free local equipotential bonding (Regulation 413-05) are not permitted.

Selection and erection of equipment

601-06   Common rules, external influences

601-06-01 Electrical equipment shall have at least the following degrees of protection:

(i) in zone 0:

IPX7, or ● ● if the equipment is not IP coded.

(ii) in zones 1 and 2:

IPX4, or ⚠ if the equipment is not IP coded.
Where water jets are likely to be used for cleaning purposes in communal baths or communal showers
IPX5, or ⚠ ⚠ if the equipment is not IP coded.

This requirement does not apply to shaver supply units to BS EN 60742, Chapter 2, Section 1 installed in zone 2 and located where direct spray from showers is unlikely.

(iii) in zone 3:

where water jets are likely to be used for cleaning purposes in communal baths or communal showers
IPX5, or ⚠ ⚠ if the equipment is not IP coded.

601-07   Wiring systems

601-07-01   The following rules apply to surface wiring systems and to wiring systems embedded in the walls at a depth not exceeding 50 mm and which do not comply with Regulation 522-06-06(i), (ii) or (iii).

601-07-02

For zone 0:

wiring systems shall be limited to those which supply fixed electrical equipment situated in that zone.

For zone 1:

wiring systems shall be limited to those which supply fixed electrical equipment situated in zones 0 and 1.

For zone 2:

wiring systems shall be limited to those which supply fixed electrical equipment in zones 0, 1 and 2.

601-08   Switchgear and controlgear

601-08-01   The following requirements do not apply to switches and controls which are incorporated in fixed current-using equipment suitable for use in that zone.

In zone 0:

switchgear or accessories shall not be installed.

In zone 1:

only switches of SELV circuits supplied at a nominal voltage not exceeding 12 V a.c. rms or 30 V ripple-free d.c. shall be installed, the safety source being installed outside zones 0, 1 and 2.

In zone 2:

switchgear, accessories incorporating switches or socket-outlets shall not be installed with the exception of:

(i)   switches and socket-outlets of SELV circuits, the safety source being installed outside zones 0, 1 and 2, and

(ii) shaver supply units complying with BS EN 60742, Chapter 2, Section 1.

In zone 3:

  (i)   socket-outlets shall not be installed except for:

      SELV socket-outlets complying with Regulation 411-02
      Shaver supply units complying with BS EN 60742 Chapter 2, Section 1

 (ii)   there shall be no provision for connecting portable equipment except for (i) above

Except as permitted by Regulation 601-08-02, outside zones 0, 1, 2 and 3 there shall be no socket-outlet other than SELV socket-outlets or shaver supply units complying with BS EN 60742 Chapter 2, Section 1.

Insulating pull cords of cord operated switches complying with BS 3676 are permitted in zones 1 and 2.

601-08-02   Where a shower cubicle is installed in a room other than a bathroom or shower room, outside zones 0, 1, 2 or 3 a socket-outlet, other than a SELV socket-outlet or shaver supply unit, shall be protected by a residual current device with rated operating current $(I_{\Delta n})$ not exceeding 30 mA in accordance with Regulation 412-06.

601-09   Fixed current-using equipment

601-09-01   In zone 0, only fixed current-using equipment which can reasonably only be located in zone 0 may be installed and shall be suitable for the conditions of that zone.

601-09-02   The following fixed current-using equipment may be installed in zone 1 if it is suitable for that zone:

  (i)   a water heater
 (ii)   a shower pump
(iii)   other fixed current-using equipment which can reasonably only be located in zone 1, provided that:

    (a) it is suitable for the conditions of that zone, and

    (b) the supply circuit is additionally protected by a residual current protective device with rated residual operating current $(I_{\Delta n})$ not exceeding 30 mA in accordance with Regulation 412-06.

 (iv)   SELV current-using equipment.

601-09-03 The following requirements do not apply to fixed current-using equipment supplied by SELV according to the conditions of Regulations 411-02 and 601-03-02.

The following fixed current-using equipment may be installed in zone 2 if it is suitable for use in that zone:

 (i) a water heater

 (ii) a shower pump

 (iii) a luminaire, fan, heating appliance or unit for a whirlpool bath complying with the relevant standards

 (iv) other fixed current-using equipment which can reasonably only be located in zone 2, provided that it is suitable for the conditions of that zone.

 (v) SELV current-using equipment.

In zone 3 current-using equipment other than fixed current-using equipment shall be protected by a residual current device with rated residual operating current ($I_{\Delta n}$) not exceeding 30 mA in accordance with Regulation 412-06.

601-09-04 Electric heating units embedded in the floor and intended for heating the location may be installed below any zone provided that they are covered by an earthed metallic grid or by an earthed metallic sheath connected to the local supplementary equipotential bonding specified in Regulation 601-04.

fig 601A - Examples of zone dimensions (plan)

NOT TO SCALE (See Regulation 601-02-01 for definitions of zones)

a) Bath tub

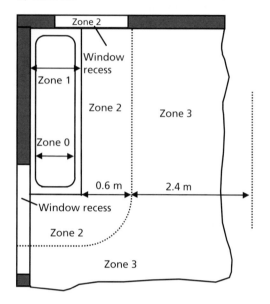

b) Bath tub, with permanently fixed partition

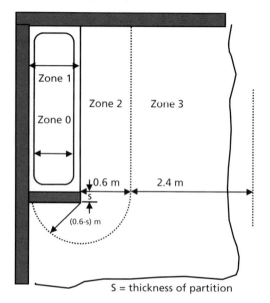

S = thickness of partition

c) Shower basin

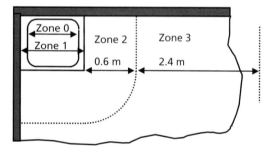

d) Shower basin with permanently fixed partition

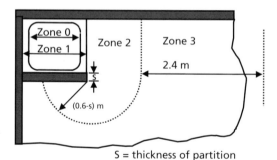

S = thickness of partition

e) Shower, without basin

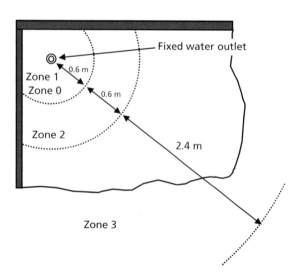

f) Shower, without basin, but with permanent fixed partition - fixed water outlet not demountable

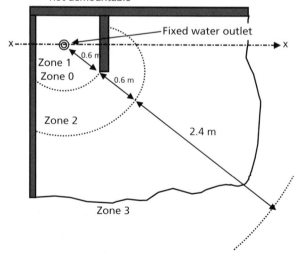

fig 601B - Examples of zone dimensions (elevation)

NOT TO SCALE (See Regulation 601-02-01 for definitions of zones)

a) Bath tub

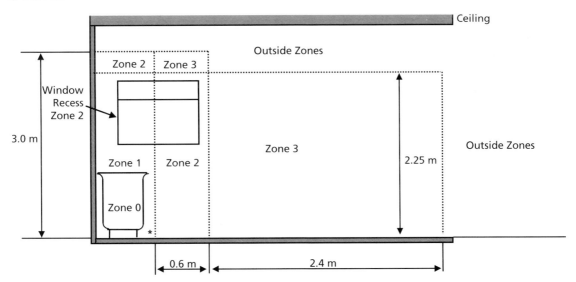

c) Shower basin

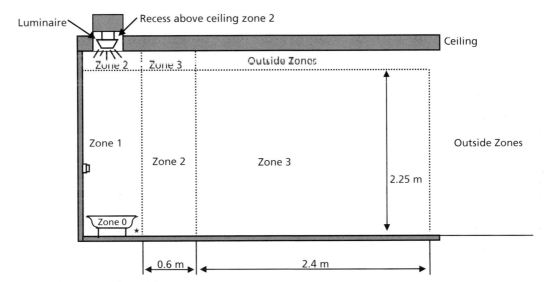

f) Shower without basin, but with permanent fixed partition - fixed water outlet not demountable

Section x-x, see fig 601A(f)

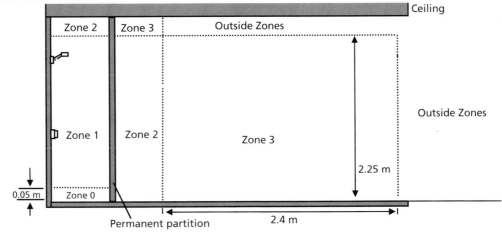

* Zone 1 if the space is accessible without the use of a tool.
Spaces under the bath accessible only with the use of a tool are outside the zones.

SECTION 602

SWIMMING POOLS

602-01   Scope

602-01-01 The particular requirements of this section shall apply to basins of swimming pools and paddling pools and their surrounding zones where the risk of electric shock is increased by a reduction in body resistance and contact of the body with earth potential.

Special requirements may be necessary for swimming pools for medical use.

602-02   Assessment of general characteristics

(see Figures 602A and 602B.)

Zone A   is the interior of the basin, chute or flume and includes the portions of essential apertures in its walls and floor which are accessible to persons in the basin.

Zone B   is limited:

by the vertical plane 2 m from the rim of the basin, and

by the floor or surface expected to be accessible to persons, and

by the horizontal plane 2.5 m above that floor or surface, except where the basin is above ground, when it shall be 2.5 m above the level of the rim of the basin.

Where the building containing the swimming pool contains diving boards, spring boards, starting blocks or a chute, zone B includes also the zone limited by - the vertical plane spaced 1.5 m from the periphery of diving boards, spring boards and starting blocks, and within that zone, by the horizontal plane 2.5 m above the highest surface expected to be occupied by persons, or to the ceiling or roof if they exist.

Zone C   is limited by:

the vertical plane circumscribing zone B, and the parallel vertical plane 1.5 m external to zone B, and

by the floor or surface expected to be occupied by persons and the horizontal plane 2.5 m above that floor or surface.

fig 602A - zone dimensions for swimming pools and paddling pools.

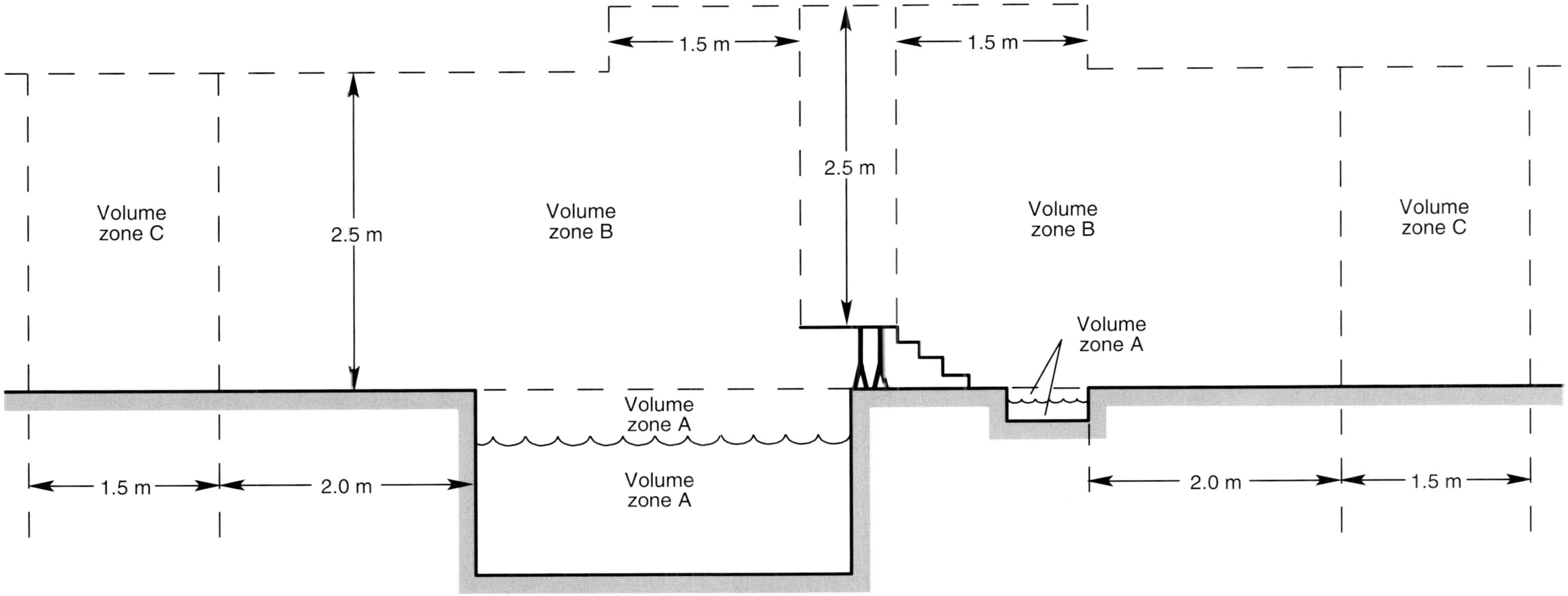

Volume zone C

Volume zone B

Volume zone A

Volume zone A

Volume zone A

Volume zone B

Volume zone C

1.5 m

2.5 m

1.5 m

2.5 m

1.5 m

2.0 m

2.0 m

1.5 m

NOTE: The dimensions are measured taking account of walls and fixed partitions

141

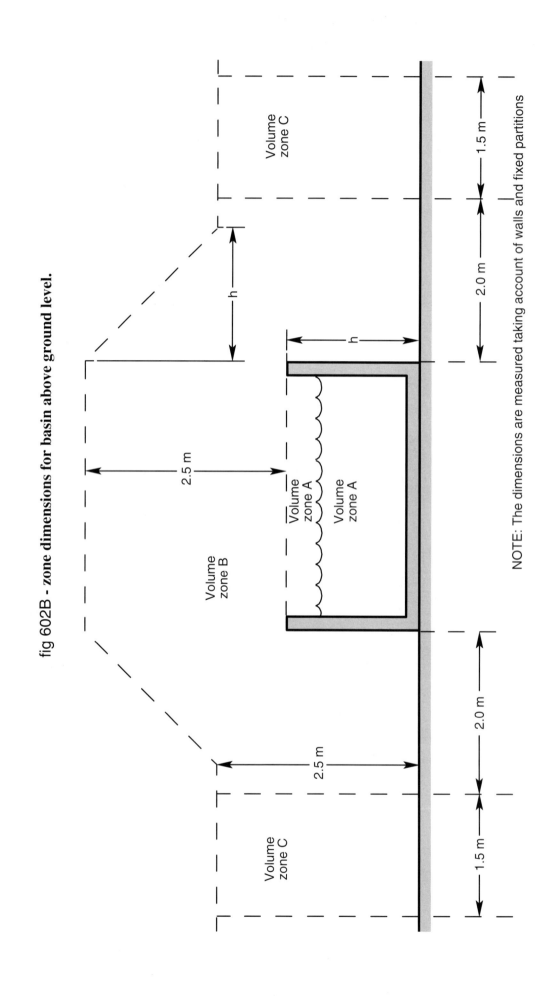

fig 602B - zone dimensions for basin above ground level.

Volume zone C

Volume zone B

h

2.5 m

Volume zone A

Volume zone A

h

Volume zone C

1.5 m

2.0 m

2.0 m

2.5 m

1.5 m

NOTE: The dimensions are measured taking account of walls and fixed partitions

Protection for safety

602-03 Protection against electric shock

602-03-01 Where SELV is used, irrespective of the nominal voltage, protection against direct contact shall be provided by:

(i) barriers or enclosures affording at least the degree of protection IP2X or IPXXB, or

(ii) insulation capable of withstanding a type-test voltage of 500 V a.c. rms for 60 seconds.

602-03-02 Local supplementary equipotential bonding shall be provided connecting all extraneous-conductive-parts in zones A, B and C together, with the protective conductors of all exposed-conductive-parts situated in these zones. This requirement is not to be applied to equipment supplied by SELV circuits. Where there is a metal grid in a solid floor it shall be connected to the local supplementary bonding.

602-04 Application of protective measures against electric shock

602-04-01 In zones A and B, only the protective measure against electric shock by SELV (Regulation 411-02) at a nominal voltage (U_o) not exceeding 12 V a.c. rms or 30 V d.c. shall be used, the safety source being installed outside the zones A, B and C, except that:

(i) where floodlights are installed, each floodlight shall be supplied from its own transformer (or an individual secondary winding of a multi-secondary transformer), having an open circuit voltage not exceeding 18 V

(ii) automatic disconnection of supply by means of a residual current device having the characteristics specified in Regulation 412-06-02 may be used to protect socket-outlets installed in accordance with Regulations 602-07-01 or 602-07-02(iii).

602-04-02 The following protective measures shall not be used in any zone:

(i) protection by means of obstacles (Regulation 412-04)

(ii) protection by means of placing out of reach (Regulation 412-05)

(iii) protection by means of a non-conducting location (Regulation 413-04)

(iv) protection by means of earth-free local equipotential bonding (Regulation 413-05).

Selection and erection of equipment

602-05 Degree of protection of enclosures

602-05-01 Equipment shall have the following minimum degrees of protection:

(i) in zone A - IPX8

(ii) in zone B - IPX5
- IPX4 for swimming pools where water jets are not likely to be used for cleaning

(iii) in zone C - IPX2 for indoor pools
- IPX4 for outdoor pools
- IPX5 for swimming pools where water jets are likely to be used for cleaning.

602-06 Wiring systems

602-06-01 In zones A and B, a surface wiring system shall not employ metallic conduit or metallic trunking or an exposed metallic cable sheath or an exposed earthing or bonding conductor.

602-06-02 Zones A and B shall contain only wiring necessary to supply equipment situated in those zones.

602-06-03 Accessible metal junction boxes shall not be installed in zones A and B.

602-07 Switchgear, controlgear and accessories

602-07-01 In zones A and B, switchgear, controlgear and accessories shall not be installed except for swimming pools where it is not possible to locate socket-outlets outside zone B, when socket-outlets complying with BS EN 60309-2 may be installed if they are:

(i) more than 1.25 m outside the border of zone A, and

(ii) at least 0.3 m above the floor, and

(iii) protected by either:

    (a) a residual current device complying with the relevant British Standard and with Regulation 412-06-02, or

    (b) electrical separation (Regulation 413-06) with the safety isolating transformer placed outside zones A, B and C.

602-07-02 In zone C, a socket-outlet, switch or accessory is permitted only if it is:

(i) protected individually by electrical separation, (Regulation 413-06), or

(ii) protected by SELV (Regulation 411-02), or

(iii) protected by a residual current device complying with the appropriate British Standard and having the characteristics specified in Regulation 412-06-02, or

(iv) a shaver socket complying with BS 3535.

This requirement does not apply to the insulating cords of cord operated switches complying with BS 3676.

602-08 Other equipment

602-08-01 Socket-outlets shall comply with BS EN 60309-2.

602-08-02 In zones A and B, only current-using equipment specifically intended for use in swimming pools shall be installed.

602-08-03 In zone C, equipment shall be protected by one of the following:

(i) individually by electrical separation (Regulation 413-06)

(ii) SELV (Regulation 411-02)

(iii) a residual current device having the characteristics specified in Regulation 412-06-02.

This requirement does not apply to instantaneous water heaters complying with the relevant requirements of the appropriate British Standard.

602-08-04 An electric heating unit embedded in the floor in zone B or C shall incorporate a metallic sheath connected to the local supplementary equipotential bonding or shall be covered by an earthed metallic grid connected to the equipotential bonding specified in Regulation 602-03-02.

602-08-05 *Deleted by BS 7671 : 1992, Amendment No 1.*

SECTION 603

HOT AIR SAUNAS

603-01   Scope

603-01-01   The particular requirements of this section shall apply to locations in which hot air sauna heating equipment according to BS EN 60335-2-53 (Safety of Household and Similar Electrical Appliances Part 2: Particular requirements, Electric sauna heating appliances) is installed.

603-02   Classification of temperature zones

603-02-01   The assessment of the general characteristics of the location shall take due consideration of the classification of the four temperature zones which are illustrated in Figure 603A. .

Protection against electric shock

603-03   Protection against both direct and indirect contact

603-03-01   Where SELV is used, irrespective of the nominal voltage, protection against direct contact shall be provided by one or more of the following:

(i)   insulation (Regulation 412-02), capable of withstanding a type-test voltage of 500 V a.c. rms for 60 seconds

(ii)   barriers or enclosures (Regulation 412-03), affording at least the degree of protection IP24 or IPX4B.

Application of protective measures against electric shock

603-04   Protection against direct contact

603-04-01   The following protective measures against direct contact shall not be used:

(i)   protection by means of obstacles (Regulation 412-04)

(ii)   protection by placing out of reach (Regulation 412-05).

603-05   Protection against indirect contact

603-05-01   The following protective measures against indirect contact shall not be used:

(i)   protection by non conducting location (Regulation 413-04)

(ii)   protection by means of earth-free local equipotential bonding (Regulation 413-05).

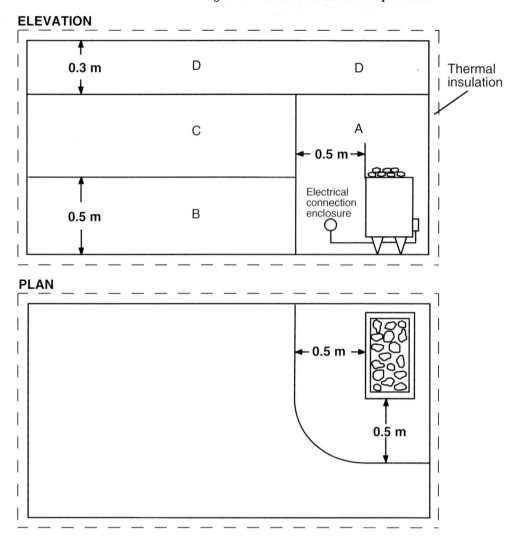

fig 603A - zones of ambient temperature.

Selection and erection of equipment

603-06   Common rules

603-06-01   All equipment shall have at least the degree of protection IP24.

603-06-02   In temperature zone A only the sauna heater and equipment directly associated with it shall be installed.

In temperature zone B there is no special requirement concerning heat resistance of equipment.

In temperature zone C equipment shall be suitable for an ambient temperature of 125 °C.

In temperature zone D only luminaires and their associated wiring, and control devices for the sauna heater and their associated wiring shall be installed. The equipment shall be suitable for an ambient temperature of 125 °C.

603-07   Wiring systems

603-07-01   Only flexible cords having 180 °C thermosetting (rubber) insulation shall be used and shall be protected against mechanical damage with material which complies with Regulation 413-03-01.

603-08   Switchgear, controlgear and accessories

603-08-01   Switchgear not built into the sauna heater, other than a thermostat and a thermal cut-out shall be installed outside the hot air sauna.

603-08-02   Except as permitted in Regulations 603-06-02 and 603-08-01 accessories shall not be installed within the hot air sauna.

603-09   Other fixed equipment

603-09-01   Luminaires shall be so mounted as to prevent overheating.

SECTION 604

CONSTRUCTION SITE INSTALLATIONS

604-01   Scope

604-01-01   The particular requirements of this section shall apply to installations provided for the purpose of electricity supply during the execution of the following works:

(i)   new building construction

(ii)   repair, alteration, extension or demolition of existing buildings

(iii)   engineering construction

(iv)   earthworks

(v)   similar works.

604-01-02   The requirements of this section are applicable to:

(i)   the assembly comprising the main switchgear and the main protective devices

(ii)   installations on the load side of the above assembly comprising mobile and transportable electrical equipment as part of the movable installation.

The assembly is the origin of the installation and is considered to be the interface between the supply system and the construction site installations.

604-01-03   The requirements of this section shall not apply:

(i)   to construction site offices, cloakrooms, meeting rooms, canteens, restaurants, dormitories and toilets, where the general requirements of the regulations shall apply

(ii)   to installations covered by BS 6907, or other installations where equipment of a similar nature to that used in surface mining applications is involved.

Assessment and general characteristics

604-02   Supplies

604-02-01   Equipment shall be identified with and be compatible with the particular supply from which it is energised and shall contain only components connected to one and the same installation, except for control or signalling circuits and inputs from standby supplies.

604-02-02   The following nominal voltages shall not be exceeded:

(i)   SELV   - portable hand lamps in confined or damp locations

(ii)   *Deleted by BS 7671 : 2001, Amendment No 1.*

(iii)   110 V, 1-phase, centre point earthed - reduced low voltage system
portable hand lamps for general use
portable hand-held tools and local lighting up to 2 kW

(iv)   110 V, 3-phase, star point earthed   - reduced low voltage system
portable hand-held tools and local lighting up to 2 kW
small mobile plant, up to 3.75 kW

(v)   230 V, 1-phase   - fixed floodlighting

(vi)   400 V, 3-phase   - fixed and movable equipment, above 3.75 kW.

This requirement shall not preclude the use of a high voltage supply for large equipment where this is necessary for functional reasons .

Protection for safety

604-03   Protection against indirect contact

604-03-01   Where an alternative system is available an IT system shall not be used. Where it is used, permanent earth fault monitoring shall be provided. Where portable generating sets are used, earth fault monitoring may be omitted.

604-03-02   Where protection against indirect contact is provided by the measure of earthed equipotential bonding and automatic disconnection of supply (Regulations 413-02 and 471-08 as appropriate to the type of earthing system), then Regulations 604-04 to 604-08 shall apply.

604-04   TN system

604-04-01   In Regulation 413-02-08, Table 41A is replaced by Table 604A.

TABLE 604A
Maximum disconnection times for TN systems
(see Regulation 604-04-02)

U_o (volts)	t* (seconds)
120	0.35
220 to 277	0.2
400, 480	0.05
580	0.02

where:

U_o is the nominal voltage to Earth.

*   If such a disconnection time cannot be guaranteed it may be necessary to take other protective measures, such as supplementary equipotential bonding.

604-04-02   Regulation 413-02-09 is replaced by:

Except for a reduced low voltage system, (see Regulation 471-15) the maximum disconnection times stated in Table 604A shall apply to circuits supplying movable installations or equipment, either directly or through socket-outlets.

604-04-03   Regulation 413-02-10 is replaced by:

Where a fuse is used to satisfy the requirements of Regulation 604-04-02, maximum values of earth fault loop impedance (Z_s) corresponding to a disconnection time of 0.2 s are stated in Table 604B1 for a nominal voltage to Earth (U_o) of 230 V. For types and rated currents of general purpose (gG) fuses other than those mentioned in Table 604B1, and for motor circuit fuses (gM), reference should be made to the appropriate British Standard, to determine the value of I_a for compliance with Regulation 604-04-02.

Maximum earth fault loop impedance (Z_s) for fuses, for 0.2 s disconnection time with U_o of 230 V
(see Regulation 604-04-03)

(a) General purpose (gG) fuses to BS 88-2.1 and BS 88-6

Rating (amperes)	6	10	16	20	25	32	40	50
Z_s (ohms)	7.74	4.71	2.53	1.60	1.33	0.92	0.71	0.53

(b) Fuses to BS 1361

Rating (amperes)	5	15	20	30	45
Z_s (ohms)	9.60	3.00	1.55	1.00	0.51

(c) Fuses to BS 3036

Rating (amperes)	5	15	20	30	45
Z_s (ohms)	7.50	1.92	1.33	0.80	0.41

(d) Fuses to BS 1362

Rating (amperes)	13
Z_s (ohms)	2.14

NOTE: The circuit loop impedances given in the table should not be exceeded when the conductors are at their normal operating temperature. If the conductors are at a different temperature when tested, the reading should be adjusted accordingly.

604-04-04 Regulation 413-02-11 is replaced by:

Where a circuit-breaker is used to satisfy the requirements of Regulation 604-04-02, the maximum value of earth fault loop impedance (Z_s) shall be determined by the formula of Regulation 413-02-08. Alternatively, for a nominal voltage to Earth (U_o) of 230 V and a disconnection time of 0.2 s, the values specified in Table 604B2 for the types and ratings of circuit-breaker listed may be used instead of calculation.

TABLE 604B2
Maximum earth fault loop impedance (Z_s) for circuit-breakers, for disconnection times of both 0.2 s with U_o of 230 V (see Regulation 604-04-04) and 5 s (see Regulations 413-02-12 and 604-04-06)

(e) Type B circuit-breakers to BS EN 60898 and RCBOs to BS EN 61009

Rating (amperes)	6	10	16	20	25	32	40	50	63	80	100	125	I_n
Z_s (ohms)	8.00	4.80	3.00	2.40	1.92	1.50	1.20	0.96	0.76	0.60	0.48	0.38	48/I_n

(f) Type C circuit-breakers to BS EN 60898 and RCBOs to BS EN 61009

Rating (amperes)	6	10	16	20	25	32	40	50	63	80	100	125	I_n
Z_s (ohms)	4.00	2.40	1.50	1.20	0.96	0.75	0.60	0.48	0.38	0.30	0.24	0.19	24/I_n

(g) Type D circuit-breakers to BS EN 60898 and RCBOs to BS EN 61009

Rating (amperes)	6	10	16	20	25	32	40	50	63	80	100	125	I_n
Z_s (ohms)	2.00	1.20	0.75	0.60	0.48	0.38	0.30	0.24	0.19	0.15	0.12	0.10	12/I_n

NOTE: The circuit loop impedances given in the table should not be exceeded when the conductors are at their normal operating temperature. If the conductors are at a different temperature when tested, the reading should be adjusted accordingly.

604-04-05 Regulation 413-02-12 is not applicable. Table 41C is not applicable.

604-04-06 Regulation 413-02-13 is replaced by:

A maximum disconnection time of 5 s shall apply to the fixed installation and to a reduced low voltage system (see Regulation 471-15).

For a nominal voltage to Earth (U_o) of 230 V and for types and rated currents of overcurrent protective devices in common use, maximum values of earth fault loop impedance (Z_s) corresponding to a disconnection time of 5 s are stated in Regulation 413-02-14.

604-04-07 The Regulation 413-02-04 reference to TN systems (3rd paragraph) is replaced by:

If the conditions of Regulations 604-04-01 and 604-04-06 cannot be fulfilled by using overcurrent protective devices, then protection shall be provided by means of a residual current device.

604-04-08 In Regulation 413-02-16, the formula is replaced by:

$$Z_s \, I_{\Delta n} \leq 25 \text{ V}$$

604-05   TT system

604-05-01 In Regulation 413-02-20, the formula is replaced by:

$$R_A \, I_a \leq 25 \text{ V}$$

604-06   IT system

604-06-01 In Regulation 413-02-23, the formula is replaced by:

$$R_A \, I_d \leq 25 \text{ V}$$

604-06-02 In Regulation 413-02-26, Table 41E is replaced by Table 604E and the definition of I_a is replaced by the following:

I_a is the current which disconnects the circuit within the time specified in Table 604E when applicable, or within 5 s for other circuits when this time is allowed (see Regulation 604-04-06).

TABLE 604E
Maximum disconnection times in IT systems (second fault)

U_o/U (volts)	Neutral not distributed t (seconds)*	Neutral distributed t (seconds)*
120/240	0.4	1
220/380 to 277/480	0.2	0.5
400/690	0.06	0.2
580/1000	0.02	0.08

where:

U_o is the voltage between phase and neutral.

U is the voltage between phases.

*   if such a disconnection time cannot be guaranteed it may be necessary to take other protective measures, such as supplementary equipotential bonding.

604-07   Supplementary equipotential bonding

604-07-01 In Regulation 413-02-28, the formula is replaced by:

$$R \leq \frac{25}{I_a}$$

604-08 Application of protective measures

604-08-01 Regulation 471-08-02 is not applicable.

604-08-02 Regulation 471-08-03 is not applicable.

604-08-03 Every socket-outlet and permanently connected hand-held equipment, with a rated current up to and including 32 A, shall be protected in accordance with Regulation 471-16.

604-08-04 Where socket-outlets or permanently connected hand-held equipment are protected in accordance with Regulation 471-16-01(ii), they each shall be supplied from a separate isolating transformer or separate windings of an isolating transformer.

Selection and erection of equipment

604-09 General

604-09-01 Every assembly for the distribution of electricity on construction and demolition sites shall comply with the requirements of BS 4363 and BS EN 60439-4.

604-09-02 Except for assemblies covered by Regulation 604-09-01 equipment shall have a degree of protection appropriate to the external influence.

604-10 Wiring systems

604-10-01 *Deleted by BS 7671 : 2001*

604-10-02 Cable shall not be installed across a site road or a walkway unless adequate protection of the cable against mechanical damage is provided.

604-10-03 For a reduced low voltage system, low temperature 300/500 V thermoplastic (pvc) or equivalent flexible cables shall be used. For applications exceeding the reduced low voltage system in compliance with (v) and (vi) of Regulation 604-02-02, flexible cable shall be H07 RN-F type or equivalent having 450/750 V rating and resistant to abrasion and water.

604-11 Isolation and switching devices

604-11-01 *Deleted by BS 7671 : 2001*

604 11-02 Each supply assembly and each distribution assembly shall incorporate devices for isolating and switching the incoming supply.

604-11-03 A means of emergency switching shall be provided on the supply to all equipment from which it may be necessary to disconnect all live conductors in order to remove a hazard.

604-11-04 *Deleted by BS 7671 : 2001*

604-11-05 Every circuit supplying current-using equipment shall be fed from a distribution assembly comprising the following:

   (i)   overcurrent protective devices

  (ii)   devices affording protection against indirect contact

 (iii)   socket-outlets, if required.

604-11-06 Safety and standby supplies shall be connected by means of devices arranged to prevent interconnection of different supplies.

604-12 Plugs and socket-outlets

604-12-01 Every socket-outlet shall be incorporated as part of an assembly complying with Regulation 604-09-01.

604-12-02 Every plug and socket-outlet shall comply with BS EN 60309-2.

604-12-03 Luminaire supporting couplers shall not be used.

604-13 Cable couplers

604-13-01 Every cable coupler shall comply with BS EN 60309-2.

SECTION 605

AGRICULTURAL AND HORTICULTURAL PREMISES

605-01 Scope

605-01-01 The particular requirements of this section apply to all parts of fixed installations of agricultural and horticultural premises outdoors and indoors, and to locations where livestock is kept (such as stables, chicken-houses, piggeries, feed-processing locations, lofts and storage areas for hay, straw and fertilizers). Where the above premises include dwellings intended solely for human habitation, the dwellings are excluded from the scope of this section.

Protection for safety

605-02 Protection against both direct and indirect contact

605-02-01 *Deleted by BS 7671 : 1992, Amendment No 1.*

605-02-02 Where SELV is used, irrespective of the nominal voltage, protection against direct contact shall be provided by one or more of the following:

(i) barriers or enclosures (Regulation 412-03), affording at least the degree of protection IP2X or IPXXB

(ii) insulation (Regulation 412-02) capable of withstanding a type-test voltage of 500 V a.c. rms for 60 seconds.

605-03 Protection against direct contact

605-03-01 Every circuit supplying a socket-outlet, except those supplied from a SELV supply, shall be protected by a residual current device complying with the appropriate British Standard and having the characteristics specified in Regulation 412-06-02(ii).

605-04 Protection against indirect contact

605-04-01 In locations in which livestock is intended to be kept and, where protection against indirect contact is provided by the measure of earthed equipotential bonding and automatic disconnection of supply (Regulations 413-02 and 471-08 as appropriate to the type of earthing system), then Regulations 605-05 to 605-09 shall apply.

605-05 TN system

605-05-01 In Regulation 413-02-08, Table 41A is replaced by Table 605A.

TABLE 605A
Maximum disconnection times for TN systems
(see Regulation 605-05-02)

Installation nominal voltage U_o (volts)	Maximum disconnection time t* (seconds)
120	0.35
220 to 277	0.2
400, 480	0.05
580	0.02

where:

U_o is the nominal voltage to Earth.

*   if such a disconnection time cannot be guaranteed it may be necessary to take other protective measures, such as supplementary equipotential bonding.

605-05-02 Except for socket-outlets complying with Regulation 605-03-01, in Regulation 413-02-09, Table 41A is replaced by Table 605A.

605-05-03 Regulation 413-02-10 is replaced by:

Where a fuse is used to satisfy the requirements of Regulation 605-05-02, maximum values of earth fault loop impedance (Z_s) corresponding to a disconnection time of 0.2 s are stated in Table 605B1 for a nominal voltage to Earth (U_o) of 230 V. For types and rated currents of general purpose (gG) fuses other than those mentioned in Table 605B1, and for motor circuit fuses (gM), reference should be made to the appropriate British Standard, to determine the value of I_a for compliance with Regulation 605-05-02.

TABLE 605B1
Maximum earth fault loop impedance (Z_s) for fuses, for 0.2 s disconnection time with U_o of 230 V
(see Regulation 605-05-03)

(a) General purpose (gG) fuses to BS 88-2.1 and BS 88-6

Rating (amperes)	6	10	16	20	25	32	40	50
Z_s (ohms)	7.74	4.71	2.53	1.60	1.33	0.92	0.71	0.53

(b) Fuses to BS 1361

Rating (amperes)	5	15	20	30	45
Z_s (ohms)	9.60	3.0	1.55	1.0	0.51

(c) Fuses to BS 3036

Rating (amperes)	5	15	20	30	45
Z_s (ohms)	7.50	1.92	1.33	0.80	0.41

(d) Fuse to BS 1362

Rating (amperes)	13
Z_s (ohms)	2.14

NOTE: The circuit loop impedances given in the table should not be exceeded when the conductors are at their normal operating temperature. If the conductors are at a different temperature when tested, the reading should be adjusted accordingly.

605-05-04 Regulation 413-02-11 is replaced by:

Where a circuit-breaker is used to satisfy the requirements of Regulation 605-05-02, the maximum value of earth fault loop impedance (Z_s) shall be determined by the formula of Regulation 413-02-08. Alternatively, for a nominal voltage to Earth (U_o) of 230 V and a disconnection time of 0.2 s, the values specified in Table 605B2 for the types and ratings of circuit-breaker listed may be used instead of calculation.

Maximum earth fault loop impedance (Z_S) for circuit-breakers, for disconnection times of both 0.2 s with U_0 of 230 V (see Regulation 605-05-04) and 5 s (see Regulations 413-02-12 and 605-05-06)

(e) Type B circuit-breakers to BS EN 60898 and RCBOs to BS EN 61009

Rating (amperes)	6	10	16	20	25	32	40	50	63	80	100	125	I_n
Z_S (ohms)	8.00		3.00		1.92		1.20		0.76		0.48		$48/I_n$
		4.80		2.40		1.50		0.96		0.60		0.38	

(f) Type C circuit-breakers to BS EN 60898 and RCBOs to BS EN 61009

Rating (amperes)	6	10	16	20	25	32	40	50	63	80	100	125	I_n
Z_S (ohms)	4.00		1.50		0.96		0.60		0.38		0.24		$24/I_n$
		2.40		1.20		0.75		0.48		0.30		0.19	

(g) Type D circuit-breakers to BS EN 60898 and RCBOs to BS EN 61009

Rating (amperes)	6	10	16	20	25	32	40	50	63	80	100	125	I_n
Z_S (ohms)	2.00		0.75		0.48		0.30		0.19		0.12		$12/I_n$
		1.20		0.60		0.38		0.24		0.15		0.10	

NOTE: The circuit loop impedances given in the table should not be exceeded when the conductors are at their normal operating temperature. If the conductors are at a different temperature when tested, the reading should be adjusted accordingly.

605-05-05 Regulation 413-02-12 is not applicable.

Table 41C is not applicable.

605-05-06 Regulation 413-02-13 is replaced by:

For a distribution circuit a disconnection time not exceeding 5 s is permitted.

For a final circuit supplying only stationary equipment and for a final circuit for which the requirement of Regulation 413-02-09 does not apply a disconnection time not exceeding 5 s is permitted. Where the disconnection time for such a final circuit exceeds that required by Table 605A and another final circuit requiring a disconnection time according to Table 605A is connected to the same distribution board or distribution circuit, one of the following conditions shall be fulfilled:

(i) the impedance of the protective conductor between the distribution board and the point at which the protective conductor is connected to the main equipotential bonding shall not exceed 25 Z_S/U_0 ohms (where Z_S is the earth fault loop impedance corresponding to a disconnection time of 5 s), or

(ii) there shall be equipotential bonding at the distribution board which involves the same types of extraneous-conductive-parts as the main equipotential bonding according to Regulation 413-02-02 and is sized in accordance with Regulation 547-02-01.

605-05-07 In Regulation 413-02-14, Regulation 413-02-13 is replaced by Regulation 605-05-06.

605-05-08 In Regulation 413-02-04, Regulations 413-02-08 to 413-02-14 are replaced by Regulations 605-05-01, 605-05-02, 605-05-03, 605-05-04, 605-05-06 and 605-05-07.

605-05-09 In Regulation 413-02-16, the formula is replaced by:

$$Z_S \, I_{\Delta n} \leq 25 \text{ V}$$

605-06 **Installations which are part of a TT system**

605-06-01 In Regulation 413-02-20, the formula is replaced by:

$$R_A \, I_a \leq 25 \text{ V}$$

605-07   Installations which are part of an IT system

605-07-01   In Regulation 413-02-23, the formula is replaced by:

$$R_A \, I_d \leq 25 \text{ V}$$

605-07-02   In Regulation 413-02-26, Table 41E is replaced by Table 605E and the definition of I_a is replaced by the following:

I_a is the current which disconnects the circuit within the time t specified in Table 605E when applicable, or within 5 s for other circuits when this time is allowed (see Regulation 605-05-06).

TABLE 605E
Maximum disconnection times in IT systems (second fault) (see Regulation 605-07-02)

Installation nominal voltage U_0/U (volts)	Disconnection time t (seconds)*	
	Neutral not distributed	Neutral distributed
120/240	0.4	1
220/380 to 277/480	0.2	0.5
400/690	0.06	0.2
580/1000	0.02	0.08

where:

U_0 is the voltage between phase and neutral.

U   is the voltage between phases.

*   if such a disconnection time cannot be guaranteed it may be necessary to take other protective measures, such as supplementary equipotential bonding.

605 08   Supplementary equipotential bonding

605-08-01   In Regulation 413-02-28, the formula is replaced by:

$$R \leq \frac{25}{I_a}$$

605-08-02   In a location intended for livestock, supplementary bonding shall connect all exposed-conductive-parts and extraneous-conductive-parts which can be touched by livestock.

605-08-03   Where a metallic grid is laid in the floor for supplementary bonding it shall be connected to the protective conductors of the installation.

Application of protective measures against indirect contact

605-09   Protection by earthed equipotential bonding and automatic disconnection of supply

605-09-01   Regulation 471-08-02 is replaced by the following:

For an installation which is part of a TN system, the limiting values of earth fault loop impedance and of circuit protective conductor impedance specified by Regulations 605-05-01, 605-05-03, 605-05-04, 605-05-06 and 605-05-07 are applicable only where the exposed-conductive-parts of the equipment concerned and any extraneous-conductive-parts are situated within the earthed equipotential zone created by the main equipotential bonding (see also Regulation 413-02-02).

Where the disconnection times specified by Regulation 605-05-01 cannot be met by the use of an overcurrent protective device, Regulation 605-05-08 shall be applied.

605-09-02   In Regulation 471-08-03, Table 41A is replaced by Table 605A.

605-09-03   Regulation 471-08-06 is not applicable and Regulation 605-03-01 applies.

605-10 Protection against fire and harmful thermal effects

605-10-01 For the purpose of protection against fire, a residual current device, having a rated residual operating current ($I_{\Delta n}$) not exceeding 0.5 A, shall be installed for the supply to equipment other than that essential to the welfare of livestock.

605-10-02 Heating appliances shall be fixed so as to maintain an appropriate distance from livestock and combustible material, to minimize any risks of burns to livestock and of fire. For radiant heaters the clearance shall be not less than 0.5 m or such other clearance as recommended by the manufacturer.

Selection and erection of equipment

605-11 External influences

605-11-01 Electrical equipment, installed as in normal use, shall have at least the degree of protection IP44. Higher degrees of protection should be provided as appropriate to the external influences.

605-12 Wiring systems

605-12-01 *Deleted by BS 7671 : 1992, Amendment No 1.*

605-12-02 *Deleted by BS 7671 : 1992, Amendment No 1.*

Switchgear and controlgear

605-13 Devices for isolation and switching

605-13-01 Each device for emergency switching including emergency stopping shall be installed where it is inaccessible to livestock and will not be impeded by livestock, due account being taken of conditions likely to arise in the event of panic by livestock.

Other equipment

605-14 Electric fence controllers

605-14-01 Mains operated electric fence controllers shall comply and be installed in accordance with BS EN 61011 and BS EN 61011-1 and account shall be taken of the effects of induction when in the vicinity of overhead power lines.

605-14-02 Every mains operated electric fence controller shall be so installed that, so far as is reasonably practicable, it is free from risk of mechanical damage or unauthorised interference.

605-14-03 A mains operated fence controller shall not be fixed to any supporting pole of an overhead power or telecommunication line; provided that, where a low voltage supply to an electric fence controller is carried by an insulated overhead line from a distribution board, the controller may be fixed to the pole carrying the supply.

605-14-04 Every earth electrode which is connected to the earthing terminal of an electric fence controller shall be separate from the earthing system of any other circuit and shall be situated outside the resistance area of any electrode used for protective earthing.

605-14-05 Not more than one controller shall be connected to each electric fence or similar system of conductors.

605-14-06 Every electric fence or similar system of conductors and the associated controller shall be so installed that it is not liable to come into contact with any other equipment or conductor.

SECTION 606

RESTRICTIVE CONDUCTIVE LOCATIONS

606-01   Scope

606-01-01   The particular requirements of this section shall apply to installations within or intended to supply equipment or appliances to be used within a restrictive conductive location. They do not apply to any location in which freedom of movement is not physically constrained.

Protection for safety

606-02   Protection against direct and indirect contact

606-02-01   Where protection by the use of SELV (Regulation 411-02) is used, irrespective of the nominal voltage, protection against direct contact shall be provided by:

(i)   a barrier or an enclosure affording at least the degree of protection IP2X or IPXXB, or

(ii)   insulation capable of withstanding a type-test voltage of 500 V a.c. rms for 60 seconds.

606-03   Protection against direct contact

606-03-01   Protection by the following means is not permitted:

(i)   obstacles (Regulations 412-04 and 471-06)

(ii)   placing out of reach (Regulations 412-05 and 471-07).

606-04   Protection against indirect contact

606-04-01   Protection against indirect contact shall be provided by one of the following:

(i)   SELV (Regulation 606-02), or

(ii)   *Deleted by BS 7671 : 1992, Amendment No 1*

(iii)   automatic disconnection (Regulations 413-02-01 to 413-02-26 and 471-08) in which case a supplementary equipotential bonding conductor (Regulations 413-02-27 and 413-02-28) shall be provided and be connected to the exposed-conductive-parts of the fixed equipment and the conductive parts of the location, or

(iv)   electrical separation (Regulation 413-06) in which case only one socket-outlet or piece of equipment shall be connected to each secondary winding of the isolating transformer, or

(v)   the use of Class II equipment adequately protected to an IP code (see Regulation 512-06) in which case the circuit shall be further protected by a residual current device having the characteristics specified in Regulation 412-06-02.

606-04-02   A supply to or a socket-outlet intended to supply a hand lamp shall be protected by SELV (Regulations 606-02 and 606-04-01(i)).

606-04-03   If a functional earth is required for certain equipment, for example measurement or control apparatus, equipotential bonding shall be provided between all exposed-conductive-parts, all extraneous-conductive-parts inside the restrictive conductive location, and the functional earth.

606-04-04   A supply to or a socket-outlet intended to supply a hand-held tool shall be protected by SELV (Regulations 606-02 and 606-04-01(i)) or electrical separation (Regulation 606-04-01(iv)).

606-04-05   A supply to fixed equipment shall be protected by one of the methods listed in Regulation 606-04-01.

606-04-06   Every safety source and isolating source, other than those specified in Regulation 411-02-02(iii), shall be situated outside the restrictive conductive location, unless it is part of a fixed installation which complies with Regulation 606-04-01 within a permanent restrictive conductive location.

SECTION 607

EARTHING REQUIREMENTS FOR THE INSTALLATION OF EQUIPMENT HAVING HIGH PROTECTIVE CONDUCTOR CURRENTS

607-01   Scope

607-01-01   The particular requirements of this section shall apply to:

(i)   that part of the wiring between the current-using equipment and the final circuit, where the protective conductor current exceeds 3.5 mA in normal use

(ii)   circuits where the total protective conductor current may exceed 10 mA in normal use.

Equipment having a high protective conductor current may include, for example, the following:

(a)   information technology equipment complying with BS EN 60950

(b)   industrial and telecommunications equipment with radio-frequency interference suppression filtering

(c)   heating elements.

Protection for safety

607-02   General

607-02-01   Except as required by Regulation 607-03-01, no special precaution is necessary for equipment having a protective conductor current not exceeding 3.5 mA.

607-02-02   Equipment having a protective conductor current exceeding 3.5 mA but not exceeding 10 mA, shall be either permanently connected to the fixed wiring of the installation without the use of a plug and socket-outlet or connected by means of a plug and socket complying with BS EN 60309- 2.

607-02-03   Equipment having a protective conductor current exceeding 10 mA shall be connected to the supply by one of the following methods:

(i)   preferably by being permanently connected to the wiring of the installation, with the protective conductor selected in accordance with Regulation 607-02-04. The permanent connection to the wiring may be by means of a flexible cable

(ii)   a flexible cable with a plug and socket-outlet complying with BS EN 60309-2, provided that either:

(a) the protective conductor of the associated flexible cable is of a cross-sectional area not less than 2.5mm^2 for plugs rated at 16A and not less than 4 mm^2 for plugs rated above 16A, or

(b) the protective conductor of the associated flexible cable is of a cross-sectional area not less than that of the phase conductor

(iii)   a protective conductor complying with Section 543 with an earth monitoring system to BS 4444 installed which, in the event of a continuity fault occurring in the protective conductor, automatically disconnects the supply to the equipment.

607-02-04   The wiring of every final circuit and distribution circuit intended to supply one or more items of equipment, such that the total protective conductor current is likely to exceed 10 mA, shall have a high integrity protective connection complying with one or more of the following:

(i)   a single protective conductor having a cross-sectional area of not less than 10 mm^2, complying with the requirements of Regulations 543-02 and 543-03

(ii)   a single copper protective conductor having a cross-sectional area of not less than 4 mm^2, complying with the requirements of Regulations 543-02 and 543-03, the protective conductor being enclosed to provide additional protection against mechanical damage, for example, within a flexible conduit

(iii)   two individual protective conductors, each complying with the requirements of Section 543. The two protective conductors may be of different types e.g. a metallic conduit together with an additional conductor of a cable enclosed in the same conduit.

Where the two individual protective conductors are both incorporated in a multicore cable, the total cross-sectional area of all the conductors including the live conductors shall be not less than 10 mm^2. One of the protective conductors may be formed by the metallic sheath, armour or wire braid screen incorporated in the construction of the cable and complying with Regulation 543-02-05

(iv) an earth monitoring system to BS 4444 may be installed which, in the event of a continuity fault occurring in the protective conductor, automatically disconnects the supply to the equipment

(v) connection of the equipment to the supply by means of a double wound transformer or equivalent unit, such as a motor-alternator set, the protective conductor of the incoming supply being connected to the exposed-conductive-parts of the equipment and to a point of the secondary winding of the transformer or equivalent device. The protective conductor(s) between the equipment and the transformer or equivalent device shall comply with one of the arrangements described in Regulation 607-02-04 (i) to (iv) above.

607-02-05   Where two protective conductors are used in accordance with Regulation 607-02-04 (iii), the ends of the protective conductors shall be terminated independently of each other at all connection points throughout the circuit, e.g. the distribution board, junction boxes and socket-outlets. This requires an accessory to be provided with two separate earth terminals.

607-03   Socket-outlet final circuits

607-03-01   For a final circuit with a number of socket-outlets or connection units intended to supply several items of equipment, where it is known or reasonably to be expected that the total protective conductor current in normal service will exceed 10 mA, the circuit shall be provided with a high integrity protective conductor connection complying with the requirements of Regulations 607-02 and 607-04. The following arrangements of the final circuit are acceptable:

(i) a ring final circuit with a ring protective conductor. Spurs, if provided, require high integrity protective conductor connection complying with the requirements of Regulation 607-02

(ii) a radial final circuit with a single protective conductor:

(a) the protective conductor being connected as a ring; or

(b) a separate protective conductor being provided at the final socket-outlet by connection to the metal conduit or ducting; or

(c) where two or more similar radial circuits supply socket-outlets in adjacent areas and are fed from the same distribution board, have identical means of short-circuit and overcurrent protection and circuit protective conductors of the same cross-sectional area, then a second protective conductor may be provided at the final socket-outlet on one circuit by connection to the protective conductor of the adjacent circuit.

(iii) other circuits complying with the requirements of Regulation 607-02.

607-03-02   At the distribution board information shall be provided indicating those circuits having a high protective conductor current. This information shall be positioned so as to be visible to a person who is modifying or extending the circuit.

607-04   Cross-sectional area of protective conductors

607-04-01   The cross-sectional area of the protective conductors shall be not less than that determined in accordance with this section or Regulation 543-01, whichever is the greater.

607-05   Requirements for TT systems

607-05-01   Where items of equipment having a protective conductor current exceeding 3.5 mA in normal service are to be supplied from an installation forming part of a TT system, it shall be verified that the product of the total protective conductor current (in amperes) and twice the resistance of the installation earth electrodes (in ohms) does not exceed 50.

Where compliance with this regulation cannot be otherwise achieved the items of equipment shall be supplied through a double wound transformer or equivalent device as described in item (v) of Regulation 607-02-04 satisfying the requirement of that regulation.

607-06   Requirements for IT systems

607-06-01   Equipment having a protective conductor current exceeding 3.5 mA in normal service shall not be connected directly to an IT system.

607-07 Compatibility of circuits with high protective conductor current with residual current protective devices

607-07-01 Where more than one item of equipment having a protective conductor current exceeding 3.5 mA in normal service is to be supplied from an installation incorporating a residual current device, the circuit arrangement shall be such that the residual current which may be expected to occur, including switch-on surges, will not trip the device.

Where compliance with this regulation cannot be otherwise achieved the items of equipment shall be supplied through a double wound transformer or equivalent device as described in item (v) of Regulation 607-02-04 satisfying the requirements of that regulation.

SECTION 608

ELECTRICAL INSTALLATIONS IN CARAVANS, MOTOR CARAVANS AND FOR CARAVAN PARKS

DIVISION ONE
ELECTRICAL INSTALLATIONS IN CARAVANS AND MOTOR CARAVANS

608-01   Scope

608-01-01   The particular requirements of this section apply to the electrical installations of caravans and motor caravans at nominal voltages not exceeding 250/440 V. They do not apply to those electrical circuits and equipment covered by the Road Vehicles Lighting Regulations 1989 nor to installations covered by BS EN 1648-1 and BS EN 1648-2. They do not apply to the internal electrical installations of mobile homes, fixed recreational vehicles, transportable sheds and the like, temporary premises or structures.

The particular requirements of Section 601 apply also to such installations in caravans or motor caravans.

Protection against shock

608-02   Protection against direct contact

608-02-01   The following methods of protection shall not be used:

   (i)   protection by obstacles (Regulations 412-04 and 471-06)

   (ii)   protection by placing out of reach (Regulations 412-05 and 471-07).

608-03   Protection against indirect contact

608-03-01   The following methods of protection shall not be used:

   (i)   non-conducting location (Regulations 413-04 and 471-10)

   (ii)   earth-free equipotential bonding (Regulations 413-05 and 471-11)

   (iii)   electrical separation (Regulations 413-06 and 471-12).

608-03-02   Where protection by automatic disconnection of supply is used (Regulations 413-02 and 471-08) a residual current device complying with BS 4293, BS EN 61008-1 or BS EN 61009-1 breaking all live conductors shall be provided having the characteristics specified in Regulation 412-06-02 and the wiring system shall include a circuit protective conductor which shall be connected to:

   (i)   the protective contact of the inlet, and

   (ii)   the exposed-conductive-parts of the electrical equipment, and

   (iii)   the protective contacts of the socket-outlets.

608-03-03   Where the protective conductor specified in Regulation 608-03-02 is not incorporated in a cable and is not enclosed in conduit or trunking, it shall have a minimum cross-sectional area of 4 mm^2 and shall be insulated.

608-03-04   Except where the caravan or motor caravan is made substantially of insulating material, and metal parts are unlikely to become live in the event of a fault, extraneous-conductive parts shall be bonded to the circuit protective conductor with a conductor of minimum cross-sectional area of 4 mm^2 and in more than one place if the construction of the caravan does not ensure continuity between extraneous-conductive-parts.

Metal sheets forming part of the structure of the caravan or motor caravan are not considered to be extraneous-conductive-parts.

Protection against overcurrent

608-04   Final circuits

608-04-01   Each final circuit shall be protected by an overcurrent protective device which disconnects all live conductors of that circuit.

Selection and erection of equipment

608-05 General

608-05-01 Where there is more than one electrically independent installation, each independent system shall be supplied by a separate connecting device and shall be segregated in accordance with Regulation 528-01-02.

608-06 Wiring systems

608-06-01 The following wiring systems shall be used with insulated conductors to the relevant British Standards:

(i) flexible single-core insulated conductors in non-metallic conduits

(ii) stranded insulated conductors with a minimum of seven strands; in non-metallic conduits

(iii) sheathed flexible cables.

Flame propagating wiring systems shall not be used.

608-06-02 The cross-sectional area of every conductor shall be not less than 1.5 mm^2

608-06-03 The limit of 6 mm^2 in Regulation 543-03-02 does not apply and all protective conductors regardless of cross-sectional area shall be insulated.

608-06-04 Cables of low voltage systems shall be run separately from the cables of extra-low voltage systems, in such a way, so far as is reasonably practicable, that there is no risk of physical contact between the two wiring systems.

608-06-05 All cables, unless enclosed in rigid conduit, and all flexible conduit shall be supported at intervals not exceeding 0.4 m for vertical runs and 0.25 m for horizontal runs.

608-06-06 No electrical equipment shall be installed in any compartment intended for the storage of gas cylinders.

608-06-07 As the wiring will be subjected to vibration, all wiring shall be protected against mechanical damage either by location or by additional protection. Wiring passing through metalwork shall be protected by means of suitable bushes or grommets, securely fixed in position. Every precaution shall be taken to avoid mechanical damage due to sharp edges or abrasive parts.

Switchgear and controlgear

608-07 Inlets

608-07-01 The electrical inlet to the caravan or motor caravan shall be an appliance inlet complying with BS EN 60309-2 of the two pole and earthing contact type with key position 6h. Where the caravan or motor caravan demands exceed 16 A single-phase, the inlet shall not be so limited.

608-07-02 The inlet shall be installed:

(i) not more than 1.8 m above ground level, and

(ii) in a readily accessible position, and

(iii) in an enclosure with a suitable cover on the outside of the caravan.

608-07-03 A notice of such durable material as to be likely to remain easily legible throughout the life of the installation shall be fixed on or near the electrical inlet recess where it can be easily read and shall bear, in indelible and easily legible characters, the following information:

(i) the nominal voltage and frequency for which the caravan or motor caravan installation concerned has been designed

(ii) the rated current of the caravan or motor caravan installation.

608-07-04 Every installation shall be provided with a main isolating switch which shall disconnect all live conductors and which shall be suitably placed for ready operation within the caravan or motor caravan. In an installation consisting of only one final circuit, the isolating switch may be the overcurrent protection device required in Regulation 608-04.

608-07-05 A notice of durable material shall be permanently fixed near the main isolating switch inside the caravan or motor caravan, bearing in indelible and easily legible characters the text shown below:

INSTRUCTIONS FOR ELECTRICITY SUPPLY

TO CONNECT

1. Before connecting the caravan installation to the mains supply, check that:

    (a) the supply available at the caravan pitch supply point is suitable for the caravan electrical installation and appliances, and

    (b) the caravan main switch is in the OFF position.

2. Open the cover to the appliance inlet provided at the caravan supply point and insert the connector of the supply flexible cable.

3. Raise the cover of the electricity outlet provided on the pitch supply point and insert the plug of the supply cable.

THE CARAVAN SUPPLY FLEXIBLE CABLE MUST BE FULLY UNCOILED TO AVOID DAMAGE BY OVERHEATING.

4. Switch on at the caravan main switch.

5. Check the operation of residual current devices, if any, fitted in the caravan by depressing the test buttons.

IN CASE OF DOUBT OR, IF AFTER CARRYING OUT THE ABOVE PROCEDURE THE SUPPLY DOES NOT BECOME AVAILABLE, OR IF THE SUPPLY FAILS, CONSULT THE CARAVAN PARK OPERATOR OR THE OPERATOR'S AGENT OR A QUALIFIED ELECTRICIAN.

TO DISCONNECT

6. Switch off at the caravan main isolating switch, unplug both ends of the cable.

PERIODIC INSPECTION

Preferably not less than once every three years and more frequently if the vehicle is used more than normal average mileage for such vehicles, the caravan electrical installation and supply cable should be inspected and tested and a report on their condition obtained as prescribed in BS 7671 Requirements for Electrical Installations published by the Institution of Electrical Engineers

---

608-08   Accessories

608-08-01   Each accessory shall be of a type without accessible conductive parts.

608-08-02   Low voltage socket-outlets, other than those supplied by an individual winding of an isolating transformer, shall incorporate a protective contact.

608-08-03   Low voltage socket-outlets shall not be compatible with plugs for socket-outlets supplied at extra-low voltage. All socket-outlets supplied at extra-low voltage shall have their voltage conspicuously marked and shall be of a form to prevent the insertion of a low voltage plug.

608-08-04   Where an accessory is located in a position in which it is exposed to the effects of moisture it shall be constructed or enclosed so as to provide a degree of protection not less than IP55.

608-08-05   Every appliance connected to the supply by a means other than a plug and socket-outlet shall be controlled by a switch incorporated in or adjacent to the appliance.

608-08-06   Each luminaire in a caravan or motor caravan shall preferably be fixed directly to the structure or lining of the caravan or motor caravan. Where a pendant luminaire is installed in a caravan or motor caravan, provision shall be made for securing the luminaire to prevent damage when the caravan or motor caravan is moved. Accessories for the suspension of pendant luminaires shall be suitable for the mass suspended.

608-08-07 A luminaire intended for dual voltage operation shall:

  (i)   be fitted with separate lampholders for each voltage, and

  (ii) have an indication of the lamp wattage and voltage clearly and permanently displayed near each lampholder, and

  (iii) be so designed and constructed that no damage will be caused if both lamps are lit at the same time, and

  (iv) be so designed and have terminals so disposed that adequate separation is maintained between LV and ELV circuits, and

  (v)   be so designed that lamps cannot be fitted in lampholders intended for lamps of other voltages.

608-08-08 The means of connection to the caravan or motor caravan pitch socket-outlet shall comprise the following:

  (i)   a plug complying with BS EN 60309-2, and

  (ii) a flexible cord or cable of 25 m (± 2 m) length, harmonized code designation HO7RN-F or HO5VV-F or equivalent, incorporating a protective conductor, and of a cross-sectional area in accordance with Table 608A, and

  (iii) a connector complying with BS EN 60309-2 and compatible with the appliance inlet installed under Regulation 608-07-01.

TABLE 608A
Cross-sectional areas of flexible cords and cables for caravan connectors

Rated current (A)	Cross-sectional area (mm^2)
16	2.5
25	4
32	6
63	16
100	35

Extra-low voltage installation

608-08-09 Any portion of a caravan installation operating at extra-low voltage shall comply with the requirements of Regulation 411-02.

For extra-low voltage d.c. power sources, the following standard voltages shall be applicable: 12 V, 24 V and 48 V.

In exceptional cases, when a.c. extra-low voltage is required, the following standard voltages (rms) are permissible: 12 V, 24 V, 42 V and 48 V.

SECTION 608

DIVISION TWO
ELECTRICAL INSTALLATIONS IN CARAVAN PARKS

608-09   Scope

608-09-01   The particular requirements of this section apply to that portion of the electrical installation in caravan parks which provides facilities for the supply of electricity to, and connection of, leisure accommodation vehicles (including caravans) or tents at nominal voltages not exceeding 250/440 V.

Protection against shock

608-10   Protection against direct contact

608-10-01   The following methods of protection shall not be used:

 (i)   protection by obstacles (Regulations 412-04 and 471-06)

 (ii)   protection by placing out of reach (Regulations 412-05 and 471-07).

608-11   Protection against indirect contact

608-11-01   The following methods of protection shall not be used:

 (i)   non-conducting location (Regulations 413-04 and 471-10)

 (ii)   earth-free local equipotential bonding (Regulations 413-05 and 471-11)

 (iii)   electrical separation (Regulations 413-06 and 471-12).

Selection and erection of equipment

608-12   Wiring systems

608-12-01   Caravan pitch supply equipment shall preferably be connected by underground cable.

608-12-02   Underground cables, unless provided with additional mechanical protection, shall be installed outside any caravan pitch or other area where tent pegs or ground anchors may be driven.

608-12-03   All overhead conductors shall be:

 (i)   of a suitable construction and insulated in accordance with Regulation 412-02, and

 (ii)   located 2 m outside the vertical surface extending from the horizontal boundary of any caravan pitch, and

 (iii)   at a height of not less than 6 m in vehicle movement areas and 3.5 m in all other areas.

Poles and other supports for overhead wiring shall be located or protected so that they are unlikely to be damaged by any reasonably foreseeable vehicle movement

608-13   Switchgear and controlgear

608-13-01   Caravan pitch supply equipment shall be located adjacent to the pitch and not more than 20 m from any point on the pitch which it is intended to serve.

608-13-02   Each socket-outlet and its enclosure forming part of the caravan pitch supply equipment shall:

 (i)   *Deleted by BS 7671 : 1992, Amendment No 1.*

 (ii)   comply with BS EN 60309-2 and meet the degree of protection provisions of IPX4

 (iii)   be placed at a height of between 0.80 m and 1.50 m from the ground to the lowest part of the socket-outlet

 (iv)   have a current rating of not less than 16 A

 (v)   have at least one socket-outlet provided for each pitch.

608-13-03   *Deleted by BS 7671 : 1992, Amendment No 1.*

608-13-04   Each socket-outlet shall be individually protected by an overcurrent device.

608-13-05 Socket-outlets shall be protected individually, or in groups of not more than three, by a residual current device complying with BS 4293, BS EN 61008-1 or BS EN 61009-1 and having the characteristics specified in Regulation 412-06 and must not be bonded to the PME terminal.

For a supply from a distributor's multiple earthed network the protective conductor of each socket-outlet circuit shall be connected to an earth electrode and shall comply with Regulations 413-02-18 to 413-02-20.

608-13-06 Grouped socket-outlets shall be on the same phase.

SECTION 609

(Reserved for marinas)

SECTION 610

(Reserved for future use)

SECTION 611

INSTALLATION OF HIGHWAY POWER SUPPLIES, STREET FURNITURE AND STREET LOCATED EQUIPMENT

611-01 Scope

611-01-01 The requirements of this section shall apply to installations comprising highway distribution circuits, street furniture and street located equipment. These requirements shall not apply to distributor's equipment as defined by the Electricity Safety, Quality and Continuity Regulations 2002 in accordance with Regulation 110-02.

611-01-02 Any measure prescribed in this section of the Regulations shall also apply to similar equipment located in other areas used by the public but not designated as a highway or part of a building.

Protection for safety

611-02 Protection against electric shock

611-02-01 Where a measure for protection against direct contact in accordance with Regulation 412-01 is used then:

(i) protection by obstacles shall not be used, and

(ii) where protection is provided by placing out of reach, it shall only apply to low voltage overhead lines constructed to the standard required by the Electricity Safety, Quality and Continuity Regulations 2002, and

(iii) except when the maintenance of equipment is to be restricted to skilled persons specially trained, where items of street furniture or street located equipment are within 1.5 m of a low voltage overhead line, protection against direct contact with the overhead line shall be provided by means other than placing out of reach.

611-02-02 A door in street furniture or street located equipment, used for access to electrical equipment, shall not be used as a barrier or an enclosure to meet Regulation 412-03-01,. A door located less than 2.50 m above ground level shall be locked with a key or secured by use of a tool. In addition, protection against direct contact shall be provided, when the door is open, by an intermediate barrier to prevent contact with live parts, such a barrier affording a degree of protection of at least IP2X or IPXXB and removable only by the use of a tool.

For luminaires located at a height less than 2.80 m above ground level, access to the light source shall only be possible after removing a barrier or enclosure requiring use of a tool.

611-02-03 Protection against indirect contact in accordance with Regulation 413-01 shall not be provided by:

(i) a non-conducting location

(ii) earth-free equipotential bonding

(iii) electrical separation.

611-02-04 A maximum disconnection time of 5 s shall apply to all circuits feeding fixed equipment used in highway power supplies for compliance with the requirements of Regulation 413-02-04.

611-02-05 Where protection against indirect contact is provided by using earthed equipotential bonding and automatic disconnection in accordance with Regulation 413 01 01(i) metallic structures, such as fences, grids, not connected to or forming part of the street furniture or street located equipment, shall not be connected to the main earthing terminal as extraneous-conductive-parts under Regulation 413-02-02.

611-02-06 Where protection against indirect contact is provided by Class II equipment or equivalent insulation, no protective conductor shall be provided and conductive parts of the lighting column, street furniture or street located equipment shall not be intentionally connected to the earthing system.

611-03   Devices for isolation and switching

611-03-01   Where it is intended that isolation and switching is carried out only by instructed persons and subject to Regulation 461-01-02 for TN systems, the requirement of Regulation 460-01-02 is considered to be fulfilled if the means of isolation is provided by a suitably rated fuse carrier.

611-03-02   Where the distributor's cut-out is used as the means of isolation of a highway power supply the approval of the distributor shall be obtained.

611-04   Identification of cables

611-04-01   On completion of an installation including highway distribution circuits and highway power supplies, detailed records in accordance with Regulation 514-09 shall be provided with the Electrical Installation Certificate required by Regulation 741-01-01.

611-04-02   Except where the method of cable installation does not permit marking the installation of underground cable shall comply with Regulation 522-06-03.

611-04-03   Ducting, marker tape or cable tiles shall be used with highway power supply cable and shall be suitably colour coded or marked for the purpose of identification and shall be distinct from other services.

611-04-04   The requirement of Regulation 514-12 need not be applied where the installation is subject to a programmed inspection and testing procedure.

611-04-05   Drawings shall be prepared showing the position and depth of underground cables supplying highway power supplies, street furniture and street located equipment.

611-05   External influences

611-05-01   *Deleted by BS 7671 : 1992, Amendment No 1.*

611-05-02   Electrical equipment shall have, by construction or by installation, a degree of protection not less than IP33.

611-06   Temporary supplies

611-06-01   Temporary supplies taken from street furniture and street located equipment shall not reduce the safety of the permanent installation and shall generally be in accordance with Section 604.

611-06-02   On every temporary supply unit there shall be a durable label externally mounted stating the maximum sustained current to be supplied from that unit.

PART 7

INSPECTION AND TESTING

CONTENTS

PART 7

INSPECTION AND TESTING

CONTENTS

CHAPTER 71

INITIAL VERIFICATION

711   GENERAL

711-01-01   Every installation shall, during erection and on completion before being put into service be inspected and tested to verify, so far as is reasonably practicable, that the requirements of the Regulations have been met.

Precautions shall be taken to avoid danger to persons and to avoid damage to property and installed equipment during inspection and testing.

711-01-02   The result of the assessment of general characteristics required by Sections 311, 312 and 313, together with the information required by Regulation 514-09-01 shall be made available to the person or persons carrying out the inspection and testing.

712   INSPECTION

712-01-01   Inspection shall precede testing and shall normally be done with that part of the installation under inspection disconnected from the supply.

712-01-02   The inspection shall be made to verify that the installed electrical equipment is:

  (i)   in compliance with Section 511 (this may be ascertained by mark or by certification furnished by the installer or by the manufacturer), and

  (ii)   correctly selected and erected in accordance with the Regulations, and

 (iii)   not visibly damaged or defective so as to impair safety.

712-01-03   The inspection shall include at least the checking of the following items, where relevant to the installation and, where necessary, during erection:

  (i)   connection of conductors

  (ii)   identification of conductors

 (iii)   routing of cables in safe zones or protection against mechanical damage, in compliance with Section 522

 (iv)   selection of conductors for current-carrying capacity and voltage drop, in accordance with the design

  (v)   connection of single-pole devices for protection or switching in phase conductors only

 (vi)   correct connection of accessories and equipment

 (vii)   presence of fire barriers, suitable seals and protection against thermal effects

(viii)   methods of protection against electric shock

     (a) protection against both direct and indirect contact, i.e.:

     -   SELV

     -   limitation of discharge of energy

     (b) protection against direct contact (including measurement of distances where appropriate), i.e.:

     -   protection by insulation of live parts

     -   protection by a barrier or an enclosure

     -   protection by obstacles

     -   protection by placing out of reach

     -   protection by PELV

     (c) protection against indirect contact:

     -   earthed equipotential bonding and automatic disconnection of supply

        presence of earthing conductor

        presence of protective conductors

        presence of main equipotential bonding conductors

        presence of supplementary equipotential bonding conductors

presence of earthing arrangements for combined protective and functional purposes

- use of Class II equipment or equivalent insulation

- non-conducting location (including measurement of distances, where appropriate)

    absence of protective conductors

- earth-free local equipotential bonding

    presence of earth-free equipotential bonding conductors

- electrical separation

(ix) prevention of mutual detrimental influence

(x) presence of appropriate devices for isolation and switching correctly located

(xi) presence of undervoltage protective devices

(xii) choice and setting of protective and monitoring devices (for protection against indirect contact and/or protection against overcurrent)

(xiii) labelling of protective devices, switches and terminals

(xiv) selection of equipment and protective measures appropriate to external influences

(xv) adequacy of access to switchgear and equipment

(xvi) presence of danger notices and other warning signs

(xvii) presence of diagrams, instructions and similar information

(xviii) erection methods.

713   TESTING

713-01   General

713-01-01 The tests of Regulations 713-02 to 713-13 where relevant shall be carried out and the results compared with relevant criteria.

The tests of Regulations 713-02 to 713-09 where relevant shall be carried out in that order before the installation is energised.

If any test indicates a failure to comply, that test and any preceding test, the results of which may have been influenced by the fault indicated, shall be repeated after the fault has been rectified.

Some methods of test are described in Guidance Note 3, Inspection & Testing, published by the Institution of Electrical Engineers. Other methods are not precluded provided they give valid results.

713-02   Continuity of protective conductors including main and supplementary equipotential bonding

713-02-01 A continuity test shall be made. It is recommended that the test be carried out with a supply having a no-load voltage between 4 V and 24 V, d.c. or a.c., and a short-circuit current of not less than 200 mA.

713-03   Continuity of ring final circuit conductors

713-03-01 A test shall be made to verify the continuity of each conductor including the protective conductor, of every ring final circuit.

713-04   Insulation resistance

713-04-01 The insulation resistance between live conductors and between each live conductor and Earth shall be measured before the installation is connected to the supply. The PEN conductor in TN-C systems shall be considered as part of the earth. Where appropriate during this measurement, phase and neutral conductors may be connected together.

713-04-02 The insulation resistance measured with the test voltages indicated in Table 71A shall be considered satisfactory if the main switchboard, and each distribution circuit tested separately with all its final circuits connected but with current-using equipment disconnected, has an insulation resistance not less than the appropriate value given in Table 71A.

713-04-03 Measurements shall be carried out with direct current. The testing apparatus shall be capable of supplying the test voltage indicated in Table 71A when loaded with 1 mA.

TABLE 71A
Minimum values of insulation resistance

Circuit nominal voltage (V)	Test voltage d.c. (V)	Minimum insulation resistance (MΩ)
SELV and PELV	250	0.25
Up to and including 500 V with the exception of the above systems	500	0.5
Above 500 V	1000	1.0

713-04-04 When the circuit includes electronic devices, only a measurement to protective earth shall be made with the phase and neutral connected together. Precautions may be necessary to avoid damage to electronic devices.

713-05   Site applied insulation

713-05-01 Where insulation applied on site in accordance with Regulation 412-02 is intended to provide protection against direct contact, it shall be verified that the insulation is capable of withstanding, without breakdown or flashover, an applied voltage test equivalent to that specified in the British Standard for similar type-tested equipment.

713-05-02 Where protection against indirect contact is provided by supplementary insulation applied to equipment during erection in accordance with Regulation 413-03, it shall be verified by test:

(i)   that the insulating enclosure affords a degree of protection not less than IP2X or IPXXB, and

(ii)   that the insulating enclosure is capable of withstanding, without breakdown or flashover, an applied voltage test equivalent to that specified in the British Standard for similar type-tested equipment.

713-06   Protection by separation of circuits

713-06-01 The separation of circuits shall be verified in accordance with Regulation 713-06-02 for protection by SELV, Regulation 713-06-03 for protection by PELV and Regulation 713-06-04 for protection by electrical separation.

713-06-02 The separation of live parts from those of other circuits and from earth, according to Regulation 411-02, shall be verified by a measurement of the insulation resistance. The resistance values shall be in accordance with Table 71A.

713-06-03 The separation of live parts from those of other circuits according to Regulation 471-14 shall be verified by a measurement of the insulation resistance. The resistance values obtained shall be in accordance with Table 71A.

713-06-04 The separation of live parts from those of other circuits and from earth, according to Regulation 413-06 shall be verified by a measurement of the insulation resistance. The resistance values obtained shall be in accordance with Table 71A.

713-06-05 Functional extra-low voltage circuits shall meet all the test requirements for low voltage circuits.

713-07   Protection against direct contact by a barrier or an enclosure provided during erection

713-07-01 Where protection against direct contact is intended to be afforded by a barrier or an enclosure provided during erection in accordance with Regulation 412-03, it shall be verified by test that each enclosure or barrier affords a degree of protection not less than IP2X or IPXXB or IP4X as appropriate, where that regulation so requires.

713-08 Insulation of non-conducting floors and walls

713-08-01 Where protection against indirect contact is to be provided by a non-conducting location intended to comply with Regulations 413-04 and 471-10, the resistance of the floors and walls of the location to the main protective conductor of the installation shall be measured at not less than three points on each relevant surface, one of which shall be not less than 1 m and not more than 1.2 m from any extraneous-conductive-part in the location. The other two measurements shall be made at greater distances.

713-08-02 Any insulation or insulating arrangement of extraneous-conductive-parts intended to satisfy Regulation 413-04-07(iii):

  (i)   when tested at 500 V d.c. shall not be less than 0.5 megohm, and

  (ii)   shall be able to withstand a test voltage of at least 2 kV a.c. rms, and

  (iii)   shall not pass a leakage current exceeding 1 mA in normal conditions of use.

713-09 Polarity

713-09-01 A test of polarity shall be made and it shall be verified that:

  (i)   every fuse and single-pole control and protective device is connected in the phase conductor only, and

  (ii)   except for E14 and E27 lampholders to BS EN 60238, in circuits having an earthed neutral conductor centre contact bayonet and Edison screw lampholders have the outer or screwed contacts connected to the neutral conductor, and

  (iii)   wiring has been correctly connected to socket-outlets and similar accessories.

713-10 Earth electrode resistance

713-10-01 Where the earthing system incorporates an earth electrode as part of the installation, the electrode resistance to earth shall be measured.

713-11 Earth fault loop impedance

713-11-01 Where protective measures are used which require a knowledge of earth fault loop impedance, the relevant impedances shall be measured, or determined by an alternative method.

Where the alternative method described in Regulation 413-02-12 (see Table 41C) is used, the impedance of the protective conductor of the circuit concerned shall also be measured.

713-12 Prospective fault current

713-12-01 The prospective short-circuit current and prospective earth fault current shall be measured, calculated or determined by another method, at the origin and at other relevant points in the installation.

713-13 Functional testing

713-13-01 Where protection against indirect contact or supplementary protection against direct contact is to be provided by a residual current device, its effectiveness shall be verified by a test simulating an appropriate fault condition and independent of any test facility incorporated in the device.

713-13-02 Assemblies, such as switchgear and controlgear assemblies, drives, controls and interlocks, shall be subjected to a functional test to show that they are properly mounted, adjusted and installed in accordance with the relevant requirements of these Regulations.

CHAPTER 72

ALTERATIONS AND ADDITIONS TO AN INSTALLATION

721 GENERAL

721-01-01 The relevant requirements of Chapter 71 shall apply to alterations and additions.

721-01-02 It shall be verified that every alteration or addition complies with the Regulations and does not impair the safety of an existing installation.

CHAPTER 73

PERIODIC INSPECTION AND TESTING

731 GENERAL

731-01-01 Where required, periodic inspection and testing of every electrical installation shall be carried out in accordance with the requirements of this Chapter.

731-01-02 Periodic inspection and testing of an electrical installation shall be carried out to determine, so far as is reasonably practicable, whether the installation is in a satisfactory condition for continued service.

731-01-03 Inspection comprising careful scrutiny of the installation shall be carried out without dismantling or with partial dismantling as required, together with the appropriate tests of Chapter 71. The scope of the periodic inspection and testing shall be decided by a competent person, taking into account the availability of records and the use, condition and nature of the installation.

731-01-04 Such inspection and testing shall provide, so far as is reasonably practicable, for:

(i) the safety of persons and livestock against the effects of electric shock and burns, in accordance with Regulation 130-01, and

(ii) protection against damage to property by fire and heat arising from an installation defect, and

(iii) confirmation that the installation is not damaged or deteriorated so as to impair safety, and

(iv) the identification of installation defects and non-compliance with the requirements of the Regulations which may give rise to danger.

731-01-05 Precautions shall be taken to ensure that the inspection and testing does not cause danger to persons or livestock and does not cause damage to property and equipment even if the circuit is defective.

732 FREQUENCY OF INSPECTION AND TESTING

732-01-01 The frequency of periodic inspection and testing of an installation shall be determined having regard to the type of installation, its use and operation, the frequency and quality of maintenance and the external influences to which it is subjected.

732-01-02 In the case of an installation under effective supervision in normal use, periodic inspection and testing may be replaced by an adequate regime of continuous monitoring and maintenance of the installation by skilled persons. Appropriate records shall be kept.

732-01-03 *Deleted by BS 7671 : 1992, Amendment No 2.*

CHAPTER 74

CERTIFICATION AND REPORTING

741   GENERAL

741-01-01 Upon completion of the verification of a new installation or changes to an existing installation, an Electrical Installation Certificate, based on the model given in Appendix 6, shall be provided. Such documentation shall include details of the extent of the installation covered by the Certificate, together with a record of the inspection and the results of testing.

741-01-02 Upon completion of the periodic inspection and testing of an existing installation, a Periodic Inspection Report, based on the model given in Appendix 6, shall be provided. Such documentation shall include details of the extent of the installation and limitations of the inspection and testing covered by the Report, together with a record of the inspection and the results of testing.

741-01-03 Where minor electrical installation work does not include the provision of a new circuit, a Minor Electrical Installation Works Certificate, based on the model given in Appendix 6, shall be provided for each circuit altered or extended.

741-01-04 Electrical Installation Certificates, Periodic Inspection Reports and Minor Electrical Installation Works Certificates shall be compiled and signed or otherwise authenticated by a competent person or persons.

741-01-05 Electrical Installation Certificates, Periodic Inspection Reports and Minor Electrical Installation Works Certificates may be produced in any durable medium, including written and electronic media. Regardless of the media used for original certificates, reports or their copies, their authenticity and integrity shall be verified by a reliable process or method. The process or method shall also verify that any copy is a true copy of the original.

742   INITIAL VERIFICATION

742-01-01 Following the initial verification required by Chapter 71, an Electrical Installation Certificate, together with a schedule of inspections and a schedule of test results, shall be given to the person ordering the work.

These schedules shall be based upon the models given in Appendix 6.

742-01-02 The schedule of test results shall identify every circuit, including its related protective device(s), and shall record the results of the appropriate tests and measurements detailed in Chapter 71.

742-01-03 The person or persons responsible for the design, construction, inspection and testing of the installation shall, as appropriate, give to the person ordering the work a Certificate which takes account of their respective responsibilities for the safety of that installation, together with the schedules described in Regulation 742-01-01.

742-01-04 Defects or omissions revealed during inspection and testing of the installation work covered by the Certificate shall be made good before the Certificate is issued.

743   ALTERATIONS AND ADDITIONS

743-01-01 The requirements of Sections 741 and 742 for the issue of an Electrical Installation Certificate or a Minor Electrical Installation Works Certificate shall apply to all the work of the alterations or additions.

743-01-02 The contractor or other person responsible for the new work, or a person authorised to act on their behalf, shall record on the Electrical Installation Certificate or the Minor Electrical Installation Works Certificate, any defects found, so far as is reasonably practicable, in the existing installation.

744   PERIODIC INSPECTION AND TESTING

744-01-01   Following the periodic inspection and testing described in Chapter 73, a Periodic Inspection Report, together with a schedule of inspections and a schedule of test results shall be given by the person carrying out the inspection, or a person authorised to act on their behalf, to the person ordering the inspection.

These schedules shall be based upon the models given in Appendix 6.

The schedule of test results shall record the results of the appropriate tests required by Chapter 71.

744-01-02   Any damage, deterioration, defects, dangerous conditions, and non-compliance with the requirements of the Regulations which may give rise to danger, together with any limitations of the inspection and testing shall be recorded.

APPENDICES

CONTENTS

APPENDIX 1

BRITISH STANDARDS TO WHICH REFERENCE IS MADE IN THE REGULATIONS

Note: Certain British Standards have been withdrawn since the issue of the 16th Edition in 1991. From the date of withdrawal, certificates and marks already awarded may continue to apply to production until a date specified in the superseding standard. During the period between these dates, the withdrawn standard may be specified in contracts. It should be noted however that this appendix may not list such standards, as only current British Standards are listed with some references to superseded standards.

BS Number	Title	Referenced in Regulations
BS 31 : 1940 (1988)	Specification. Steel conduit and fittings for electrical wiring.	521-04-01(i)
BS 67 : 1987 (1999)	Specification for ceiling roses.	412-03-04 553-04-01(i)
BS 88 :	Cartridge fuses for voltages up to and including 1000 V a.c. and 1500 V d.c.	Part 2 gG Part 2 gM 433-02-04 Appx. 4 Preface
BS 88-1 : 1988	General requirements. Also numbered as BS EN 60269-1 : 1994 and replaced by BS EN 60269-1 : 1999, but remains current.	
BS 88-2.1 : 1988	Specification for fuses for use by authorized persons (mainly for industrial applications). Also numbered as BS EN 60269-2 : 1995.	433-02-02 Tables 41B1, 41C, 41D, 471A, 604B1, 605B1 Figures 3.3A, 3.3B
BS 88-6 : 1988 (1992)	Specification of supplementary requirements for fuses of compact dimensions for use in 240/415 V a.c. industrial and commercial electrical installations.	433-02-02 Tables 41B1, 41C, 41D, 471A, 604B1, 605B1 Figures 3.3A, 3.3B
BS 196 : 1961	Specification for protected-type non-reversible plugs, socket-outlets, cable couplers and appliance couplers with earthing contacts for single-phase a.c. circuits up to 250 volts.	Table 55A 553-01-05 553-02-01
BS 476 :	Fire tests on building materials and structure.	
BS 476-4 : 1970 (1984)	Non-combustibility test for materials.	526-03-02(iv)
BS 476 Part 5 : 1979	Method of test for ignitability, now withdrawn. BS 476-12 : 1991 Method of test for ignitability also refers but methods of test are not identical.	521-05-01 526-03-02(v) 527 01 06 553-03-01 554-06-01
BS 476-23 : 1987	Methods for determination of the contribution of components to the fire resistance of a structure.	527-02-02
BS 546 : 1950 (1988)	Specification. Two-pole and earthing pin plugs, socket-outlets and socket-outlet adaptors.	Table 55A 553-01-05
BS 559 : 1998	Specification for electric signs and high voltage luminous discharge tube installations.	110-01-01(xvi) 554-02-01
BS 646 : 1958 (1991)	Specification. Cartridge fuse links (rated up to 5 amperes) for a.c. and d.c. service.	Table 55A 553-01-05(i)

BS Number	Title	Referenced in Regulations
BS 731 :	Flexible steel conduit for cable protection and flexible steel tubing to enclose flexible drives.	521-04-01(ii)
BS 731-1 : 1952 (1993)	Flexible steel conduit and adaptors for the protection of electric cables.	521-04-01(ii)
BS 951 : 1999	Specification for clamps for earthing and bonding purposes.	514-13-01
BS 1361 : 1971 (1986)	Specification for cartridge fuses for a.c. circuits in domestic and similar premises.	Tables 41B1, 41C, 41D, 604B1, 605B1 433-02-02 433-02-04 Figure 3.1 Appx. 4 Preface
BS 1362 : 1973 (1992)	Specification for general purpose fuse links for domestic and similar purposes (primarily for use in plugs).	Tables 41B1, 41C, 41D, 55A, 604B1, 605B1 553-01-05(i)
BS 1363 :	13 A plugs, socket-outlets, connection units and adaptors.	433-02-04 Table 55A 553-01-04 553-01-05
BS 1363-1 : 1995	Specification for rewirable and non-rewirable 13 A fused plugs.	
BS 1363-2 : 1995	Specification for 13 A switched and unswitched socket-outlets.	
BS 1363-3 : 1995	Specification for adaptors.	
BS 1363-4 : 1995	Specification for 13 A fused connection units: switched and unswitched.	537-02-02 553-04-01(vi)
BS 1710 : 1984 (1991)	*Deleted by BS 7671 : 2001, Amendment No 2, 2004.*	
BS 2754 : 1976 (1999)	Memorandum. Construction of electrical equipment for protection against electric shock.	Part 2 Class I, II & III equipment
BS 2848 : 1973	Specification for flexible insulating sleeving for electrical purposes. Note partially replaced by BS 6893 : Part 3 : 1987 and BS EN 60684-1 : 1996	543-03-02
BS 3036 : 1958 (1992)	Specification. Semi-enclosed electric fuses (rating up to 100 amperes and 240 volts to earth).	Tables 41B1, 41C, 41D, 604B1, 605B1 433-02-03 433-02-04 Figures 3.3A, 3.3B Appx. 4 Preface Appx. 4 Tables ...
BS 3456 :	*Deleted by BS 7671 : 2001.*	

BS Number	Title	Referenced in Regulations
BS 3535 :	Isolating transformers and safety isolating transformers. This standard is partially replaced by the BS EN 61558 series of standards, and these standards should be read jointly.	411-02-02(i) 413-06-02(i)(a) 413-06-03(iv) 471-12-01 553-01-05(ii) 602-07-02(iv)
BS 3535-1 : 1990	General requirements. (Also numbered as BS EN 60742 : 1996). Remains current only for use with BS 3535-2 and where application not covered by BS EN 61558 series.	
BS 3535-2 : 1990	Specification for transformers for reduced system voltage. To be read in conjunction with BS 3535-1.	471-15-03(i)
BS 3676 :	Switches for houschold and similar fixed electrical installations.	412-03-04 537-02-02 553-04-01 601-08-01 602-07-02
BS 3676-1 : 1989	Specification for general requirements. Now replaced by BS EN 60669-1 : 2000, but remains current. BS EN 60669-1 : 2000 is dual numbered BS 3676 : 2000	
BS 3858 : 1992	Specification for binding and identification sleeves for use on electric cables and wires.	514-03-02
BS 3871 :	Replaced by BS EN 60898 : 1991.	
BS 3939 :	*Deleted by BS 7671 : 1992, Amendment No 2.* BS EN 60617	
BS 4066 :	Tests on electric cables under fire conditions.	
	Part 1 . 1980 (1995) Method of test on a single insulated vertical wire or cable. Replaced by BS EN 50265-1 : 1999.	
BS 4066-3 : 1994	Tests on bunched wires or cables.	482-02-04
BS 4293 : 1983 (1993)	Specification for residual current operated circuit-breakers. (Replaced by BS EN 61008-1 : 1995, BS EN 61008-2-1 : 1995 and BS IEC 61008-2-2 : 1990).	412-06-02(ii) 608-03-02 608-13-05
BS 4343 : 1992	Replaced by BS EN 60309 series.	
BS 4363 : 1998	Specification for distribution assemblies for electricity supplies for construction and building sites.	604-09-01
BS 4444 : 1989 (1995)	Guide to electrical earth monitoring and protective conductor proving.	543-03-05 607-02-03(iii) 607-02-04(iv)
BS 4491 :	Appliance couplers for household and similar general purposes.	553-02-01

BS Number	Title	Referenced in Regulations
BS 4553 :	Specification for 600/1000 V single-phase split concentric electric cables.	
BS 4553-1 : 1998	Cables having PVC insulation.	522-06-06 Table 4A2
BS 4553-2 : 1998	Cables having thermosetting insulation.	522-06-06 Table 4A2
BS 4553-3 : 1998	Cables having thermosetting insulation and low emission of smoke and corrosive gases when affected by fire.	522-06-06 Table 4A2
BS 4568 :	Specification for steel conduit and fittings with metric threads of ISO form for electrical installations.	521-04-01(iii)
BS 4568 Part 1 : 1970 (1973)	Steel conduit, bends and couplers.	
BS 4573 : 1970 (1979)	Specification for 2-pin reversible plugs and shaver socket-outlets.	553-01-05(ii)
BS 4607 :	Non-metallic conduits and fittings for electrical installations.	521-04-01(iv)
BS 4678 :	Cable trunking.	521-05-01
BS 4678-1 : 1971	Steel surface trunking.	
BS 4678-2 : 1973	Steel underfloor (duct) trunking.	
BS 4678-4 : 1982	Specification for cable trunking made of insulation material.	
BS 4727 :	Glossary of electrotechnical, power, telecommunications, electronics, lighting and colour terms.	Part 2 First Para
BS 5042 : 1987	Specification for bayonet lampholders. Replaced by BS EN 61184 : 1997.	
BS 5266 :	Emergency lighting.	110-01-01(xvii) 482-01-01(iv) 528-01-04
BS 5345 :	Replaced in part by BS EN 60079 Electrical apparatus for explosive gas atmospheres and BS EN 50014 : 1998 Electrical apparatus for potentially explosive atmospheres. General requirements.	
BS 5467 : 1997	Specification for 600/1000 V and 1900/3300 V armoured electric cables having thermosetting insulation.	522-06-06 Table 4A2
BS 5490 : 1977 (1985)	*Deleted by BS 7671 : 1992, Amendment No 2.*	
BS 5518 : 1977 (1999)	Specification for electronic variable control switches (dimmer switches) for tungsten filament lighting.	553-04-01
BS 5593 : 1978 (1991)	Specification for impregnated paper insulated cables with aluminium sheath/neutral conductor and three shaped solid aluminium phase conductors (CONSAC), 600/1000 V, for electricity supply. Standard withdrawn.	546-02-04(ii)

BS Number	Title	Referenced in Regulations
BS 5655 :	Lifts and service lifts. BS 5655 is a multiple set of standards.	110-02-01(x) 528-02-06
BS 5655-1 : 1986 BS 5655-2 : 1988 BS 5655-11 : 1989	-1, -2 and -11 are obsolescent and apply only to modernization of existing installations. Replaced partly by BS EN 81-2 : 1998 pending implementation of the EU Lift Directive.	
BS 5733 : 1995	Specification for general requirements for electrical accessories.	553-04-01(vi)
BS 5839 :	Fire detection and alarm systems for buildings. BS 5839 is a multiple part standard.	110-01-01(xx) 528-01-04
BS 5839-4 : 1988	Specification for control and indicating equipment, remains current but is replaced by BS EN 54-2 : 1998 and BS EN 54-4 : 1988.	
BS 6004 : 2000	Electric cables. PVC insulated, non-armoured cables for voltages up to and including 450/750 V, for electric power, lighting and internal wiring.	Table 4A2
BS 6007 : 1993	*Deleted by BS 7671 : 2001, Amendment No 2, 2004.*	
BS 6053 : 1981 (1991)	Replaced by BS EN 60423 : 1995.	
BS 6099 :	Replaced by BS EN 50086 Specification for conduit systems for electrical installations.	
BS 6141 : 1991	Specification for insulated cables and flexible cords for use in high temperature zones.	Table 4A2
BS 6207 :	Mineral insulated cables with a rated voltage not exceeding 750 V.	433-02-04 546-02-07
BS 6207-1 : 1995	Cables.	Table 4A2
BS 6207-2 : 1995	Terminations.	
BS 6231 : 1998	*Deleted by BS 7671 : 2001.*	
BS 6346 : 1997	Specification for 600/1000 V and 1900/3000 V armoured cables having pvc insulation.	522-06-06 Table 4A2
BS 6351 :	Electric surface heating.	110-01-01(xxii) 554-07-01
BS 6351-1 : 1983 (1993)	Specification for electric surface heating devices.	
BS 6351-2 : 1983 (1993)	Guide to the design of electric surface heating systems.	
BS 6351-3 : 1983 (1993)	Code of practice for the installation, testing and maintenance of electric surface heating systems.	
BS 6387 : 1994	*Deleted by BS 7671 : 1992, Amendment No 2.*	
BS 6458 : BS 6458-2.1 : 1984	Fire hazard testing for electrotechnical products. Glow-wire test.	526-03-02(iii)
BS 6480 : 1988 (1997)	*Deleted by BS 7671 : 2001.*	
BS 6500 : 2000	Electric cables. Flexible cords rated up to 300/500 V, for use with appliances and equipment intended for domestic, office and similar environments.	Table 4A2

BS Number	Title	Referenced in Regulations
BS 6651 : 1999	Code of practice for protection of structures against lightning.	110-02-01(ix) 541-01-03
BS 6701 : 1994	Code of practice for installation of apparatus intended for connection to certain telecommunications systems.	110-01-01(xxi) 528-01-04
BS 6724 : 1997	Specification for 600/1000 V and 1900/3300 V armoured cables having thermosetting insulation and low emission of smoke and corrosive gases when affected by fire.	522-06-06 Table 4A2
BS 6765 :	*Deleted by BS 7671 : 2001, see BS EN 1648.*	
BS 6883 : 1999	Elastomer insulated cables for fixed wiring in ships and on mobile and fixed offshore units. Requirements and test methods.	Table 4A2
BS 6907 :	Electrical installations for open cast mines and quarries.	110-01-01(xxiii) 604-01-03(ii)
BS 6972 : 1988	Specification for general requirements for luminaire supporting couplers for domestic, light industrial and commercial use.	553-04-01(ii)
BS 6991 : 1990	Specification for 6/10 amp two pole weather-resistant couplers for household, commercial and light industrial equipment.	553-02-01
BS 7001 : 1988	Specification for interchangeability and safety of a standardized luminaire supporting coupler. To be read in conjunction with BS 6972 : 1988.	553-04-01(ii)
BS 7071 : 1992 (1998)	Specification for portable residual current devices.	412-06-02(ii)
BS 7211 : 1998	Specification for thermosetting insulated cables (non-armoured) for electric power and lighting with low emission of smoke and corrosive gases when affected by fire.	Table 4A2
BS 7288 : 1990 (1998)	Specification for socket-outlets incorporating residual current devices. (SRCDs).	412-06-02(ii)
BS 7430 : 1998	Code of practice for earthing.	542-03-01
BS 7454 : 1991	Method for calculation of thermally permissible short-circuit currents taking into account non-adiabatic heating effects.	434-03-03 543-01-03
BS 7629-1 : 1997	Specification for 300/500 V fire-resistant electric cables having low emission of smoke and corrosive gases when affected by fire. Multicore cables.	Table 4A2
BS 7697 :	Nominal voltages for low voltage public electricity supply systems.	Appx. 2
BS 7769 :	Electric cables, Calculation of current rating. Parts 1, 2, 3 : 1997	Appx. 4 Preface

BS Number	Title	Referenced in Regulations
BS 7822 :	Insulation coordination for equipment within low voltage systems.	Table 44A
BS 7822-1 : 1995	Principles, requirements and tests.	
BS 7846 : 2000	Electric cables. 600/1000 V armoured fire-resistant electric cables having thermosetting insulation and low emission of smoke and corrosive gases when affected by fire.	522-06-06 Table 4A2
BS 7889 : 1997	Specification for 600/1000 V single-core unarmoured electric cables having thermosetting insulation.	Table 4A2
BS 7895 : 1997	Specification for bayonet lampholders with enhanced safety.	553-04-01(iii)
BS 7919 : 2001	Electric cables. Flexible cables rated up to 450/750 V, for use with appliances and equipment intended for industrial and similar environments.	Table 4A2
BS 8436 : 2004	300/500 V screened electric cables having low emission of smoke and corrosive gases when affected by fire, for use in thin partitions and building voids.	522-06-06 Table 4A2
BS EN 1648 :	Leisure accommodation vehicles. 12 V direct current extra low voltage electrical installations	
BS EN 1648-1 : 1998	Caravans.	608-01-01
BS EN 1648-2 : 1998	Motor caravans.	608-01-01
BS EN 50014 : (1998)	Electrical apparatus for potentially explosive atmospheres. General requirements.	110-01-01(xviii) 482-01-01(iii)
BS EN 50081 :	Electromagnetic compatibility Generic emission standard.	515-02-02 528-01-02
BS EN 50082 :	Electromagnetic compatibility Generic immunity standard. Partially replaced by BS EN 6100-6-2 : 1999 but remains current.	515-02-01 528-01-02
BS EN 50085 :	Specification for cable trunking and ducting systems for electrical installations.	527-01-05
BS EN 50085-1 : 1999	General requirements.	482-03-04 521-05-01
BS EN 50086 :	Specification for conduit systems for electrical installations.	527-01-05
BS EN 50086-1 : 1994	General requirements.	482-03-04 521-04-01(i) 521-04-01(ii) 521-04-01(iii)
BS EN 50086-2-1 : 1996	Rigid conduit systems. Replaces BS 6099 Part 2 Section 2.2 : 1982 which remains current.	521-04-01(iv)

BS Number	Title	Referenced in Regulations
BS EN 50265 :	Common test methods for cables under fire conditions. Test for resistance to vertical flame propagation for a single insulated conductor or cable.	
BS EN 50265-1 : 1999	Tests for resistance to vertical flame propagation for a single insulated conductor or cable. Apparatus.	527-01-03 527-01-04
BS EN 50265-2-1 : 1999	Procedures. 1kW pre-mixed flame.	482-02-04 482-03-03
BS EN 50265-2-2 : 1999	Procedures. Diffusion flame.	482-02-04 482-03-03
BS EN 50281 :	Electrical apparatus for use in the presence of combustible dust.	110-01-01(xix)
BS EN 50310 : 2000	Application of equipotential bonding and earthing in buildings with information technology equipment.	545-01-01
BS EN 60073 : 1997	*Deleted by BS 7671 : 2001, Amendment No 2, 2004.*	
BS EN 60079 :	Electrical apparatus for potentially explosive gas atmospheres.	110-01-01(xviii)
BS EN 60079-10 : 1996	Classification of hazardous areas.	
BS EN 60079-14 : 1997	Electrical installations in hazardous areas (other than mines)	
BS EN 60079-17 : 1997	Inspection and maintenance of electrical installations in hazardous areas (other than mines)	
BS EN 60238 : 1999	Specification for Edison screw lampholders. Replaces BS EN 60238 : (1996) (which remains current) and BS 6776 : 1990.	412-03-04 Table 55B 553-03-04 553-04-01(iii) 713-09-01(ii)
BS EN 60269 :	Low voltage fuses	
BS EN 60269-1 : 1999	General requirements. Replaces BS EN 60269-1 : 1994, which remains current and is also numbered as BS 88-1 : 1988.	
BS EN 60269-2 : 1995	Supplementary requirements for fuses for use by authorized persons. Replaces BS 88-2.1 : 1988.	
BS EN 60309 :	Plugs, socket-outlets and couplers for industrial purposes. Replaces BS 4343 : 1968.	
BS EN 60309-1 : 1999	General requirements. Replaces BS EN 60309-1 : 1998 which remains current.	
BS EN 60309-2 : 1998	Dimensional interchangeability requirements for pin and contact-tube accessories of harmonised configurations (replaces BS 4343 : 1992).	Table 55A 553-01-05 553-02-01 602-07-01 602-08-01 604-12-02 604-13-01 607-02-02 607-02-03(ii) 608-07-01 608-08-08(i) 608-08-08(iii) 608-13-02(ii)

BS Number	Title	Referenced in Regulations
BS EN 60335-2-53 : 1997	Electric sauna heating appliances.	603-01-01
BS EN 60423 : 1995	Conduits for electrical purposes. Outside diameters of conduits for electrical installations and threads for conduits and fittings (replaces BS 6053).	521-04-01
BS EN 60439 :	Specification for low voltage switchgear and controlgear assemblies.	413-03-01(i)b
BS EN 60439-1 : 1999	Specification for type-tested and partially type-tested assemblies.	Part 2 LV switch… 543-02-04(ii)
BS EN 60439-2 : 1993	Particular requirements for busbar trunking systems (busways). Formerly numbered as BS 5486 : Part 2 : 1988.	521-01-02
BS EN 60439-3 : 1991	Specification for low-voltage switchgear and controlgear assemblies. Particular requirements for low-voltage switchgear and controlgear assemblies intended to be installed in places where unskilled persons have access to their use.	
BS EN 60439-4 : 1991	Particular requirements for assemblies for construction sites (ACS).	604-09-01
BS EN 60445 : 2000	Basic and safety principles for man-machine interface, marking and identification. Identification of equipment terminals and of terminations of certain designated conductors, including general rules for an alphanumeric system.	Introduction to Amendment No 2
BS EN 60446 : 2000	Basic and safety principles for the man-machine interface, marking and identification. Identification of conductors by colours or numerals.	Introduction to Amendment No 2
BS EN 60570 : 1997	Electrical supply track systems for luminaires. Replaces BS 4533 : Section 102.57 : 1990. (See note).	521-06-01
BS EN 60598 :	Luminaires. Partly replaces BS 4533.	
BS EN 60598-2-24 : (1999)	Luminaires with limited surface temperature.	482-02-12
BS EN 60617 :	Graphical symbols for diagrams. Replaces BS 3939.	514-09-01
BS EN 60669 :	Switches for household and similar fixed electrical equipment.	
BS EN 60669-2-4 :	Particular requirements - Isolating switches.	537-02-02
BS EN 60702-1 : 2002	Mineral insulated cables and their terminations with a rated voltage not exceeding 750 V. Cables.	433-02-04 522-06-06 546-02-07 Table 4A2
BS EN 60742 : 1996 :	Isolating transformers and safety isolating transformers. Requirements. Replaces BS 3535, which remains current for use with Part 2. In turn, this document is also being partially replaced by documents in the BS EN 61558 series.	601-06-01 601-08-01 zone2(ii) 601-08-01 zone3(i)

BS Number	Title	Referenced in Regulations
BS EN 60898 : 1991 :	Specification for circuit-breakers for overcurrent protection for household and similar installations. Replaces BS 3871 Part 1 : 1965.	433-02-02 433-02-04 537-02-02 Tables 41B2, 41C, 471A, 604B2, 605B2 Figures 3.4, 3.5, 3.6 Appx. 4 Preface
BS EN 60947 :	Specification for low voltage switchgear and controlgear.	
BS EN 60947-1 : 1999	General rules.	
BS EN 60947-2 : 1996	Circuit-breakers. To be read in conjunction with BS EN 60947-1 : 1992.	433-02-02 433-02-04 537-02-02 Appx. 4 Prefix
BS EN 60947-3 : 1999	Switches, disconnectors, switch-disconnectors and fuse-combination units.	537-02-02
BS EN 60947-4 :	Contactors and motor starters.	
BS EN 60947-4-1 : 1992	Electromechanical contactors and motor starters.	435-01-01
BS EN 60950 : 1992	Specification for safety of information technology equipment including electrical business equipment. Replaces BS 7002 : 1989.	607-01-01
BS EN 61008 :	Residual current operated circuit-breakers without integral overcurrent protection for household and similar uses (RCCBs).	
BS EN 61008-1 : 1995	General rules. Replaces BS 4293 : 1983 which remains current.	412-06-02(ii) 537-02-02 608-03-02 608-13-05
BS EN 61009 :	Residual current operated circuit-breakers with integral overcurrent protection for household and similar uses (RCBOs).	Tables 41B2, 41C, 471A, 604B2, 605B2 Figures 3.4, 3.5, 3.6
BS EN 61009-1 : 1995	General rules.	412-06-02(ii) 433-02-02 433-02-04 537-02-02 608-03-02 608-13-05 Appx. 4 Preface
BS EN 61011 : 1993	Electric fence energizers. Safety requirements for mains operated electric fence energizers. Replaces BS 2632 : 1980. Replaced by BS EN 60335-2-76 : 1999, but remains current.	471-03-01 605-14-01
BS EN 61011-1 : 1993	Electric fence energizers. Safety requirements for battery operated electric fence energizers suitable for connection to the supply mains. Replaces BS 6369 : 1983. To be read in conjunction with BS EN 61011 : 1993. Replaced by BS EN 60335-2-76 : 1999, but remains current.	471-03-01 605-14-01

BS Number	Title	Referenced in Regulations
BS EN 61184 : 1997	Bayonet lampholders. Replaces BS 5042 : 1987. Replaces BS EN 61184 : 1995, which remains current.	412-03-04 471-05-02 Table 55B 553-03-03 553-04-01(iii)
BS EN 61558 :	Safety of power transformers, power supply units and similar. In view of the changes made to this series of standards, it is necessary to read these in conjunction with BS 3535-1 : 1996 and BS 3535-2 : 1990.	
BS EN 61558-2-1 : 1998	General requirements and tests. Partially replaces dual numbered standard BS EN 60742 : 1996, BS 3535-1 : 1996 and BS 3535-2 : 1990..	
BS EN 61558-2-2 : 1998	Particular requirements for separating transformers for general use. Partially replaces dual numbered standard BS EN 60742 : 1996, BS 3535-1 : 1996 and BS 3535-2 : 1990.	
BS EN 61558-2-4 : 1998	Particular requirements for isolating transformers for general use.	
BS EN 61558-2-5 : 1998	Particular requirements for shaver transformers and shaver units.	
BS EN 61558-2-6 :	Particular requirements for safety isolating transformers for general use.	
BS EN 61558-2-8 : 1999	Particular requirements for bell and chime transformers.	
BS EN 61558-2-17 : 1998	Particular requirements for switch mode power supplies.	

APPENDIX 2

STATUTORY REGULATIONS AND ASSOCIATED MEMORANDA

1. In Great Britain the following classes of electrical installations are required to comply with the Statutory Regulations indicated below. The regulations listed represent the principal legal requirements. Information concerning these regulations may be obtained from the appropriate authority also indicated below.

Provisions relating to electrical installations are also to be found in other legislation relating to particular activities.

(i)	Distributors' installations generally, subject to certain exemptions	Electricity Safety, Quality and Continuity Regulations 2002 SI 2002 No 2665	President of the Board of Trade and Secretary of State for Trade and Industry, and Secretary of State for Scotland
(ii)	Building generally (for Scotland only), subject to certain exemptions	Building Standards (Scotland) Regulations 1990 as amended SI 1990 No 2179 (S.187) SI 1993 No 1457 (S.191) SI 1994 No 1266 (S.65) SI 1996 No 2251 (S.183) SI 1997 No 2157 (S.150)	Secretary of State for Scotland
(iii)	Work activity Places of work Non-domestic installations	The Electricity at Work Regulations 1989 as amended SI 1989 No 635 SI 1997 No 1993 SI 1999 No 2550	Health and Safety Commission
(iv)	Cinematograph installations	Cinematograph (Safety) Regulations 1955, as amended made under the Cinematograph Act, 1909, and/or Cinematograph Act, 1952 SI 1982 No 1856	The Secretary of State for the Home Department, and Secretary of State for Scotland
(v)	Machinery	The Supply of Machinery (Safety) Regulations 1992 as amended SI 1992 No 3073 SI 1994 No 2063	Department of Trade and Industry

(vi)	Theatres and other places licensed for public entertainment, music, dancing, etc.	Conditions of licence under:
		(a) in England and Wales,
		    The Local Government
		    (Miscellaneous provisions)
		    Act 1982
		
		(b) in Scotland,
		    The Civic Government
		    (Scotland) Act 1982
			(a) The Secretary of State
			    for the Home
			    Department
			
			(b) Secretary of State
			    for Scotland

(vii)	High voltage luminous tube signs	As (a) and (b) above	As (a) and (b) above

2. Failure to comply in a consumer's installation in Great Britain with the requirements of Chapter 13 of BS 7671, Requirements for Electrical Installations (the IEE Wiring Regulations 16th Edition) places the distributor in the position of not being compelled to commence or, in certain circumstances, to continue to give, a supply of energy to that installation.

Under Regulation 26 of the Electricity Safety, Quality and Continuity Regulations 2002, any dispute which may arise between a consumer and the distributor having reference to the consumer's installation shall be determined by a person nominated by the Secretary of State on the application of the consumer or consumer's authorised agent or the distributor.

Regulation 28 of the Electricity Safety, Quality and Continuity Regulations 2002 requires distributors to provide the following information to relevant persons free of charge:

The maximum prospective short-circuit current at the supply terminals

The maximum earth loop impedance of the earth fault path outside the installation (Z_e)

The type and rating of the distributor's protective device or devices nearest to the supply terminals

The type of earthing system applicable to the connection

The number of phases of the supply

The frequency of the supply and the extent of the permitted variations

The voltage of the supply and the extent of the permitted variations.

3. Where it is intended to use protective multiple earthing the distributor and the consumer must comply with the Electricity Safety, Quality and Continuity Regulations 2002.

4. For further guidance on the application of the Electricity at Work Regulations, reference may be made to the following publication:

(i)   Memorandum of Guidance on the Electricity at Work Regulations 1989 (HSR25).

5. For installations in potentially explosive atmospheres reference should be made to:

(i)   the Electricity at Work Regulations 1989

(ii)   the Highly Flammable Liquids and Liquefied Petroleum Gases Regulations 1972

(iii) the Petroleum (Consolidation) Act 1928

(iv)   the Equipment and Protective Systems intended for use in potentially explosive atmospheres Regulations 1996 (SI 1996 No 192)

(v)   relevant British Standards.

Under the Petroleum (Consolidation) Act 1928 local authorities are empowered to grant licences in respect of premises where petroleum spirit is stored and as the authorities may attach such conditions as they think fit, the requirements may vary from one local authority to another. Guidance may be obtained from the Health and Safety Executive (Guidance Note HS(G)41. Petrol Filling Stations : Instructions and Operation), and from the Association for Petroleum and Explosive Administration (APEA) and the Institute of Petroleum (IP) publication: Guidance for the Design, Construction, Modification and Maintenance of Petrol Filling Stations. .

6. For installations in theatres and other places of public entertainment, and on caravan parks, the requirements of the licensing authority should be ascertained. Model Standards were issued by the Department of the Environment in 1977 under the Caravan Sites and Control of Development Act 1960 as guidance for local authorities.

7. The Electrical Equipment (Safety) Regulations 1994 (SI 1994 No 3260), administered by the Department of Trade and Industry, contain requirements for safety of equipment designed or suitable for general use. Information on the application of the Regulations is given in guidance issued by the DTI.

8. The Plugs and Sockets etc. (Safety) Regulations 1994 (SI 1994 No 1768) made under the Consumer Safety Act 1978, administered by the Department of Trade and Industry, contains requirements for the safety of plugs, sockets, adaptors and fuse links etc. designed for use at a voltage of not less than 200 volts.

9 The Health and Safety (Safety Signs and Signals) Regulations 1996 (SI 1996 No 341) require employers to ensure that safety signs are provided. Guidance from the Health and Safety Executive L64, Safety Signs and Signals specifies signs including emergency escape, first aid and fire safety signs.

10. The Management of Health and Safety at Work Regulations 1999 (SI 1999 No 3242) require employers and self-employed persons to assess risks to workers and others who may be affected by their work or business. This is intended to enable them to identify measures they need to take to comply with the law. The Health and Safety Commission has published an Approved Code of Practice L21, Management of health and safety at work, which gives advice that has special legal status.

11. The Provision and Use of Work Equipment Regulations 1998 (SI 1988 No 2306) require employers to ensure that all work equipment is suitable for the purpose for which it is used, is properly maintained and that appropriate training is given. The Health and Safety Commission has published an Approved Code of Practice L22, Safe use of work equipment, which gives advice that has special legal status.

12. The Electromagnetic Compatibility Regulations 1992 as amended (SI 1992 No 2372, SI 1994 No 3080, SI 1995 No 3180) provide requirements for electrical and electronic products for electromagnetic compatibility.

13. Other Regulations relevant to electrical installation include:

The Personal Protective Equipment at Work Regulations 1992 as amended
(European Directive 89/656/EEC, HSE Publication L25)

The Workplace (Health Safety and Welfare) Regulations 1992
(European Directive 89/654/EEC, HSE Publication L24)

The Manual Handling Operations Regulations 1992
(European Directive 90/269/EEC, HSE Publication L23).

14. In November 1988 the European electrical standards body CENELEC agreed on harmonization of "low voltage" electricity supplies within Europe (CENELEC document HD 472 S1), implemented by BS 7697 Nominal voltages for low voltage public electricity supply systems. The measure is intended to harmonize mains electricity supplies at 230 V within Europe. CENELEC has proposed three stages of harmonization, the first two stages of which are shown below.

Effective date	Nominal voltage	Permitted tolerance	Permitted voltage range
Pre-1995	240 V	+6 % / -6 %	225.6 - 254.4 V
1 January 1995	230 V	+10 % / -6 %	216.2 - 253.0 V
1 January 2008 (proposed)	230 V	+10 % / -10 %	207.0 - 253.0 V

APPENDIX 3

TIME/CURRENT CHARACTERISTICS OF OVERCURRENT PROTECTIVE DEVICES

This appendix gives the time/current characteristics of the following overcurrent protective devices:

figure 3.1   Fuses to BS 1361

figures 3.2A & 3.2B Semi-enclosed fuses to BS 3036

figures 3.3A & 3.3B Fuses to BS 88-2.1 and BS 88-6

Circuit-breakers

figure 3.4   Type B to BS EN 60898 and RCBOs to BS EN 61009

figure 3.5   Type C to BS EN 60898 and RCBOs to BS EN 61009

figure 3.6   Type D to BS EN 60898 and RCBOs to BS EN 61009

In all of these cases time/current characteristics are based on the slowest operating times for compliance with the Standard and have been used as the basis for determining the limiting values of earth fault loop impedance prescribed in Sections 413, 604 and 605.

Maximum Earth Fault Loop Impedance

Regulations 413-02-09 and 413-02-13 specify maximum disconnection times for circuits. Regulations 413-02-10, 413-02-11 and 413-02-14 provide maximum earth fault loop impedances (Z_S) that will result in protective devices operating within the required disconnection times (of Regulations 413-02-09 and 413-02-13).

The maximum earth loop impedance for a protective device is given by:

$$Z_S = \frac{U_{oc}}{I_a}$$

where:

U_{oc} is the open circuit voltage at the distribution transformer.

I_a is the current causing operation of the protective device within the specified time.

For the purposes of Regulations 413-02-10 and 413-02-13 (Tables 41B1, 41B2, 41D, 604B1, 604B2, 605B1 and 605B2) the open circuit voltage has been presumed to be 240 V for a nominal supply voltage (U_o) of 230 V.

The tabulated values are applicable for supplies from regional electricity companies. For other supplies the designer will need to determine open circuit voltages and calculate Z_S accordingly.

fig 3.1 Fuses to BS 1361

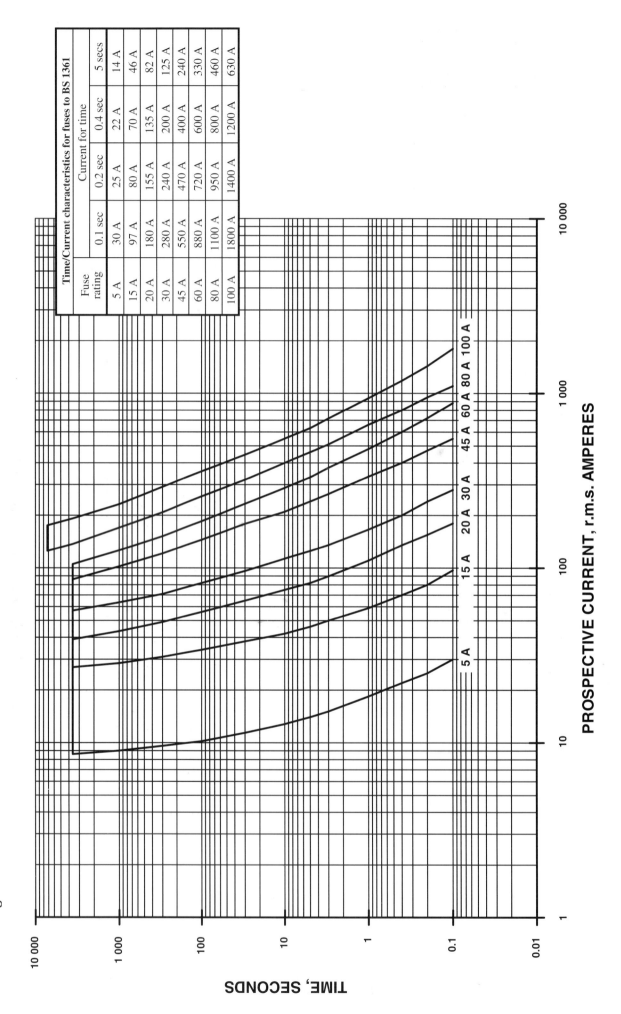

Time/Current characteristics for fuses to BS 1361					
Fuse rating	Current for time				
	0.1 sec	0.2 sec	0.4 sec	5 secs
5 A	30 A	25 A	22 A	14 A
15 A	97 A	80 A	70 A	46 A
20 A	180 A	155 A	135 A	82 A
30 A	280 A	240 A	200 A	125 A
45 A	550 A	470 A	400 A	240 A
60 A	880 A	720 A	600 A	330 A
80 A	1100 A	950 A	800 A	460 A
100 A	1800 A	1400 A	1200 A	630 A

PROSPECTIVE CURRENT, r.m.s. AMPERES

TIME, SECONDS

fig 3.2A Semi-enclosed fuses to BS 3036

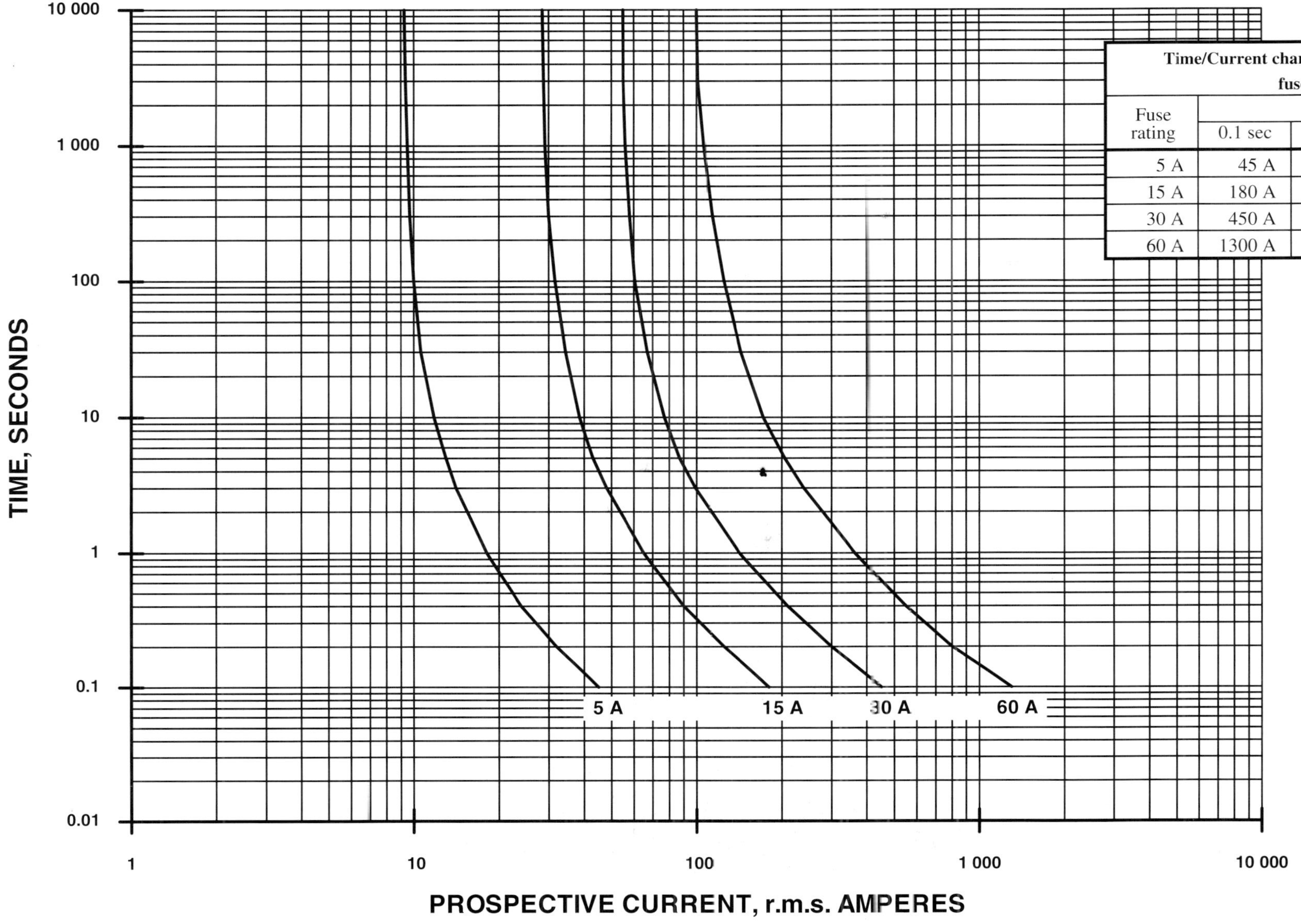

Time/Current characteristics for semi-enclosed fuses to BS 3036				
Fuse rating	Current for time			
	0.1 sec	0.2 sec	0.4 sec	5 secs
5 A	45 A	32 A	24 A	13 A
15 A	180 A	125 A	90 A	43 A
30 A	450 A	300 A	210 A	87 A
60 A	1300 A	800 A	550 A	205 A

PROSPECTIVE CURRENT, r.m.s. AMPERES

TIME, SECONDS

fig 3.2B **Semi-enclosed fuses to BS 3036**

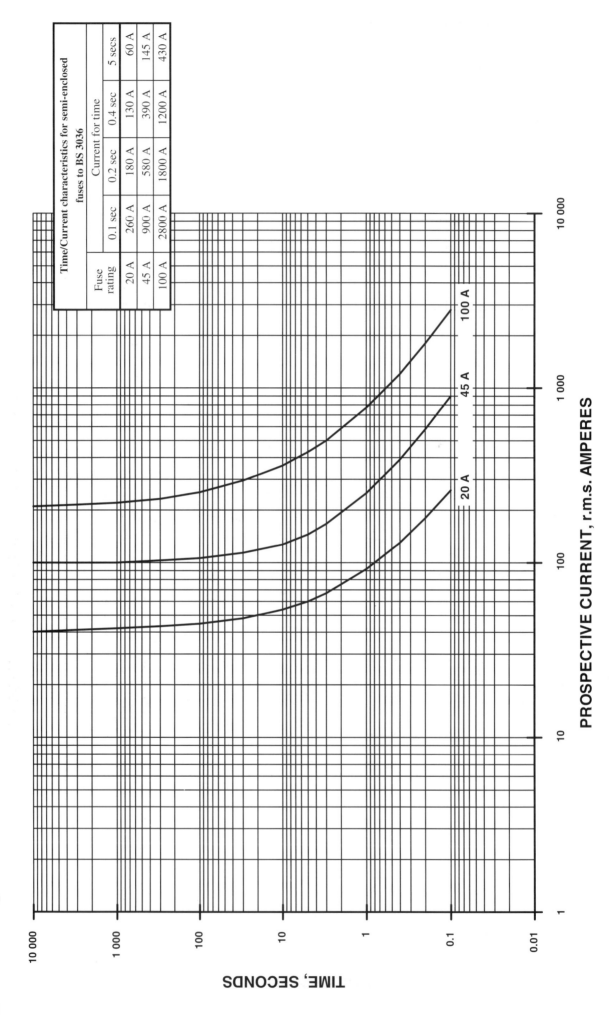

Time/Current characteristics for semi-enclosed fuses to BS 3036					
Fuse rating	Current for time				
	0.1 sec	0.2 sec	0.4 sec	5 secs	
20 A	260 A	180 A	130 A	60 A	
45 A	900 A	580 A	390 A	145 A	
100 A	2800 A	1800 A	1200 A	430 A	

TIME, SECONDS

PROSPECTIVE CURRENT, r.m.s. AMPERES

fig 3.3A Fuses to BS 88-2.1 and BS 88-6

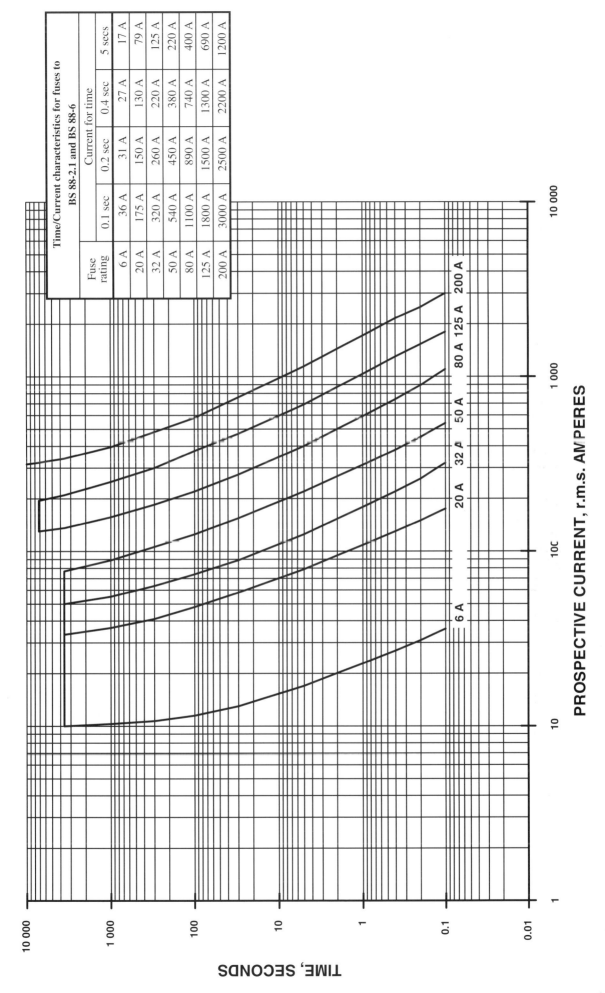

Time/Current characteristics for fuses to BS 88-2.1 and BS 88-6				
Fuse rating	Current for time			
	0.1 sec	0.2 sec	0.4 sec	5 secs
6 A	36 A	31 A	27 A	17 A
20 A	175 A	150 A	130 A	79 A
32 A	320 A	260 A	220 A	125 A
50 A	540 A	450 A	380 A	220 A
80 A	1100 A	890 A	740 A	400 A
125 A	1800 A	1500 A	1300 A	690 A
200 A	3000 A	2500 A	2200 A	1200 A

PROSPECTIVE CURRENT, r.m.s. AMPERES

TIME, SECONDS

197

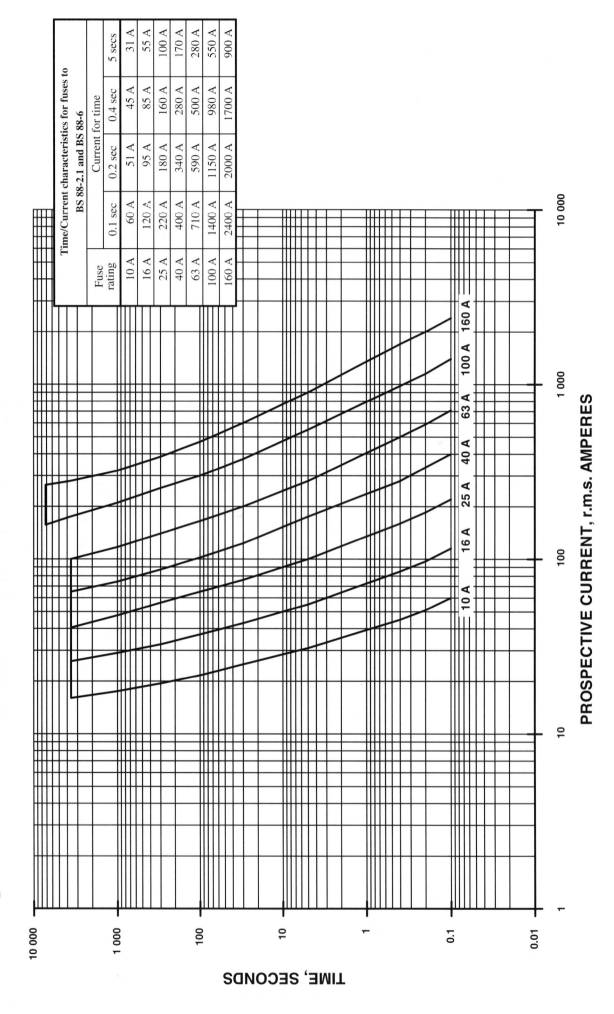

fig 3.3B **Fuses to BS 88-2.1 and BS 88-6**

Fuse rating	Time/Current characteristics for fuses to BS 88-2.1 and BS 88-6				
	Current for time				
	0.1 sec	0.2 sec	0.4 sec	5 secs	
10 A	60 A	51 A	45 A	31 A	
16 A	120 A	95 A	85 A	55 A	
25 A	220 A	180 A	160 A	100 A	
40 A	400 A	340 A	280 A	170 A	
63 A	710 A	590 A	500 A	280 A	
100 A	1400 A	1150 A	980 A	550 A	
160 A	2400 A	2000 A	1700 A	900 A	

PROSPECTIVE CURRENT, r.m.s. AMPERES

TIME, SECONDS

198

fig 3.4 Type B circuit-breakers to BS EN 60898 and RCBOs to BS EN 61009

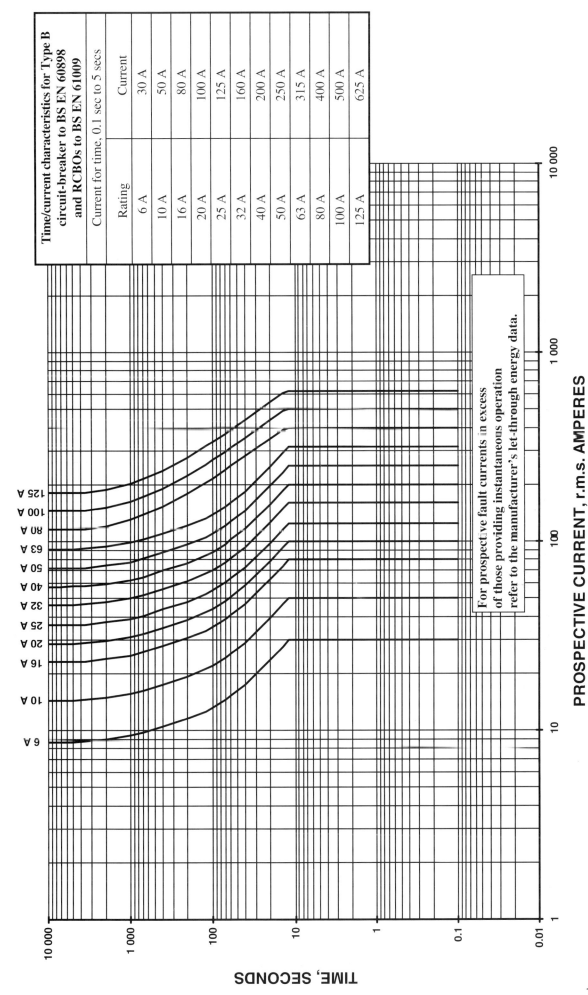

Time/current characteristics for Type B circuit-breaker to BS EN 60898 and RCBOs to BS EN 61009	
Current for time, 0.1 sec to 5 secs	
Rating	Current
6 A	30 A
10 A	50 A
16 A	80 A
20 A	100 A
25 A	125 A
32 A	160 A
40 A	200 A
50 A	250 A
63 A	315 A
80 A	400 A
100 A	500 A
125 A	625 A

For prospective fault currents in excess of those providing instantaneous operation refer to the manufacturer's let-through energy data.

PROSPECTIVE CURRENT, r.m.s. AMPERES

TIME, SECONDS

fig 3.5 Type C circuit-breakers to BS EN 60898 and RCBOs to BS EN 61009

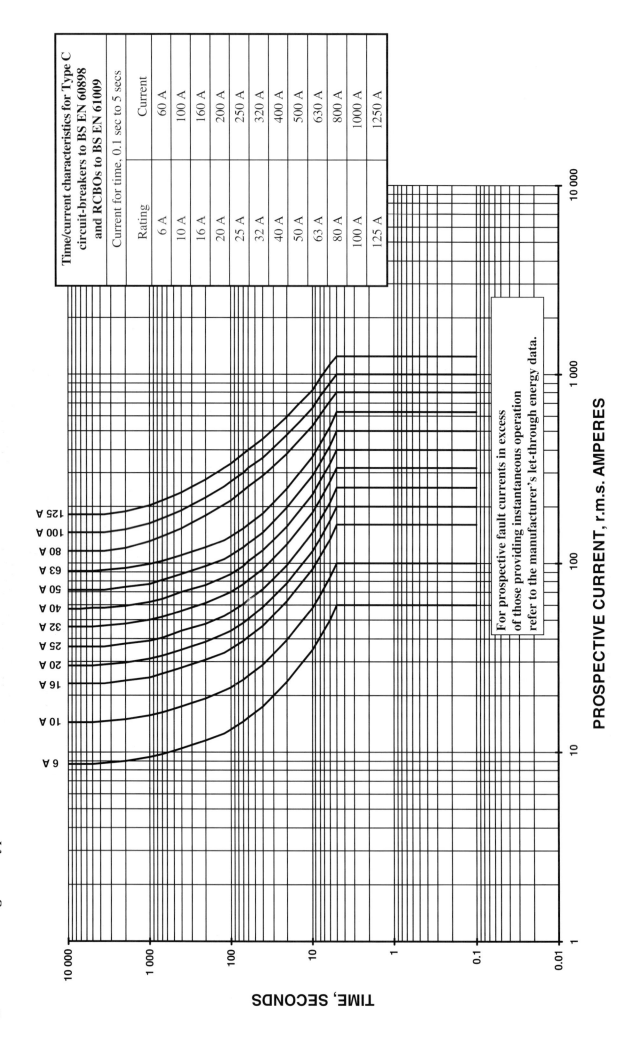

Time/current characteristics for Type C circuit-breakers to BS EN 60898 and RCBOs to BS EN 61009	
Current for time, 0.1 sec to 5 secs	
Rating	Current
6 A	60 A
10 A	100 A
16 A	160 A
20 A	200 A
25 A	250 A
32 A	320 A
40 A	400 A
50 A	500 A
63 A	630 A
80 A	800 A
100 A	1000 A
125 A	1250 A

For prospective fault currents in excess of those providing instantaneous operation refer to the manufacturer's let-through energy data.

PROSPECTIVE CURRENT, r.m.s. AMPERES

TIME, SECONDS

fig 3.6 Type D circuit-breakers to BS EN 60898 and RCBOs to BS EN 61009

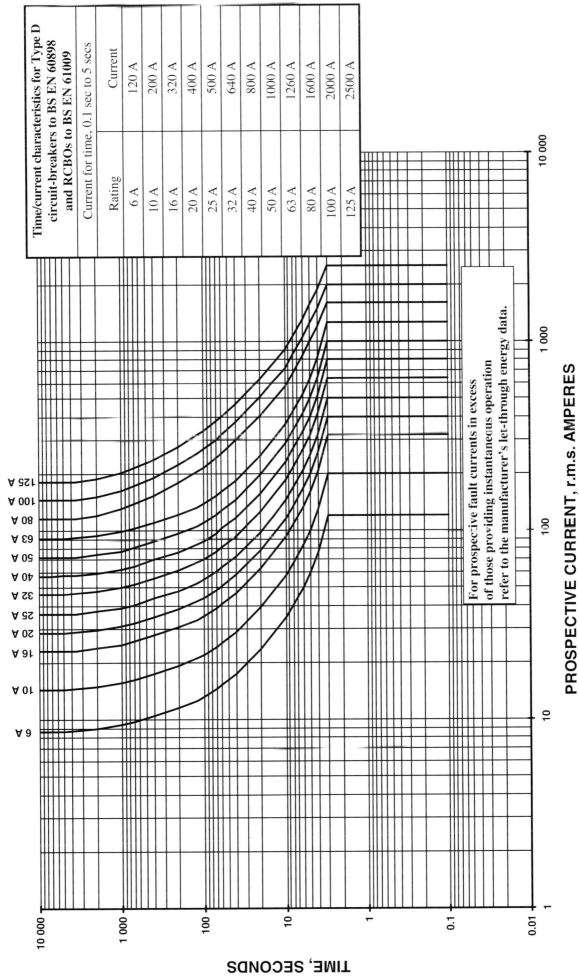

Time/current characteristics for Type D circuit-breakers to BS EN 60898 and RCBOs to BS EN 61009	
Current for time, 0.1 sec to 5 secs	
Rating	Current
6 A	120 A
10 A	200 A
16 A	320 A
20 A	400 A
25 A	500 A
32 A	640 A
40 A	800 A
50 A	1000 A
63 A	1260 A
80 A	1600 A
100 A	2000 A
125 A	2500 A

For prospective fault currents in excess of those providing instantaneous operation refer to the manufacturer's let-through energy data.

PROSPECTIVE CURRENT, r.m.s. AMPERES

TIME, SECONDS

201

APPENDIX 4

CURRENT-CARRYING CAPACITY AND VOLTAGE DROP FOR

CABLES AND FLEXIBLE CORDS

CONTENTS

Preface to the tables

Tables:

COPPER CONDUCTORS

70 °C THERMOPLASTIC (PVC) INSULATED CABLES

70 °C THERMOSETTING-INSULATED CABLES

CABLES HAVING 90 °C THERMOSETTING INSULATION

85 °C THERMOSETTING (RUBBER) INSULATED CABLES

FLEXIBLE CABLES AND CORDS

MINERAL INSULATED CABLES

ALUMINIUM CONDUCTORS

70 °C THERMOPLASTIC (PVC) INSULATED CABLES

4K1   Single-core non-armoured, with or without sheath
4K2   Multicore non-armoured
4K3   Single-core armoured (non-magnetic armour)
4K4   Multicore armoured

CABLES HAVING 90 °C THERMOSETTING INSULATION

4L1   Single-core, non-armoured
4L2   Multicore, non-armoured
4L3   Single-core armoured (non-magnetic armour)
4L4   Multicore armoured

APPENDIX 4

CURRENT-CARRYING CAPACITY AND VOLTAGE DROP FOR CABLES AND FLEXIBLE CORDS

PREFACE TO THE TABLES

1. Basis of tabulated current-carrying capacity

The current-carrying capacity set out in this appendix takes account of IEC Publication 364-5-523 (1983), so far as the latter is applicable. For types of cable not treated in the IEC publication (e.g. armoured cables) the current-carrying capacities given in this appendix are based on data provided by ERA Technology Ltd and the British Cables Association. See also the ERA Report 69-30 "Current rating standards for distribution cables"*.

The tabulated current-carrying capacity relates to continuous loading and is also known as the 'full thermal current rating' of the cable, corresponding to the conductor operating temperature indicated in the headings to the tables concerned. It is intended to provide for a satisfactory life of conductor and insulation subject to the thermal effects of carrying current for sustained periods in normal service. A cable may be seriously damaged, leading to early failure, or its service life may be significantly reduced, if it is operated for any prolonged period at a temperature higher than the indicated value.

In addition, there are other considerations affecting the choice of the cross-sectional area of a conductor, such as the requirements for protection against electric shock (see Chapter 41), protection against thermal effects (see Chapter 42), overcurrent protection (see Chapter 43 and item 5 below), voltage drop (see item 7 below) and the limiting temperatures for terminals of equipment to which the conductors are connected.

The tabulated current-carrying capacity relates to a single circuit in the installation methods shown in Table 4A1, in an ambient air temperature of 30 °C. The current-carrying capacities given in the tables for a.c. operation apply only to frequencies in the range 49 to 61 Hz. For other conditions appropriate correction factors are to be applied as described below.

The current ratings given for single-core armoured cable are for the condition of armour bonded at both ends and to earth.

Further information on cables installed in thermal insulation may be obtained from ERA Report 85-0111. "The temperature rise of cables passing through short lengths of thermal insulation"*.

*ERA Technology Ltd, Cleeve Road, LEATHERHEAD, Surrey, United Kingdom KT22 7SA.

Current-carrying capacities may also be obtained by calculation using the method described in BS 7769.

2. Correction factors for current-carrying capacity

The current-carrying capacity of a cable for continuous service is affected by ambient temperature, by grouping, by partial or total enclosure in thermal insulating material and, for a.c., by frequency. This appendix provides correction factors in these respects as follows:

2.1 *Ambient temperature*

Tables 4C1 and 4C2 give the correction factor to be applied to the tabulated current-carrying capacity depending upon the actual ambient temperature of the location in which the cable is to be installed.

In practice the ambient air temperatures may be determined by thermometers placed in free air as close as practicable to the position at which the cables are installed or are to be installed, subject to the proviso that the measurements are not to be influenced by the heat arising from the cables; thus if the measurements are made while the cables are loaded, the thermometers should be placed about 0.5 m or ten times the overall diameter of the cable, whichever is the lesser, from the cables, in the horizontal plane, or 150 mm below the lowest of the cables.

Tables 4C1 and 4C2 do not take account of temperature increase, if any, due to solar or other infra-red radiation. Where cables are subject to such radiation, the current-carrying capacity may need to be specially calculated.

2.2 *Grouping*

Tables 4B1, 4B2 and 4B3 give the correction factor to be applied to the tabulated current-carrying capacity where cables or circuits are grouped.

In extreme cases, notably for large multicore cables, the reduction in current-carrying capacity of cables carrying, for example, balanced 400 Hz a.c. compared with the current-carrying capacity at 50 Hz, may be as much as 50 %. For small cables and flexible cords, such as may be used to supply individual tools, the difference in the 50 Hz and the 400 Hz current-carrying capacities may be negligible.

3. Effective current-carrying capacity

The current-carrying capacity of a cable corresponds to the maximum current that can be carried in specified conditions without the conductors exceeding the permissible limit of steady state temperature for the type of insulation concerned.

The values of current tabulated represent the effective current-carrying capacity only where no correction factor is applicable. Otherwise, the current-carrying capacity corresponds to the tabulated value multiplied by the appropriate factor or factors for ambient temperature, grouping and thermal insulation, as applicable.

Irrespective of the type of overcurrent protective device associated with the conductors concerned, the ambient temperature correction factors to be used when calculating current-carrying capacity (as opposed to those used when selecting cable sizes) are those given in Table 4C1.

4. Relationship of current-carrying capacity to other circuit parameters

The relevant symbols used in the Regulations are as follows:

I_z the current-carrying capacity of a cable for continuous service, under the particular installation conditions concerned.

I_t the value of current tabulated in this appendix for the type of cable and installation method concerned, for a single circuit in an ambient temperature of 30 °C.

I_b the design current of the circuit, i.e. the current intended to be carried by the circuit in normal service.

I_n the nominal current or current setting of the device protecting the circuit against overcurrent.

I_2 the operating current (i.e. the fusing current or tripping current for the conventional operating time) of the device protecting the circuit against overload.

C a correction factor to be applied where the installation conditions differ from those for which values of current-carrying capacity are tabulated in this appendix. The various correction factors are identified as follows:

C_a for ambient temperature

C_g for grouping

C_i for thermal insulation

C_t for operating temperature of conductor.

In all circumstances I_z must be not less than I_b and I_n also must be not less than I_b.

Where the overcurrent device is intended to afford protection against overload, I_2 must not exceed 1.45 I_z and I_n must not exceed I_z (see item 5 below).

Where the overcurrent device is intended to afford short-circuit protection only, I_n can be greater than I_z and I_2 can be greater than 1.45 I_z. The protective device is then to be selected for compliance with Regulation 434-03-03.

5. Overload protection

Where overload protection is required, the type of protection provided does not affect the current-carrying capacity of a cable for continuous service (I_z) but it may affect the choice of conductor size. The operating conditions of a cable are influenced not only by the limiting conductor temperature for continuous service, but also by the conductor temperature which might be attained during the conventional operating time of the overload protection device, in the event of an overload.

This means that the operating current of the protective device must not exceed 1.45 I_z. Where the protective device is a fuse to BS 88 or BS 1361, a circuit-breaker to BS EN 60898 or BS EN 60947-2 or a residual current circuit-breaker with integral overcurrent protection to BSEN 61009-1 (RCBO), this requirement is satisfied by selecting a value of I_z not less than I_n.

In practice, because of the standard steps in nominal rating of fuses and circuit-breakers, it is often necessary to select a value of I_n exceeding I_b. In that case, because it is also necessary for I_z in turn to be not less than the selected value of I_n, the choice of conductor cross-sectional area may be dictated by the overload conditions and the current-carrying capacity (I_z) of the conductors will not always be fully used.

The size needed for a conductor protected against overload by a BS 3036 semi-enclosed fuse can be obtained by the use of a correction factor, 1.45/2=0.725, which results in the same degree of protection as that afforded by other overload protective devices. This factor is to be applied to the nominal rating of the fuse as a divisor, thus indicating the minimum value of I_t required of the conductor to be protected. In this case also, the choice of conductor size is dictated by the overload conditions and the current-carrying capacity (I_z) of the conductors cannot be fully used.

6. Determination of the size of cable to be used

Having established the design current (I_b) of the circuit under consideration, the appropriate procedure described in items 6.1 to 6.4 below will enable the designer to determine the size of the cable it will be necessary to use.

As a preliminary step it is useful to identify the length of the cable run and the permissible voltage drop for the equipment being supplied, as this may be an overriding consideration (see Regulation 525-01 and item 7 of this appendix). The permissible voltage drop in mV, divided by I_b and by the length of run, will give the value of voltage drop in mV/A/m which can be tolerated. A voltage drop not exceeding that value is identified in the appropriate table and the corresponding cross-sectional area of conductor needed on this account can be read off directly before any other calculations are made.

The conductor size necessary from consideration of the conditions of normal load and overload is then determined. All correction factors affecting I_z (i.e. the factors for ambient temperature, grouping and thermal insulation) can, if desired, be applied to the values of I_t as multipliers. This involves a process of trial and error until a cross-sectional area is reached which ensures that I_z is not less than I_b and not less than I_n of any protective device it is intended to select. In any event, if a correction factor for protection by a semi-enclosed fuse is necessary, this has to be applied to I_n as a divisor. It is therefore more convenient to apply all the correction factors to I_n as divisors.

This method is used in items 6.1 to 6.3 and produces a value of current and that value (or the next larger value) can readily be located in the appropriate table of current-carrying capacity and the corresponding cross-sectional area of conductor can be identified directly. It should be noted that the value of I_t appearing against the chosen cross-sectional area is not I_z. It is not necessary to know I_z where the size of conductor is chosen by this method, but if it is desired to identify I_z the value is determined by the method indicated in item 3 above.

However, this method cannot be used for cables installed in enclosed trenches (installation methods 18, 19 and 20 of Table 4A1) because the correction factors given in Table 4B3 are related to conductor cross-sectional areas. For such cables it is therefore necessary to use the process of trial and error described in the third paragraph above, selecting on a trial basis a particular size of cable from, for instance, voltage drop considerations.

6.1 *Where overload protection is afforded by a fuse to BS 88 or BS 1361, or a circuit-breaker to BS EN 60898 or BS EN 60947-2 or a residual current circuit-breaker with integral overcurrent protection to BS EN 61009-1 (RCBO).*

6.1.1 *For single circuits*

- DIVIDE the nominal current of the protective device (I_n) by any applicable correction factor for ambient temperature (C_a) given in Table 4Cl.

- then further DIVIDE by any applicable correction factor for thermal insulation (C_i).

The size of cable to be used is to be such that its tabulated current-carrying capacity (I_t) is not less than the value of nominal current of the protective device adjusted as above:

$$I_t \geq \frac{I_n}{C_a C_i} \tag{1}$$

6.1.2 *For groups*

- DIVIDE the nominal current of the protective device (I_n) by the correction factor for grouping (C_g) given in Tables 4B1, 4B2 or 4B3:

$$I_t \geq \frac{I_n}{C_g} \tag{2}$$

Alternatively, it may be selected in accordance with the following formulae, provided that the circuits of the group are not liable to simultaneous overload:

$$I_t \geq \frac{I_b}{C_g} \text{, and} \tag{3}$$

$$I_t \geq \sqrt{I_n^2 + 0.48\,I_b^2\left(\frac{1 - C_g^2}{C_g^2}\right)} \tag{4}$$

The size of cable to be used is to be such that its tabulated single-circuit current-carrying capacity (I_t) is not less than the value of I_t calculated in accordance with formula (2) above or, where formulae (3) and (4) are used not less than the larger of the resulting two values of I_t.

Where correction factors C_a and/or C_i are applicable, they are to be applied as divisors to the value of I_t determined by the above formulae.

6.2 *Where the protective device is a semi-enclosed fuse to BS 3036:*

6.2.1 *For single circuits*

- DIVIDE the nominal current of the fuse (I_n) by any applicable correction factor for ambient temperature (C_a) given in Table 4C2

- then further DIVIDE by any applicable correction factor for thermal insulation, (C_i)

- then further DIVIDE by 0.725.

The size of cable to be used is to be such that its tabulated current-carrying capacity (I_t) is not less than the value of nominal current of the fuse adjusted as above:

$$I_t \geq \frac{I_n}{0.725\,C_a\,C_i} \tag{5}$$

6.2.2 *For groups*

- DIVIDE the nominal current of the fuse I_n by 0.725 and by the applicable correction factor for grouping (C_g) given in Table 4B1, 4B2 or 4B3:

$$I_t \geq \frac{I_n}{0.725\,C_g} \tag{6}$$

Alternatively, it may be selected by the following formulae, provided that the circuits of the group are not liable to simultaneous overload:

$$I_t \geq \frac{I_b}{C_g} \text{, and} \tag{7}$$

$$I_t \geq \sqrt{1.9\,I_n^2 + 0.48\,I_b^2\left(\frac{1 - C_g^2}{C_g^2}\right)} \tag{8}$$

The size of cable to be used is to be such that its tabulated single-circuit current-carrying capacity (I_t) is not less than the value of I_t calculated in accordance with formula (6) above or, where formulae (7) and (8) are used, not less than the larger of the resulting two values of I_t.

Where correction factors C_a and/or C_i are applicable, they are to be applied as divisors to the value of I_t determined by the above formulae.

6.3 *Where overload protection is not required:*

Where Regulation 473-01-04 applies, and the cable under consideration is not required to be protected against overload, the design current of the circuit (I_b) is to be divided by any applicable correction factors, and the size of the cable to be used is to be such that its tabulated current-carrying capacity (I_t) for the installation method concerned is not less than the value of I_b adjusted as above:

$$I_t \geq \frac{I_b}{C_a\,C_g\,C_i} \tag{9}$$

6.4 *Variation of installation conditions along a cable route*

The procedures in items 6.1 to 6.3 above are based on the assumption that all the conditions necessitating the use of correction factors apply to the same part of the route of the conductors of the circuit. Where various factors apply to different parts of the route, each part may be treated separately, or alternatively only the factor or combination of factors appropriate to the most onerous conditions encountered along the route may be applied to the whole of the route. It is permissible to obtain more precise factors by calculation of the various conductor temperature rises that will occur along such a route, provided that the appropriate limiting temperature of the conductor is nowhere exceeded (see Regulation 523-01).

7. Tables of voltage drop

In the tables, values of voltage drop are given for a current of one ampere for a metre run, i.e. for a distance of 1 m along the route taken by the cables, and represent the result of the voltage drops in all the circuit conductors. The values of voltage drop assume that the conductors are at their maximum permitted normal operating temperatures.

The values in the tables, for a.c. operation, apply only to frequencies in the range 49 to 61 Hz and for single-core armoured cables the tabulated values apply where the armour is bonded to earth at both ends. The values of voltage drop for cables operating at higher frequencies may be substantially greater.

For a given run, to calculate the voltage drop (in mV) the tabulated value of voltage drop per ampere per metre for the cable concerned has to be multiplied by the length of the run in metres and by the current the cable is intended to carry, namely the design current of the circuit (I_b) in amperes. For three-phase circuits the tabulated mV/A/m values relate to the line voltage and balanced conditions have been assumed.

For cables having conductors of 16 mm^2 or less cross-sectional area their inductances can be ignored and (mV/A/m)$_r$ values only are tabulated. For cables having conductors greater than 16 mm^2, cross-sectional area the impedance values are given as (mV/A/m)$_z$, together with the resistive component (mV/A/m)$_r$ and the reactive component (mV/A/m)$_x$.

The *direct* use of the tabulated (mV/A/m)$_r$ or (mV/A/m)$_z$ values, as appropriate, may lead to pessimistically high calculated values of voltage drop or, in other words, to unnecessarily low values of permitted circuit lengths.

For example, where the design current of a circuit is significantly less than the effective current-carrying capacity of the cable chosen, the actual voltage drop would be less than the calculated value because the conductor temperature (and hence its resistance) will be less than that on which the tabulated mV/A/m had been based.

As regards power factor in a.c. circuits, the use of the tabulated mV/A/m values (for the larger cable sizes, the tabulated (mV/A/m)$_z$ values) to calculate the voltage drop is strictly correct only when the phase angle of the cable equals that of the load. When the phase angle of the cable does not equal that of the load, the direct use of the tabulated mV/A/m or (mV/A/m)$_z$ values leads to a calculated value of voltage drop higher than the actual value. In some cases it may be advantageous to take account of the load power factor when calculating voltage drop.

Where a more accurate assessment of voltage drop is desirable the following methods may be used.

7.1 *Correction for operating temperature*

For cables having conductors of cross-sectional area 16 mm^2 or less the design value of mV/A/m is obtained by multiplying the tabulated value by a factor C_t, given by

$$C_t = \frac{230 + t_p - \left(C_a^2 \, C_g^2 - \dfrac{I_b^2}{I_t^2} \right)(t_p - 30)}{230 + t_p} \tag{10}$$

where t_p is the maximum permitted normal operating temperature (°C).

This equation applies only where the overcurrent protective device is other than a BS 3036 fuse and where the actual ambient temperature is equal to or greater than 30 °C

NOTE: For convenience, the above formula is based on the approximate resistance-temperature coefficient of 0.004 per °C at 20 °C for both copper and aluminium conductors.

For cables having conductors of cross-sectional area greater than 16 mm^2, only the resistive component of the voltage drop is affected by the temperature and the factor C_t is therefore applied only to the tabulated value of (mV/A/m)$_r$ and the design value of (mV/A/m)$_z$ is given by the vector sum of C_t (mV/A/m)$_r$ and (mV/A/m)$_x$.

For very large conductor sizes where the resistive component of voltage drop is much less than the corresponding reactive part (i.e. when x/r ≥3) this correction factor need not be considered.

7.2   *Correction for load power factor*

For cables having conductors of cross-sectional area of 16 mm² or less the design value of mV/A/m is obtained approximately by multiplying the tabulated value by the power factor of the load, cos Ø.

For cables having conductors of cross-sectional area greater than 16 mm² the design value of mV/A/m is given approximately by:

$$\cos \emptyset \ (\text{tabulated } (\text{mV/A/m})_r) + \sin \emptyset \ (\text{tabulated } (\text{mV/A/m})_x)$$

For single-core cables in flat formation the tabulated values apply to the outer cables and may under-estimate for the voltage drop between an outer cable and the centre cable for cross-sectional areas above 240 mm², and power factors greater than 0.8.

7.3   *Combined correction for both operating temperature and load power factor*

From items 7.1 and 7.2 above, where it is considered appropriate to correct the tabulated mV/A/m values for both operating temperature and load power factor, the design values of mV/A/m are given by:

for cables having conductors of 16 mm² or less cross-sectional area

$$C_t \cos \emptyset \ (\text{tabulated mV/A/m})$$

for cables having conductors of cross-sectional area greater than 16 mm²

$$C_t \cos \emptyset \ (\text{tabulated } (\text{mV/A/m})_r) + \sin \emptyset \ (\text{tabulated } (\text{mV/A/m})_x).$$

8. Methods of installation of cables

Table 4A1 lists the methods of installation for which this appendix provides guidance for the selection of the appropriate cable size. Table 4A2 lists the appropriate tables for selection of current ratings for specific cable constructions. The methods of installation distinguished by bold type are reference methods for which the current-carrying capacities given in Tables 4D1 to 4L4 have been determined. For the other methods, an indication is given of the appropriate reference method having values of current-carrying capacity which can safely be applied.

As stated in Regulation 521-07-01 the use of other methods is not precluded, where specified by a suitably qualified electrical engineer; in that case the evaluation of current-carrying capacity may need to be based on experimental work

Schedule of Installation Methods of Cables (including Reference Method)

Installation method		Examples	Appropriate Reference Method for determining current-carrying capacity
Number	Description		
1	2	3	4

Open and clipped direct:

| 1 | **Sheathed cables clipped direct to or lying on a non-metallic surface** | | **Method 1** |

Cables embedded direct in building materials:

| 2 | Sheathed cables embedded directly in masonry, brickwork, concrete, plaster or the like (other than thermally insulating materials) | | Method 1 |

In conduit:

3	**Single-core non-sheathed cables in metallic or non-metallic conduit on a wall or ceiling**		**Method 3**
4	**Single-core non-sheathed cables in metallic or non-metallic conduit in a thermally insulating wall or above a thermally insulating ceiling, the conduit being in contact with a thermally conductive surface on one side †**		**Method 4**
5	Multicore cables having non-metallic sheath, in metallic or non-metallic conduit on a wall or ceiling		Method 3

† The wall is assumed to consist of an outer weatherproof skin, thermal insulation and an inner skin of plasterboard or wood-like material having a coefficient of heat transfer not less than 10 W/m²K. The conduit is fixed so as to be close to, but not necessarily touching, the inner skin. Heat from the cables is assumed to escape through the inner skin only.

Installation method		Examples	Appropriate Reference Method for determining current-carrying capacity
Number	Description		
1	2	3	4
6	Sheathed cables in conduit in a thermally insulating wall etc. (otherwise as Reference Method 4)		Method 4 **or** **Method 6 for cable type covered by Table 4D5A.**
7	Cables in conduit embedded in masonry, brickwork, concrete, plaster or the like (other than thermally insulating materials)		Method 3

In trunking:

8	Cables in trunking on a wall or suspended in the air		Method 3
9	Cables in flush floor trunking		Method 3
10	Single-core cables in skirting trunking		Method 3

On trays:

11	**Sheathed cables on a perforated cable tray, bunched and unenclosed. A perforated cable tray is a ventilated tray in which the holes occupy 30 % or more of the surface area**		**Method 11**

Installation method		Examples	Appropriate Reference Method for determining current-carrying capacity
Number	Description		
1	2	3	4

In free air, on cleats, brackets or a ladder:

12	**Sheathed single-core cables in free air (any supporting metalwork under the cables occupying less than 10 % of the plan area):** **Two or three cables vertically one above the other, minimum distance between cable surfaces equal to the overall cable diameter (D_e); distance from the wall not less than 0.5 D_e** **Two or three cables horizontally, with spacings as above** **Three cables in trefoil, distance between wall and surface of nearest cable 0.5 D_e or nearest cables 0.75 D_e**		**Method 12**
13	**Sheathed multicore cables on ladder or brackets, separation greater than 2 D_e** **Sheathed multicore cables in free air distance between wall and cable surface not less than 0.3 D_e** **Any supporting metalwork under the cables occupying less than 10 % of the plan area**		**Method 13**
14	Cables suspended from or incorporating a catenary wire		Method 12 or 13, as appropriate

Cables in building voids:

15	Sheathed cables installed directly in a thermally insulating wall or above a thermally insulating ceiling, the cable being in contact with a thermally conductive surface on one side (otherwise as Reference Method 4)		Method 4 **or** **Method 15 for cable type covered by Table 4D5A.**

Installation method		Examples	Appropriate Reference Method for determining current-carrying capacity
Number	Description		
1	2	3	4
16	Sheathed cables in ducts or voids formed by the building structure, other than thermally insulating materials		Method 4 Where the cable has a diameter D_e and the duct has a diameter not greater than 5 D_e or a perimeter not greater than 20 D_e Method 3 Where the duct has either a diameter greater than 5 D_e or a perimeter greater than 20 D_e NOTE 1 - Where the perimeter is greater than 60 D_e, installation Methods 18 to 20, as appropriate, should be used. NOTE 2 - D_e is the overall cable diameter. For groups of cables D_e is the sum of the cable diameters.

Cables in trenches:

Number	Description	Examples	Appropriate Reference Method for determining current-carrying capacity
17	Cables supported on the wall of an open or ventilated trench, with spacings as indicated for Reference Method 12 or 13 as appropriate		Method 12 or 13, as appropriate
18	**Cables in enclosed trench 450 mm wide by 300 mm deep (minimum dimensions) including 100 mm cover**	Two to six single-core cables with surfaces separated by a minimum of one cable diameter. One or two groups of three single-core cables in trefoil formation. One to four 2-core cables or one to three 3 or 4 core cables with all cables separated by a minimum of 50 mm	**Method 18 Use rating factors in Table 4B3**

213

Installation method		Examples	Appropriate Reference Method for determining current-carrying capacity
Number	Description		
1	2	3	4
19	**Cables in enclosed trench 450 mm wide by 600 mm deep (minimum dimensions) including 100 mm cover**	Six to twelve single-core cables arranged in flat groups of two or three on the vertical trench wall with cables separated by one cable diameter and a minimum of 50 mm between groups or two to four groups of three single-core cables in trefoil formation with a minimum of 50 mm between trefoil formations or four to eight cables of 2-core or three to six cables of 3 or 4 cores with cables separated by a minimum of 75 mm. All cables spaced at least 25 mm from the trench wall.	**Method 19** **Use rating factors in Table 4B3**

Installation method		Examples	Appropriate Reference Method for determining current-carrying capacity
Number	Description		
1	2	3	4
20	**Cables in enclosed trench 600 mm wide by 760 mm deep (minimum dimensions) including 100 mm cover**	Twelve to twenty four single-core cables arranged in either flat formation of two or three cables in a group with cables separated by one cable diameter and each cable group separated by a minimum of 50 mm either horizontally or vertically or single-core cables in trefoil formation with each group or trefoil formation separated by a minimum of 50 mm either horizontally or vertically. or eight to sixteen 2-core cables or six to twelve cables of 3 or 4 cores with cables separated by a minimum of 75 mm either horizontally or vertically. All cables spaced at least 25 mm from trench wall.	**Method 20** **Use rating factors in Table 4B3**

* Larger spacing to be used where practicable.

TABLE 4A2
Schedule of appropriate current rating tables

Specification Number	Specification Title	Applicable Current Rating Tables	Conductor Operating Temperature
BS 5467 : 1997	Specification for 600/1000 V and 1900/3300 V armoured electric cables having thermosetting insulation.	4E3, 4E4, 4L3, 4L4	90 °C
BS 6004 : 2000	Electric cables. PVC insulated, non-armoured cables for voltages up to and including 450/750 V, for electric power, lighting and internal wiring.	4D1, 4D2 4E1	70 °C, 90 °C
	PVC insulated and sheathed flat cable with protective conductor to Table 8.	4D5	70 °C
BS 6207-1 : 1995	Mineral insulated cables with a rated voltage not exceeding 750 V.	4J1, 4J2	70 °C*, 105 °C*
BS 6346 : 1997	Specification for 600/1000 V and 1900/3300 V armoured electric cables having pvc insulation.	4D3, 4D4, 4K3, 4K4	70 °C
BS 6500 : 2000	Electric cables. Flexible cords rated up to 300/500 V, for use with appliances and equipment intended for domestic, office and similar environments.	4H3	60 °C, 90 °C
BS 6724 : 1997	Specification for 600/1000 V and 1900/3300 V armoured electric cables having thermosetting insulation and low emission of smoke and corrosive gases when affected by fire.	4E3, 4E4, 4L3, 4L4	90 °C
BS 6883 : 1999	Elastomer insulated cables for fixed wiring in ships and on mobile and fixed offshore units. Requirements and test methods.	4F1, 4F2	85 °C
BS 7211 : 1998	Specification for thermosetting insulated cables (non-armoured) for electric power and lighting with low emission of smoke and corrosive gases when affected by fire.	4E1, 4E2	90 °C
BS 7629-1 : 1997	Specification for 300/500 V fire-resistant electric cables having low emission of smoke and corrosive gases when affected by fire. Multicore cables.	4D2	70 °C
BS 7846 : 2000	Electric cables. 600/1000 V armoured fire-resistant electric cables having thermosetting insulation and low emission of smoke and corrosive gases when affected by fire.	4E4	90 °C
BS 7889 : 1997	Specification for 600/1000 V single-core unarmoured electric cables having thermosetting insulation.	4E1, 4L1	90 °C
BS 7919 : 2001	Electric cables. Flexible cables rated up to 450/750 V, for use with appliances and equipment intended for industrial and similar environments.	4H1, 4H2 4H3	60 °C, 110 °C
BS 8436 : 2004	300/500 V screened electric cables having low emission of smoke and corrosive gases when affected by fire, for use in thin partitions and building voids.	4D2	70 °C
BS EN 60702-1 : 2002	Mineral insulated cables and their terminations with a rated voltage not exceeding 750 V. Cables.	4J1, 4J2	70 °C*, 105 °C*

* Sheath operating temperature

Current rating tables 4K1, 4K2 and 4L2 are not listed in the table as currently there are no British Standards for these particular aluminium cable constructions.

Correction factors for groups of more than one circuit of single-core cables, or more than one multicore cable (to be applied to the corresponding current-carrying capacity for a single circuit in Tables 4D1 to 4D4, 4E1 to 4E4, 4F1 and 4F2, 4J1, 4K1 to 4K4, 4L1 to 4L4)**

Reference method of installation (see Table 4A1)		Correction factor (Cg)													
		Number of circuits or multicore cables													
		2	3	4	5	6	7	8	9	10	12	14	16	18	20
Enclosed (Method 3 or 4) or bunched and clipped direct to a non-metallic surface (Method 1) *CONDUIT*		0.80	0.70	0.65	0.60	0.57	0.54	0.52	0.50	0.48	0.45	0.43	0.41	0.39	0.38
Single layer clipped to a non-metallic surface (Method 1)	Touching	0.85	0.79	0.75	0.73	0.72	0.72	0.71	0.70	-	-	-	-	-	-
	Spaced*	0.94	0.90	0.90	0.90	0.90	0.90	0.90	0.90	0.90	0.90	0.90	0.90	0.90	0.90
Single layer *multicore* on a perforated metal cable tray, vertical or horizontal (Method 11)	Touching	0.86	0.81	0.77	0.75	0.74	0.73	0.73	0.72	0.71	0.70	-	-	-	-
	Spaced*#	0.91	0.89	0.88	0.87	0.87	-	-	-	-	-	-	-	-	-
Single layer *single-core* on a perforated metal cable tray, touching (Method 11)	Horizontal	0.90	0.85	-	-	-	-	-	-	-	-	-	-	-	-
	Vertical	0.85	-	-	-	-	-	-	-	-	-	-	-	-	-
Single layer multicore touching on ladder supports (Method 13)		0.86	0.82	0.80	0.79	0.78	0.78	0.78	0.77	-	-	-	-	-	-

* Spaced by a clearance between adjacent surfaces of at least one cable diameter (De). Where the horizontal clearance between adjacent cables exceeds 2 De no correction factor need be applied.

** When cables having differing conductor operating temperatures are grouped together, the current rating shall be based upon the lowest operating temperature of any cable in the group.

\- Correction factor not tabulated.

\# Not applicable to mineral insulated cables, see Table 4B2.

TABLE 4B2
Correction factors for mineral insulated cables installed on perforated tray, (to be applied to the corresponding current-carrying capacity for single circuits for Reference Method 11 in Table 4J1A)

Tray orientation	Arrangement of cables	Number of trays	Number of multicore cables or circuits					
			1	2	3	4	6	9
Horizontal	Multiconductor cables touching	1	1.0	0.90	0.80	0.80	0.75	0.75
Horizontal	Multiconductor cables spaced ‡	1	1.0	1.0	1.0	0.95	0.90	-
Vertical	Multiconductor cables touching	1	1.0	0.90	0.80	0.75	0.75	0.70
Vertical	Multiconductor cables spaced ‡	1	1.0	0.90	0.90	0.90	0.85	-
Horizontal	Single conductor cables trefoil separated ‡‡	1	1.0	1.0	0.95			
Vertical	Single conductor cables trefoil separated ‡‡	1	1.0	0.90	0.90			

‡ Spaced by a clearance between adjacent surfaces of at least one cable diameter (De).

‡‡ Separated by a clearance between adjacent surfaces of at least two cable diameters (2 De).

\- Correction factor not tabulated.

NOTES to Tables 4B1 and 4B2

1. The factors in the table are applicable to groups of cables all of one size. The value of current derived from application of the appropriate factors is the maximum current to be carried by any of the cables in the group.

2. If, due to known operating conditions, a cable is expected to carry not more than 30 % of its *grouped* rating, it may be ignored for the purpose of obtaining the rating factor for the rest of the group.
   For example, a group of N loaded cables would normally require a group reduction factor of Cg applied to the tabulated It. However, if M cables in the group carry loads which are not greater than 0.3 CgIt amperes the other cables can be sized by using the group rating factor corresponding to (N-M) cables.

3. When cables having differing conductor operating temperatures are grouped together, the current rating shall be based on the lowest operating temperature of any cable in the group.

4. Where the horizontal clearance between adjacent cables exceeds 2 De, no correction factor need be applied.

TABLE 4B3
Correction factors for cables installed in enclosed trenches
(Installation Methods 18, 19 and 20 of Table 4A1)*

The correction factors tabulated below relate to the disposition of cables illustrated in items 18 to 20 of Table 4A1 and are applicable to the current-carrying capacities for Reference Methods 12 or 13 of Table 4A1 as given in the relevant tables of this appendix.

	Correction factor									
	Installation Method 18				Installation Method 19			Installation Method 20		
Conductor cross-sectional area	2 single-core cables, or 1 three- or four-core cable	3 single-core cables, or 2 two-core cables	4 single-core cables, or 2 three- or four-core cables	6 single-core cables, 4 two-core cables, or 3 three- or four-core cables	6 single-core cables, 4 two-core cables, or 3 three- or four-core cables	8 single-core cables, or 4 three- or four-core cables	12 single-core cables, 8 two-core cables, or 6 three- or four-core cables	12 single-core cables, 8 two-core cables, or 6 three- or four-core cables	18 single-core cables, 12 two-core cables, or 9 three- or four-core cables	24 single-core cables, 16 two-core cables, or 12 three- or four-core cables
1	2	3	4	5	6	7	8	9	10	11
(mm^2)										
4	0.93	0.90	0.87	0.82	0.86	0.83	0.76	0.81	0.74	0.69
6	0.92	0.89	0.86	0.81	0.86	0.82	0.75	0.80	0.73	0.68
10	0.91	0.88	0.85	0.80	0.85	0.80	0.74	0.78	0.72	0.66
16	0.91	0.87	0.84	0.78	0.83	0.78	0.71	0.76	0.70	0.64
25	0.90	0.86	0.82	0.76	0.81	0.76	0.69	0.74	0.67	0.62
35	0.89	0.85	0.81	0.75	0.80	0.74	0.68	0.72	0.66	0.60
50	0.88	0.84	0.79	0.74	0.78	0.73	0.66	0.71	0.64	0.59
70	0.87	0.82	0.78	0.72	0.77	0.72	0.64	0.70	0.62	0.57
95	0.86	0.81	0.76	0.70	0.75	0.70	0.63	0.68	0.60	0.55
120	0.85	0.80	0.75	0.69	0.73	0.68	0.61	0.66	0.58	0.53
150	0.84	0.78	0.74	0.67	0.72	0.67	0.59	0.64	0.57	0.51
185	0.83	0.77	0.73	0.65	0.70	0.65	0.58	0.63	0.55	0.49
240	0.82	0.76	0.71	0.63	0.69	0.63	0.56	0.61	0.53	0.48
300	0.81	0.74	0.69	0.62	0.68	0.62	0.54	0.59	0.52	0.46
400	0.80	0.73	0.67	0.59	0.66	0.60	0.52	0.57	0.50	0.44
500	0.78	0.72	0.66	0.58	0.64	0.58	0.51	0.56	0.48	0.43
630	0.77	0.71	0.65	0.56	0.63	0.57	0.49	0.54	0.47	0.41

* When cables having different conductor operating temperatures are grouped together the current rating shall be based on the lowest operating temperature of any cable in the group.

NOTES:

1. The factors in Table 4B3 are applicable to groups of cables all of one size. The value of current derived from application of the appropriate factors is the maximum current to be carried by any of the cables in the group.

2. If, due to known operating conditions, a cable is expected to carry not more than 30% of its *grouped* rating, it may be ignored for the purpose of obtaining the rating factor for the rest of the group.

3. When cables having different conductor operating temperatures are grouped together the current rating shall be based on the lowest operating temperature of any cable in the group.

4. When the number of cables used differs from those stated in the table, the derating factor for the next higher stated number of cables shall be used.

TABLE 4C1

Correction factors for ambient temperature where protection is against short-circuit

NOTE: This table applies where the associated overcurrent protective device is intended to provide short-circuit protection only. Except where the device is a semi-enclosed fuse to BS 3036 the table also applies where the device is intended to provide overload protection.

Type of insulation	Operating temperature	Ambient temperature (°C)														
		25	30	35	40	45	50	55	60	65	70	75	80	85	90	95
Thermosetting (rubber) (flexible cables only)	60 °C	1.04	1.0	0.91	0.82	0.71	0.58	0.41	-	-	-	-	-	-	-	-
Thermoplastic (General purpose pvc)	70 °C	1.03	1.0	0.94	0.87	0.79	0.71	0.61	0.50	0.35	-	-	-	-	-	-
Paper	80 °C	1.02	1.0	0.95	0.89	0.84	0.77	0.71	0.63	0.55	0.45	0.32	-	-	-	-
Thermosetting (rubber)	85 °C	1.02	1.0	0.95	0.90	0.85	0.80	0.74	0.67	0.60	0.52	0.43	0.30	-	-	-
Thermoplastic (high temperature pvc)*	90 °C	1.03	1.0	0.97	0.94	0.91	0.87	0.84	0.80	0.76	0.71	0.61	0.50	0.35	-	-
Thermosetting	90 °C	1.02	1.0	0.96	0.91	0.87	0.82	0.76	0.71	0.65	0.58	0.50	0.41	0.29	-	-
Mineral	70 °C sheath	1.03	1.0	0.93	0.85	0.77	0.67	0.57	0.45	0.31	-	-	-	-	-	-
	105 °C sheath	1.02	1.0	0.96	0.92	0.88	0.84	0.80	0.75	0.70	0.65	0.60	0.54	0.47	0.40	0.32

NOTES:
1. Correction factors for flexible cords and for 85 °C and 180 °C thermosetting (rubber) insulated flexible cables are given in the relevant table of current-carrying capacity.
2. This table also applies when determining the current-carrying capacity of a cable.
3. * These factors are applicable only to ratings in columns 2 to 5 of Table 4D1A.

TABLE 4C2

Correction factors for ambient temperature where the overload protective device is a semi-enclosed fuse to BS 3036.

Type of insulation	Operating temperature	Ambient temperature (°C)														
		25	30	35	40	45	50	55	60	65	70	75	80	85	90	95
Thermosetting (rubber) (flexible cables only)	60 °C	1.04	1.0	0.96	0.91	0.87	0.79	0.56	-	-	-	-	-	-	-	-
Thermoplastic (General purpose pvc)	70 °C	1.03	1.0	0.97	0.94	0.91	0.87	0.84	0.69	0.48	-	-	-	-	-	-
Paper	80 °C	1.02	1.0	0.97	0.95	0.92	0.90	0.87	0.84	0.76	0.62	0.43	-	-	-	-
Thermosetting (rubber)	85 °C	1.02	1.0	0.97	0.95	0.93	0.91	0.88	0.86	0.83	0.71	0.58	0.41	-	-	-
Thermoplastic (high temperature pvc)*	90 °C	1.03	1.0	0.97	0.94	0.91	0.87	0.84	0.80	0.76	0.72	0.68	0.63	0.49	-	-
Thermosetting	90 °C	1.02	1.0	0.98	0.95	0.93	0.91	0.89	0.87	0.85	0.79	0.69	0.56	0.39	-	-
Mineral: bare and exposed to touch or pvc covered	70 °C sheath	1.03	1.0	0.96	0.93	0.89	0.86	0.79	0.62	0.42	-	-	-	-	-	-
Mineral: bare and not exposed to touch	105 °C sheath	1.02	1.0	0.98	0.96	0.93	0.91	0.89	0.86	0.84	0.82	0.79	0.77	0.64	0.55	0.43

NOTES:
1. Correction factors for flexible cords and for 85 °C and 180 °C thermosetting (rubber) insulated flexible cables are given in the relevant table of current-carrying capacity.
2. * These factors are applicable only to ratings in columns 2 to 5 of Table 4D1A.

TABLE 4D1A

Single-core 70 °C thermoplastic (pvc) insulated cables, non-armoured, with or without sheath
(COPPER CONDUCTORS)

Ambient temperature: 30 °C
Conductor operating temperature: 70 °C

CURRENT-CARRYING CAPACITY (amperes):

Conductor cross-sectional area	Reference Method 4 (enclosed in conduit in thermally insulating wall etc.)		Reference Method 3 (enclosed in conduit on a wall or in trunking etc.)		Reference Method 1 (clipped direct)		Reference Method 11 (on a perforated cable tray horizontal or vertical)		Reference Method 12 (free air)		
	2 cables, single-phase a.c. or d.c.	3 or 4 cables, three-phase a.c.	2 cables, single-phase a.c. or d.c.	3 or 4 cables, three-phase a.c.	2 cables, single-phase a.c. or d.c. flat and touching	3 or 4 cables, three-phase a.c. flat and touching or trefoil	2 cables, single-phase a.c. or d.c. flat and touching	3 or 4 cables, three-phase a.c. flat and touching or trefoil	Horizontal flat spaced — 2 cables, single-phase a.c. or d.c. or 3 cables three-phase a.c.	Vertical flat spaced — 2 cables, single-phase a.c. or d.c. or 3 cables three-phase a.c.	Trefoil — 3 cables trefoil, three-phase a.c.
1	2	3	4	5	6	7	8	9	10	11	12
(mm²)	(A)	(A)	(A)	(A)	(A)	(A)	(A)	(A)	(A)	(A)	(A)
1	11	10.5	13.5	12	15.5	14	-	-	-	-	-
1.5	14.5	13.5	17.5	15.5	20	18	-	-	-	-	-
2.5	20	18	24	21	27	25	-	-	-	-	-
4	26	24	32	28	37	33	-	-	-	-	-
6	34	31	41	36	47	43	-	-	-	-	-
10	46	42	57	50	65	59	-	-	-	-	-
16	61	56	76	68	87	79	-	-	-	-	-
25	80	73	101	89	114	104	126	112	146	130	110
35	99	89	125	110	141	129	156	141	181	162	137
50	119	108	151	134	182	167	191	172	219	197	167
70	151	136	192	171	234	214	246	223	281	254	216
95	182	164	232	207	284	261	300	273	341	311	264
120	210	188	269	239	330	303	349	318	396	362	308
150	240	216	300	262	381	349	404	369	456	419	356
185	273	245	341	296	436	400	463	424	521	480	409
240	320	286	400	346	515	472	549	504	615	569	485
300	367	328	458	394	594	545	635	584	709	659	561
400	-	-	546	467	694	634	732	679	852	795	656
500	-	-	626	533	792	723	835	778	982	920	749
630	-	-	720	611	904	826	953	892	1138	1070	855
800	-	-	-	-	1030	943	1086	1020	1265	1188	971
1000	-	-	-	-	1154	1058	1216	1149	1420	1337	1079

TABLE 4D1B

VOLTAGE DROP (per ampere per metre): Conductor operating temperature: 70 °C

Conductor cross-sectional area	2 cables d.c.	2 cables, single-phase a.c.									3 or 4 cables, three-phase a.c.											
		Reference Methods 3 & 4 (enclosed in conduit etc. in or on a wall)			Reference Methods 1 & 11 (clipped direct or on trays, touching)			Reference Method 12 (spaced*)			Reference Methods 3 & 4 (enclosed in conduit etc. in or on a wall)			Reference Methods 1, 11 & 12 (in trefoil)			Reference Methods 1 & 11 (flat and touching)			Reference Method 12 (flat spaced*)		
(mm²)	(mV/A/m)	(mV/A/m)			(mV/A/m)			(mV/A/m)			(mV/A/m)			(mV/A/m)			(mV/A/m)			(mV/A/m)		
1	2	3			4			5			6			7			8			9		
		r	x	z	r	x	z	r	x	z	r	x	z	r	x	z	r	x	z	r	x	z
1	44	44			44			44			38			38			38			38		
1.5	29	29			29			29			25			25			25			25		
2.5	18	18			18			18			15			15			15			15		
4	11	11			11			11			9.5			9.5			9.5			9.5		
6	7.3	7.3			7.3			7.3			6.4			6.4			6.4			6.4		
10	4.4	4.4			4.4			4.4			3.8			3.8			3.8			3.8		
16	2.8	2.8			2.8			2.8			2.4			2.4			2.4			2.4		
25	1.75	1.80	0.33	1.80	1.75	0.20	1.75	1.75	0.29	1.80	1.50	0.29	1.55	1.50	0.175	1.50	1.50	0.25	1.55	1.50	0.32	1.55
35	1.25	1.30	0.31	1.30	1.25	0.195	1.25	1.25	0.28	1.30	1.10	0.27	1.10	1.10	0.170	1.10	1.10	0.24	1.10	1.10	0.32	1.15
50	0.93	0.95	0.30	1.00	0.93	0.190	0.95	0.93	0.28	0.97	0.81	0.26	0.85	0.80	0.165	0.82	0.80	0.24	0.84	0.80	0.32	0.86
70	0.63	0.65	0.29	0.72	0.63	0.185	0.66	0.63	0.27	0.69	0.56	0.25	0.61	0.55	0.160	0.57	0.55	0.24	0.60	0.55	0.31	0.63
95	0.46	0.49	0.28	0.56	0.47	0.180	0.50	0.47	0.27	0.54	0.42	0.24	0.48	0.41	0.155	0.43	0.41	0.23	0.47	0.40	0.31	0.51
120	0.36	0.39	0.27	0.47	0.37	0.175	0.41	0.37	0.26	0.45	0.33	0.23	0.41	0.32	0.150	0.36	0.32	0.23	0.40	0.32	0.30	0.44
150	0.29	0.31	0.27	0.41	0.30	0.175	0.34	0.29	0.26	0.39	0.27	0.23	0.36	0.26	0.150	0.30	0.26	0.23	0.34	0.26	0.30	0.40
185	0.23	0.25	0.27	0.37	0.24	0.170	0.29	0.24	0.26	0.35	0.22	0.23	0.32	0.21	0.145	0.26	0.21	0.22	0.31	0.21	0.30	0.36
240	0.180	0.195	0.26	0.33	0.185	0.165	0.25	0.185	0.25	0.31	0.17	0.23	0.29	0.160	0.145	0.22	0.160	0.22	0.27	0.160	0.29	0.34
300	0.145	0.160	0.26	0.31	0.150	0.165	0.22	0.150	0.25	0.29	0.14	0.23	0.27	0.130	0.140	0.190	0.130	0.22	0.25	0.130	0.29	0.32
400	0.105	0.130	0.26	0.29	0.120	0.160	0.20	0.115	0.25	0.27	0.12	0.22	0.25	0.105	0.140	0.175	0.105	0.21	0.24	0.100	0.29	0.31
500	0.086	0.110	0.26	0.28	0.098	0.155	0.185	0.093	0.24	0.26	0.10	0.22	0.25	0.086	0.135	0.160	0.086	0.21	0.23	0.081	0.29	0.30
630	0.068	0.094	0.25	0.27	0.081	0.155	0.175	0.076	0.24	0.25	0.08	0.22	0.24	0.072	0.135	0.150	0.072	0.21	0.22	0.066	0.28	0.29
800	0.053	-	-		0.068	0.150	0.165	0.061	0.24	0.25	-	-		0.060	0.130	0.145	0.060	0.21	0.22	0.053	0.28	0.29
1000	0.042	-	-		0.059	0.150	0.160	0.050	0.24	0.24	-	-		0.052	0.130	0.140	0.052	0.20	0.21	0.044	0.28	0.28

NOTE: * Spacings larger than those specified in Method 12 (see Table 4A1) will result in larger voltage drop.

221

TABLE 4D2A

Multicore 70 °C thermoplastic (pvc) insulated and thermosetting insulated cables, non-armoured
(COPPER CONDUCTORS)

Ambient temperature: 30 °C
Conductor operating temperature: 70 °C

CURRENT-CARRYING CAPACITY (amperes):

Conductor cross-sectional area	Reference Method 4 (enclosed in an insulated wall, etc.)		Reference Method 3 (enclosed in conduit on a wall or ceiling, or in trunking)		Reference Method 1 (clipped direct)		Reference Method 11 (on a perforated cable tray) or Reference Method 13 (free air)	
	1 two-core cable*, single-phase a.c. or d.c.	1 three-core cable* or 1 four-core cable, three-phase a.c.	1 two-core cable*, single-phase a.c. or d.c.	1 three-core cable* or 1 four-core cable, three-phase a.c.	1 two-core cable*, single-phase a.c. or d.c.	1 three-core cable* or 1 four-core cable, three-phase a.c.	1 two-core cable*, single-phase a.c. or d.c.	1 three-core cable* or 1 four-core cable, three-phase a.c.
1	2	3	4	5	6	7	8	9
(mm²)	(A)	(A)	(A)	(A)	(A)	(A)	(A)	(A)
1	11	10	13	11.5	15	13.5	17	14.5
1.5	14	13	16.5	15	19.5	17.5	22	18.5
2.5	18.5	17.5	23	20	27	24	30	25
4	25	23	30	27	36	32	40	34
6	32	29	38	34	46	41	51	43
10	43	39	52	46	63	57	70	60
16	57	52	69	62	85	76	94	80
25	75	68	90	80	112	96	119	101
35	92	83	111	99	138	119	148	126
50	110	99	133	118	168	144	180	153
70	139	125	168	149	213	184	232	196
95	167	150	201	179	258	223	282	238
120	192	172	232	206	299	259	328	276
150	219	196	258	225	344	299	379	319
185	248	223	294	255	392	341	434	364
240	291	261	344	297	461	403	514	430
300	334	298	394	339	530	464	593	497
400	-	-	470	402	634	557	715	597

NOTES:
1. **Where the conductor is to be protected by a semi-enclosed fuse to BS 3036, see item 6.2 of the preface to this appendix.**
2. Circular conductors are assumed for sizes up to and including 16 mm². Values for larger sizes relate to shaped conductors and may safely be applied to circular conductors.
3. * With or without a protective conductor.

TABLE 4D2B

VOLTAGE DROP (per ampere per metre):   Conductor operating temperature: 70 °C

Conductor cross-sectional area	Two-core cable, d.c.	Two-core cable, single-phase a.c.			Three- or four-core cable, three-phase a.c.		
1	2	3			4		
(mm²)	(mV/A/m)	(mV/A/m)			(mV/A/m)		
1	44	44			38		
1.5	29	29			25		
2.5	18	18			15		
4	11	11			9.5		
6	7.3	7.3			6.4		
10	4.4	4.4			3.8		
16	2.8	2.8			2.4		
		r	x	z	r	x	z
25	1.75	1.75	0.170	1.75	1.50	0.145	1.50
35	1.25	1.25	0.165	1.25	1.10	0.145	1.10
50	0.93	0.93	0.165	0.94	0.80	0.140	0.81
70	0.63	0.63	0.160	0.65	0.55	0.140	0.57
95	0.46	0.47	0.155	0.50	0.41	0.135	0.43
120	0.36	0.38	0.155	0.41	0.33	0.135	0.35
150	0.29	0.30	0.155	0.34	0.26	0.130	0.29
185	0.23	0.25	0.150	0.29	0.21	0.130	0.25
240	0.180	0.190	0.150	0.24	0.165	0.130	0.21
300	0.145	0.155	0.145	0.21	0.135	0.130	0.185
400	0.105	0.115	0.145	0.185	0.100	0.125	0.160

COPPER CONDUCTORS

NOTE:
Where the conductor is to be protected by a semi-enclosed fuse to BS 3036, see item 6.2 of the preface to this appendix.

TABLE 4D3A
**Single-core 70 °C armoured thermoplastic (pvc) insulated cables
(non-magnetic armour)
(COPPER CONDUCTORS)**

Ambient temperature: 30 °C
Conductor operating temperature: 70 °C

CURRENT-CARRYING CAPACITY (amperes):

	Reference Method 1 (clipped direct)		Reference Method 11 (on perforated cable tray)		Reference Method 12 (free air)						
					2 cables, single-phase a.c.		2 cables, d.c.		3 or 4 cables, three-phase a.c.		
Conductor cross-sectional area	2 cables, single-phase a.c. or d.c. flat and touching	3 or 4 cables, three-phase a.c. flat and touching	2 cables, single-phase a.c. or d.c. flat and touching	3 or 4 cables, three-phase a.c. flat and touching	Horizontal flat spaced	Vertical flat spaced	Horizontal spaced	Vertical spaced	Horizontal flat spaced	Vertical flat spaced	3 cables trefoil
1	2	3	4	5	6	7	8	9	10	11	12
(mm²)	(A)	(A)	(A)	(A)	(A)	(A)	(A)	(A)	(A)	(A)	(A)
50	193	179	205	189	229	217	229	216	230	212	181
70	245	225	259	238	287	272	294	279	286	263	231
95	296	269	313	285	349	332	357	340	338	313	280
120	342	309	360	327	401	383	415	396	385	357	324
150	393	352	413	373	449	429	479	458	436	405	373
185	447	399	469	422	511	489	548	525	490	456	425
240	525	465	550	492	593	568	648	622	566	528	501
300	594	515	624	547	668	640	748	719	616	578	567
400	687	575	723	618	737	707	885	851	674	632	657
500	763	622	805	673	810	777	1035	997	721	676	731
630	843	669	891	728	893	856	1218	1174	771	723	809
800	919	710	976	777	943	905	1441	1390	824	772	886
1000	975	737	1041	808	1008	967	1685	1627	872	816	945

VOLTAGE DROP (per ampere per metre):

TABLE 4D3B

Conductor operating temperature: 70 °C

Conductor cross-sectional area	2 cables d.c.	2 cables, single-phase a.c.						3 or 4 cables, three-phase a.c.								
		Reference Methods 1 & 11 (touching)			Reference Method 12 (spaced*)			Reference Methods 1, 11 & 12 (in trefoil touching)			Reference Methods 1 & 11 (flat and touching)			Reference Method 12 (flat spaced*)		
1	2	3			4			5			6			7		
(mm²)	(mV/A/m)	(mV/A/m)			(mV/A/m)			(mV/A/m)			(mV/A/m)			(mV/A/m)		
		r	x	z	r	x	z	r	x	z	r	x	z	r	x	z
50	0.93	0.93	0.22	0.95	0.92	0.30	0.97	0.80	0.190	0.82	0.79	0.26	0.84	0.79	0.34	0.86
70	0.63	0.64	0.21	0.68	0.66	0.29	0.72	0.56	0.180	0.58	0.57	0.25	0.62	0.59	0.32	0.68
95	0.46	0.48	0.20	0.52	0.51	0.28	0.58	0.42	0.175	0.45	0.44	0.25	0.50	0.47	0.31	0.57
120	0.36	0.39	0.195	0.43	0.42	0.28	0.50	0.33	0.170	0.37	0.36	0.24	0.43	0.40	0.30	0.50
150	0.29	0.31	0.190	0.37	0.34	0.27	0.44	0.27	0.165	0.32	0.30	0.24	0.38	0.34	0.30	0.45
185	0.23	0.26	0.190	0.32	0.29	0.27	0.39	0.22	0.160	0.27	0.25	0.23	0.34	0.29	0.29	0.41
240	0.180	0.20	0.180	0.27	0.23	0.26	0.35	0.175	0.160	0.23	0.20	0.23	0.30	0.24	0.28	0.37
300	0.145	0.160	0.180	0.24	0.190	0.26	0.32	0.140	0.155	0.21	0.165	0.22	0.28	0.20	0.28	0.34
400	0.105	0.140	0.175	0.22	0.180	0.24	0.30	0.120	0.130	0.195	0.160	0.21	0.26	0.21	0.25	0.32
500	0.086	0.120	0.170	0.21	0.165	0.23	0.29	0.105	0.145	0.180	0.145	0.20	0.25	0.190	0.24	0.30
630	0.068	0.105	0.165	0.195	0.150	0.22	0.27	0.091	0.145	0.170	0.135	0.195	0.23	0.175	0.22	0.28
800	0.053	0.095	0.160	0.185	0.145	0.21	0.25	0.082	0.140	0.160	0.125	0.180	0.22	0.170	0.195	0.26
1000	0.042	0.091	0.155	0.180	0.140	0.190	0.24	0.079	0.135	0.155	0.125	0.165	0.21	0.165	0.170	0.24

NOTE: * Spacings larger than those specified in Method 12 (see Table 4A1) will result in larger voltage drop.

225

TABLE 4D4A

**Multicore 70 °C armoured thermoplastic (pvc) insulated cables
(COPPER CONDUCTORS)**

Ambient temperature: 30 °C

Conductor operating temperature: 70 °C

CURRENT-CARRYING CAPACITY (amperes):

NOTE:

Where the conductor is to be protected by a semi-enclosed fuse to BS 3036, see item 6.2 of the preface to this appendix.

Conductor cross-sectional area	Reference Method 1 (clipped direct)		Reference Method 11 (on a perforated horizontal or vertical cable tray) or Reference Method 13 (free air)	
	1 two-core cable, single-phase a.c. or d.c.	1 three- or four-core cable, three-phase a.c.	1 two-core cable, single-phase a.c. or d.c.	1 three- or four-core cable, three-phase a.c.
1	2	3	4	5
(mm²)	(A)	(A)	(A)	(A)
1.5	21	18	22	19
2.5	28	25	31	26
4	38	33	41	35
6	49	42	53	45
10	67	58	72	62
16	89	77	97	83
25	118	102	128	110
35	145	125	157	135
50	175	151	190	163
70	222	192	241	207
95	269	231	291	251
120	310	267	336	290
150	356	306	386	332
185	405	348	439	378
240	476	409	516	445
300	547	469	592	510
400	621	540	683	590

TABLE 4D4B

VOLTAGE DROP (per ampere per metre): Conductor operating temperature: 70 °C

Conductor cross-sectional area	Two-core cable, d.c.	Two-core cable, single-phase a.c.			Three- or four-core cable, three-phase a.c.		
1	2	3			4		
(mm²)	(mV/A/m)	(mV/A/m)			(mV/A/m)		
	29	29			25		
		r	x	z	r	x	z
2.5	18	18			15		
4	11	11			9.5		
6	7.3	7.3			6.4		
10	4.4	4.4			3.8		
16	2.8	2.8			2.4		
25	1.75	1.75	0.170	1.75	1.50	0.145	1.50
35	1.25	1.25	0.165	1.25	1.10	0.145	1.10
50	0.93	0.93	0.165	0.94	0.80	0.140	0.81
70	0.63	0.63	0.160	0.65	0.55	0.140	0.57
95	0.46	0.47	0.155	0.50	0.41	0.135	0.43
120	0.36	0.38	0.155	0.41	0.33	0.135	0.35
150	0.29	0.30	0.155	0.34	0.26	0.130	0.29
185	0.23	0.25	0.150	0.29	0.21	0.130	0.25
240	0.180	0.190	0.150	0.24	0.165	0.130	0.21
300	0.145	0.155	0.145	0.21	0.135	0.130	0.185
400	0.105	0.115	0.145	0.185	0.100	0.125	0.160

NOTES:

1. Where the conductor is to be protected by a semi-enclosed fuse to BS 3036, see item 6.2 of the preface to this appendix.

2. * These methods are regarded as Reference Methods for the cable types specified by the Table 4A1.

TABLE 4D5A

70 °C thermoplastic (pvc) insulated and sheathed flat cable with protective conductor (COPPER CONDUCTORS)

CURRENT-CARRYING CAPACITY (amperes):

Ambient temperature: 30 °C
Conductor operating temperature: 70 °C

Conductor cross-sectional area	Installation Method 6* (enclosed in conduit in an insulated wall)	Installation Method 15* (installed directly in an insulated wall)	Reference Method 1 (clipped direct)	Voltage drop (per ampere per metre)
		1 two-core cable, single-phase a.c. or d.c.		
1	2	3	4	5
(mm²)	(A)	(A)	(A)	(mV/A/m)
1	11.5	12	16	44
1.5	14.5	15	20	29
2.5	20	21	27	18
4	26	27	37	11
6	32	35	47	7.3
10	44	47	64	4.4
16	57	63	85	2.8

THIS PAGE HAS BEEN INTENTIONALLY LEFT BLANK

TABLE 4E1A

Single-core 90 °C thermosetting insulated cables, unarmoured, with or without sheath
(COPPER CONDUCTORS)

Ambient temperature: 30 °C
Conductor operating temperature: 90 °C

CURRENT-CARRYING CAPACITY (amperes):

Conductor cross-sectional area	Reference Method 4 (enclosed in conduit in thermally insulating wall etc.)		Reference Method 3 (enclosed in conduit on a wall or in trunking etc.)		Reference Method 1 (clipped direct)		Reference Method 11 (on a perforated cable tray horizontal or vertical)		Reference Method 12 (free air)		
	2 cables, single-phase a.c. or d.c.	3 or 4 cables, three-phase a.c.	2 cables, single-phase a.c. or d.c.	3 or 4 cables, three-phase a.c.	2 cables, single-phase a.c. or d.c. flat and touching	3 or 4 cables, three-phase a.c. flat and touching or trefoil	2 cables, single-phase a.c. or d.c. flat and touching	3 or 4 cables, three-phase a.c. flat and touching or trefoil	Horizontal flat spaced 2 cables, single-phase a.c. or d.c. or 3 cables three-phase	Vertical flat spaced 2 cables, single-phase a.c. or d.c. or 3 cables three-phase	Trefoil 3 cables trefoil, three phase a.c.
	2	3	4	5	6	7	8	9	10	11	12
(mm²)	(A)	(A)	(A)	(A)	(A)	(A)	(A)	(A)	(A)	(A)	(A)
1	14	13	17	15	19	17.5	-	-	-	-	-
1.5	18	17	22	19	25	23	-	-	-	-	-
2.5	24	23	30	26	34	31	-	-	-	-	-
4	33	30	40	35	46	41	-	-	-	-	-
6	43	39	51	45	59	54	-	-	-	-	-
10	58	53	71	63	81	74	-	-	-	-	-
16	76	70	95	85	109	99	-	-	-	-	-
25	100	91	126	111	143	130	158	140	183	163	138
35	124	111	156	138	176	161	195	176	226	203	171
50	149	135	189	168	228	209	239	215	274	246	209
70	189	170	240	214	293	268	308	279	351	318	270
95	228	205	290	259	355	326	375	341	426	389	330
120	263	235	336	299	413	379	436	398	495	453	385
150	300	270	375	328	476	436	505	461	570	524	445
185	341	306	426	370	545	500	579	530	651	600	511
240	400	358	500	433	644	590	686	630	769	711	606
300	459	410	573	493	743	681	794	730	886	824	701
400	-	-	683	584	868	793	915	849	1065	994	820
500	-	-	783	666	990	904	1044	973	1228	1150	936
630	-	-	900	764	1130	1033	1191	1115	1423	1338	1069
800	-	-	-	-	1288	1179	1358	1275	1581	1485	1214
1000	-	-	-	-	1443	1323	1520	1436	1775	1671	1349

NOTES:

1. **Where the conductor is to be protected by a semi-enclosed fuse to BS 3036, see item 6.2 of the preface to this appendix.**

2. The current-carrying capacities in columns 2 to 5 are also applicable to flexible cables where the cables are used in fixed installations.

3. For cable in rigid pvc conduit the values stated in Table 4D1 are applicable (see Regulation 521-05).

4. Where a conductor operates at a temperature exceeding 70 °C it shall be ascertained that the equipment connected to the conductor is suitable for the conductor operating temperature (see Regulation 512-02).

5. Where cables in this table are connected to equipment or accessories designed to operate at a temperature not exceeding 70 °C, the current ratings given in the equivalent table for 70 °C thermoplastic (pvc) insulated cables (Table 4D1A) shall be used (see also Regulation 523-01-01).

TABLE 4E1B

VOLTAGE DROP (per ampere per metre):

Conductor operating temperature: 90 °C

Conductor cross-sectional area (mm²)	2 cables d.c. (mV/A/m)	2 cables, single-phase a.c. — Ref Methods 3 & 4 (enclosed in conduit etc. in or on a wall) (mV/A/m)			Ref Methods 1 & 11 (clipped direct or on trays, touching) (mV/A/m)			Ref Method 12 (spaced*) (mV/A/m)			3 or 4 cables, three-phase a.c. — Ref Methods 3 & 4 (enclosed in conduit etc. in or on a wall) (mV/A/m)			Ref Methods 1, 11 & 12 (in trefoil) (mV/A/m)			Ref Methods 1 & 11 (flat and touching) (mV/A/m)			Ref Method 12 (flat spaced*) (mV/A/m)		
		r	x	z	r	x	z	r	x	z	r	x	z	r	x	z	r	x	z	r	x	z
1	46		46			46			46			40			40			40			40	
1.5	31		31			31			31			27			27			27			27	
2.5	19		19			19			19			16			16			16			16	
4	12		12			12			12			10			10			10			10	
6	7.9		7.9			7.9			7.9			6.8			6.8			6.8			6.8	
10	4.7		4.7			4.7			4.7			4.0			4.0			4.0			4.0	
16	2.9		2.9			2.9			2.9			2.5			2.5			2.5			2.5	
25	1.85	1.85	0.31	1.90	1.85	0.190	1.85	1.85	0.28	1.85	1.60	0.27	1.65	1.60	0.165	1.60	1.60	0.190	1.60	1.60	0.27	1.65
35	1.35	1.35	0.29	1.35	1.35	0.180	1.35	1.35	0.27	1.35	1.15	0.25	1.15	1.15	0.155	1.15	1.15	0.180	1.15	1.15	0.26	1.20
50	0.99	1.00	0.29	1.05	0.99	0.180	1.00	0.99	0.27	1.00	0.87	0.25	0.90	0.86	0.155	0.87	0.86	0.180	0.87	0.86	0.26	0.89
70	0.68	0.70	0.28	0.75	0.68	0.175	0.71	0.68	0.26	0.73	0.60	0.24	0.65	0.59	0.150	0.61	0.59	0.175	0.62	0.59	0.25	0.65
95	0.49	0.51	0.27	0.58	0.49	0.170	0.52	0.49	0.26	0.56	0.44	0.23	0.50	0.43	0.145	0.45	0.43	0.170	0.46	0.43	0.25	0.49
120	0.39	0.41	0.26	0.48	0.39	0.165	0.43	0.39	0.25	0.47	0.35	0.23	0.42	0.34	0.140	0.37	0.34	0.165	0.38	0.34	0.24	0.42
150	0.32	0.33	0.26	0.43	0.32	0.165	0.36	0.32	0.25	0.41	0.29	0.23	0.37	0.28	0.140	0.31	0.28	0.165	0.32	0.28	0.24	0.37
185	0.25	0.27	0.26	0.37	0.25	0.165	0.30	0.25	0.25	0.36	0.23	0.23	0.32	0.22	0.140	0.26	0.22	0.165	0.28	0.22	0.24	0.33
240	0.190	0.21	0.26	0.33	0.23	0.160	0.25	0.195	0.25	0.31	0.185	0.22	0.29	0.170	0.140	0.22	0.170	0.165	0.24	0.170	0.24	0.29
300	0.155	0.175	0.25	0.31	0.150	0.160	0.22	0.155	0.25	0.29	0.150	0.22	0.27	0.140	0.140	0.195	0.135	0.160	0.21	0.135	0.24	0.27
400	0.120	0.140	0.25	0.29	0.130	0.155	0.20	0.125	0.24	0.27	0.125	0.22	0.25	0.110	0.135	0.175	0.110	0.160	0.195	0.110	0.24	0.26
500	0.093	0.120	0.25	0.28	0.105	0.155	0.185	0.098	0.24	0.26	0.100	0.22	0.24	0.090	0.135	0.160	0.088	0.160	0.180	0.085	0.24	0.25
630	0.072	0.100	0.25	0.27	0.086	0.155	0.175	0.078	0.24	0.25	0.088	0.21	0.23	0.074	0.135	0.150	0.071	0.160	0.170	0.068	0.23	0.24
800	0.056	-	-		0.072	0.150	0.170	0.064	0.24	0.25	-			0.062	0.130	0.145	0.059	0.155	0.165	0.055	0.23	0.24
1000	0.045	-	-		0.063	0.150	0.165	0.054	0.24	0.24	-			0.055	0.130	0.140	0.050	0.155	0.165	0.047	0.23	0.24

NOTE: * Spacings larger than those specified in Method 12 (see Table 4A1) will result in larger voltage drop.

COPPER CONDUCTORS

TABLE 4E2A

Multicore 90 °C thermosetting insulated cables, non armoured
(COPPER CONDUCTORS)

CURRENT-CARRYING CAPACITY (amperes):

Ambient temperature: 30 °C
Conductor operating temperature: 90 °C

Conductor cross-sectional area	Reference Method 4 (enclosed in an insulated wall, etc.)		Reference Method 3 (enclosed in conduit on a wall or ceiling, or in trunking)		Reference Method 1 (clipped direct)		Reference Method 11 (on a perforated cable tray) or Reference Method 13 (free air)	
	1 two-core cable*, single-phase a.c. or d.c.	1 three- or four-core cable*, three-phase a.c.	1 two-core cable*, single-phase a.c. or d.c.	1 three- or four-core cable*, three-phase a.c.	1 two-core cable*, single-phase a.c. or d.c.	1 three- or four-core cable*, three-phase a.c.	1 two-core cable*, single-phase a.c. or d.c.	1 three- or four-core cable*, three-phase a.c.
1	2	3	4	5	6	7	8	9
(mm²)	(A)	(A)	(A)	(A)	(A)	(A)	(A)	(A)
1	14.5	13	17	15	19	17	21	18
1.5	18.5	16.5	22	19.5	24	22	26	23
2.5	25	22	30	26	33	30	36	32
4	33	30	40	35	45	40	49	42
6	42	38	51	44	58	52	63	54
10	57	51	69	60	80	71	86	75
16	76	68	91	80	107	96	115	100
25	99	89	119	105	138	119	149	127
35	121	109	146	128	171	147	185	158
50	145	130	175	154	209	179	225	185
70	183	164	221	194	269	229	289	246
95	220	197	265	233	328	278	352	298
120	253	227	305	268	382	322	410	346
150	290	259	334	300	441	371	473	399
185	329	295	384	340	506	424	542	456
240	386	346	459	398	599	500	641	538
300	442	396	532	455	693	576	741	621
400	-	-	625	536	803	667	865	741

NOTES:

1. **Where the conductor is to be protected by a semi-enclosed fuse to BS 3036, see item 6.2 of the preface to this appendix.**

2. Where a conductor operates at a temperature exceeding 70 °C it shall be ascertained that the equipment connected to the conductor is suitable for the conductor operating temperature (see Regulation 512-02).

3. * With or without a protective conductor.

4. For cables in rigid pvc conduit the values stated in Table 4D2 are applicable (see Regulation 521-05).

5. Where cables in this table are connected to equipment or accessories designed to operate at a temperature not exceeding 70 °C, the current ratings given in the equivalent table for 70 °C thermoplastic (pvc) insulated cables (Table 4D2A) shall be used (see also Regulation 523-01-01).

6. Circular conductors are assumed for sizes up to and including 16 mm². Values for larger sizes relate to shaped conductors and may safely be applied to circular conductors.

TABLE 4E2B

VOLTAGE DROP (per ampere per metre): Conductor operating temperature: 90 °C

Conductor cross-sectional area	Two-core cable, d.c.	Two-core cable, single-phase a.c.			Three- or four-core cable, three-phase a.c.		
1	2	3			4		
(mm^2)	$(mV/A/m)$	$(mV/A/m)$			$(mV/A/m)$		
1	46	46			40		
1.5	31	31			27		
2.5	19	19			16		
4	12	12			10		
6	7.9	7.9			6.8		
10	4.7	4.7			4.0		
16	2.9	2.9			2.5		
		r	x	z	r	x	z
25	1.85	1.85	0.160	1.90	1.60	0.140	1.65
35	1.35	1.35	0.155	1.35	1.15	0.135	1.15
50	0.98	0.99	0.155	1.00	0.86	0.135	0.87
70	0.67	0.67	0.150	0.69	0.59	0.130	0.60
95	0.49	0.50	0.150	0.52	0.43	0.130	0.45
120	0.39	0.40	0.145	0.42	0.34	0.130	0.37
150	0.31	0.32	0.145	0.35	0.28	0.125	0.30
185	0.25	0.26	0.145	0.29	0.22	0.125	0.26
240	0.195	0.200	0.140	0.24	0.175	0.125	0.21
300	0.155	0.160	0.140	0.21	0.140	0.120	0.185
400	0.120	0.130	0.140	0.190	0.115	0.120	0.165

TABLE 4E3A
Single-core 90 °C armoured thermosetting insulated cables (non-magnetic armour)
(COPPER CONDUCTORS)

CURRENT-CARRYING CAPACITY (amperes):

Ambient temperature: 30 °C
Conductor operating temperature: 90 °C

Conductor cross-sectional area	Reference Method 1 (clipped direct)		Reference Method 11 (on perforated cable tray)		Reference Method 12 (free air)							
					2 cables, single-phase a.c.		2 cables, d.c.		3 or 4 cables, three-phase a.c.			
	2 cables, single-phase a.c. or d.c. flat and touching	3 or 4 cables, three-phase a.c. flat and touching	2 cables, single-phase a.c. or d.c. flat and touching	3 or 4 cables, three-phase a.c. flat and touching	Horizontal flat spaced	Vertical flat spaced	Horizontal spaced	Vertical spaced	Horizontal flat spaced	Vertical flat spaced	3 cables trefoil
1	2	3	4	5	6	7	8	9	10	11	12
(mm²)	(A)	(A)	(A)	(A)	(A)	(A)	(A)	(A)	(A)	(A)	(A)
50	237	220	253	232	282	266	284	270	288	266	222
70	303	277	322	293	357	337	356	349	358	331	285
95	367	333	389	352	436	412	446	426	425	393	346
120	425	383	449	405	504	477	519	497	485	449	402
150	488	437	516	462	566	539	600	575	549	510	463
185	557	496	587	524	643	614	688	660	618	574	529
240	656	579	689	612	749	714	815	782	715	666	625
300	755	662	792	700	842	805	943	906	810	755	720
400	853	717	899	767	929	889	1137	1094	848	797	815
500	962	791	1016	851	1032	989	1314	1266	923	871	918
630	1082	861	1146	935	1139	1092	1528	1474	992	940	1027
800	1170	904	1246	987	1204	1155	1809	1744	1042	978	1119
1000	1261	961	1345	1055	1289	1238	2100	2026	1110	1041	1214

NOTES:

1. **Where the conductor is to be protected by a semi-enclosed fuse to BS 3036, see item 6.2 of the preface to this appendix.**

2. Where a conductor operates at a temperature exceeding 70 °C it shall be ascertained that the equipment connected to the conductor is suitable for the conductor operating temperature (see Regulation 512-02).

3. Where cables in this table are connected to equipment or accessories designed to operate at a temperature not exceeding 70 °C, the current ratings given in the equivalent table for 70 °C thermoplastic (pvc) insulated cables (Table 4D3A) shall be used (see also Regulation 523-01-01).

TABLE 4E3B

VOLTAGE DROP (per ampere per metre): Conductor operating temperature: 90 °C

Conductor cross-sectional area	2 cables, d.c.	2 cables, single-phase a.c.						3 or 4 cables, three-phase a.c.								
		Reference Methods 1 &11 (touching)			Reference Method 12 (spaced*)			Reference Methods 1, 11 & 12 (in trefoil touching)			Reference Methods 1 &11 (flat and touching)			Reference Method 12 (flat spaced*)		
1	2	3			4			5			6			7		
(mm²)	(mV/A/m)	(mV/A/m)			(mV/A/m)			(mV/A/m)			(mV/A/m)			(mV/A/m)		
		r	x	z	r	x	z	r	x	z	r	x	z	r	x	z
50	0.98	0.99	0.21	1.00	0.98	0.29	1.00	0.86	0.180	0.87	0.84	0.25	0.88	0.84	0.33	0.90
70	0.67	0.68	0.200	0.71	0.69	0.29	0.75	0.59	0.170	0.62	0.60	0.25	0.65	0.62	0.32	0.73
95	0.49	0.51	0.195	0.55	0.53	0.28	0.60	0.44	0.170	0.47	0.46	0.24	0.52	0.49	0.31	0.58
120	0.39	0.41	0.190	0.45	0.43	0.27	0.51	0.35	0.165	0.39	0.38	0.24	0.44	0.41	0.30	0.51
150	0.31	0.33	0.185	0.38	0.36	0.27	0.45	0.29	0.160	0.33	0.31	0.23	0.39	0.34	0.29	0.45
185	0.25	0.27	0.185	0.33	0.30	0.26	0.40	0.23	0.160	0.28	0.26	0.23	0.34	0.29	0.29	0.41
240	0.195	0.21	0.180	0.28	0.24	0.26	0.35	0.180	0.155	0.24	0.21	0.22	0.30	0.24	0.28	0.37
300	0.155	0.170	0.175	0.25	0.195	0.25	0.32	0.145	0.150	0.21	0.170	0.22	0.28	0.20	0.27	0.34
400	0.115	0.145	0.170	0.22	0.180	0.24	0.30	0.125	0.150	0.195	0.160	0.21	0.27	0.20	0.27	0.33
500	0.093	0.125	0.170	0.21	0.165	0.24	0.29	0.105	0.145	0.180	0.145	0.20	0.25	0.190	0.24	0.31
630	0.073	0.105	0.165	0.195	0.150	0.23	0.27	0.092	0.145	0.170	0.135	0.195	0.24	0.175	0.23	0.29
800	0.056	0.090	0.160	0.190	0.145	0.23	0.27	0.086	0.140	0.165	0.130	0.180	0.23	0.175	0.195	0.26
1000	0.045	0.092	0.155	0.180	0.140	0.21	0.25	0.080	0.135	0.155	0.125	0.170	0.21	0.165	0.180	0.24

NOTE: * Spacings larger than those specified in Method 12 (see Table 4A1) will result in a larger voltage drop.

TABLE 4E4A

Multicore 90 °C armoured thermosetting insulated cables (COPPER CONDUCTORS)

Ambient temperature: 30 °C
Conductor operating temperature: 90 °C

CURRENT-CARRYING CAPACITY (amperes):

Conductor cross-sectional area	Reference Method 1 (clipped direct)		Reference Method 11 (on a perforated horizontal or vertical cable tray) or Reference Method 13 (free air)	
	1 two-core cable, single-phase a.c. or d.c.	1 three- or four-core cable, three-phase a.c.	1 two-core cable, single-phase a.c. or d.c.	1 three- or four-core cable, three-phase a.c.
1	2	3	4	5
(mm²)	(A)	(A)	(A)	(A)
1.5	27	23	29	25
2.5	36	31	39	33
4	49	42	52	44
6	62	53	66	56
10	85	73	90	78
16	110	94	115	99
25	146	124	152	131
35	180	154	188	162
50	219	187	228	197
70	279	238	291	251
95	338	289	354	304
120	392	335	410	353
150	451	386	472	406
185	515	441	539	463
240	607	520	636	546
300	698	599	732	628
400	787	673	847	728

NOTES:

1. **Where the conductor is to be protected by a semi-enclosed fuse to BS 3036, see item 6.2 of the preface to this appendix.**

2. Where a conductor operates at a temperature exceeding 70 °C it shall be ascertained that the equipment connected to the conductor is suitable for the conductor operating temperature (see Regulation 512-02).

3. Where cables in this table are connected to equipment or accessories designed to operate at a temperature not exceeding 70 °C, the current ratings given in the equivalent table for 70 °C thermoplastic (pvc) insulated cables (Table 4D4A) shall be used (see also Regulation 523-01-01).

TABLE 4E4B

VOLTAGE DROP (per ampere per metre):   Conductor operating temperature: 90 °C

Conductor cross-sectional area	Two-core cable, d.c.	Two-core cable, single-phase a.c.			Three- or four-core cable, three-phase a.c.		
1	2	3			4		
(mm²)	(mV/A/m)	(mV/A/m)			(mV/A/m)		
1.5	31	31			27		
2.5	19	19			16		
4	12	12			10		
6	7.9	7.9			6.8		
10	4.7	4.7			4.0		
16	2.9	2.9			2.5		
		r	x	z	r	x	z
25	1.85	1.85	0.160	1.90	1.60	0.140	1.65
35	1.35	1.35	0.155	1.35	1.15	0.135	1.15
50	0.98	0.99	0.155	1.00	0.86	0.135	0.87
70	0.67	0.67	0.150	0.69	0.59	0.130	0.60
95	0.49	0.50	0.150	0.52	0.43	0.130	0.45
120	0.39	0.40	0.145	0.42	0.34	0.130	0.37
150	0.31	0.32	0.145	0.35	0.28	0.125	0.30
185	0.25	0.26	0.145	0.29	0.22	0.125	0.26
240	0.195	0.20	0.140	0.24	0.175	0.125	0.21
300	0.155	0.16	0.140	0.21	0.140	0.120	0.185
400	0.120	0.13	0.140	0.190	0.115	0.120	0.165

COPPER CONDUCTORS

TABLE 4F1A

Single-core 85 °C thermosetting (rubber) insulated cables with sheath, non-armoured
(COPPER CONDUCTORS)

Ambient temperature: 30 °C
Conductor operating temperature: 85 °C

CURRENT-CARRYING CAPACITY (amperes):

Conductor cross-sectional area	Reference Method 3 (enclosed in conduit etc. in or on a wall)		Reference Method 1 (clipped direct)		Reference Method 11 (on a perforated cable tray) Horizontal or Vertical		Reference Method 12 (free air)	
	2 cables, single-phase a.c. or d.c.	3 or 4 cables, three-phase a.c.	2 cables, single-phase a.c. or d.c. flat and touching	3 or 4 cables, three-phase a.c. flat and touching or trefoil	2 cables, single-phase a.c. or d.c. flat and touching	3 or 4 cables, three-phase a.c. flat and touching or trefoil	2 cables, single-phase a.c. or d.c. or 3 or 4 cables, three-phase a.c. flat spaced horizontal or vertical	3 cables trefoil, three-phase a.c.
1	2	3	4	5	6	7	8	9
(mm²)	(A)	(A)	(A)	(A)	(A)	(A)	(A)	(A)
1	17	15	19	17.5	-	-	-	-
1.5	22	19.5	25	23	-	-	-	-
2.5	30	27	34	31	-	-	-	-
4	40	36	45	42	-	-	-	-
6	52	46	59	54	-	-	-	-
10	72	63	81	75	-	-	-	-
16	96	85	108	100	-	-	-	-
25	127	112	143	133	153	140	154	134
35	157	138	177	164	189	174	192	167
50	190	167	215	199	229	211	235	204
70	242	213	274	254	293	269	303	262
95	293	258	332	308	356	327	370	320
120	339	298	384	357	412	379	431	373
150	372	334	442	411	475	437	499	432
185	428	379	519	469	542	499	573	495
240	510	443	607	553	639	589	679	587
300	593	506	695	636	735	679	786	680
400	719	602	827	755	860	798	929	799
500	835	689	946	865	989	918	1081	919
630	975	791	1088	996	1143	1062	1263	1060

NOTES:

1. **Where the conductor is to be protected by a semi-enclosed fuse to BS 3036, see item 6.2 of the preface to this appendix.**

2. Where a conductor operates at a temperature exceeding 70 °C it shall be ascertained that the equipment connected to the conductor is suitable for the conductor operating temperature (see Regulation 512-02).

3. For cables in rigid pvc conduit the values stated in Table 4D1 are applicable (see Regulation 521-05).

4. Where cables in this table are connected to equipment or accessories designed to operate at a temperature not exceeding 70 °C, the current ratings given in the equivalent table for 70 °C thermoplastic (pvc) insulated cables (Table 4D1A) shall be used (see also Regulation 523-01-01).

TABLE 4F1B

VOLTAGE DROP (per ampere per metre):

Conductor operating temperature: 85 °C

Conductor cross-sectional area	2 cables, d.c.	2 cables, single-phase a.c. Reference Method 3 (enclosed in conduit etc. in or on a wall)			2 cables, single-phase a.c. Reference Methods 1 &11 (clipped direct or on trays, touching)			2 cables, single-phase a.c. Reference Method 12 (spaced*)			3 or 4 cables, three-phase a.c. Reference Method 3 (enclosed in conduit etc. in or on a wall)			3 or 4 cables, three-phase a.c. Reference Methods 1, 11 & 12 (in trefoil touching)			3 or 4 cables, three-phase a.c. Reference Methods 1 &11 (flat and touching)			3 or 4 cables, three-phase a.c. Reference Method 12 (flat spaced*)		
1	2	3			4			5			6			7			8			9		
(mm²)	(mV/A/m)	(mV/A/m)			(mV/A/m)			(mV/A/m)			(mV/A/m)			(mV/A/m)			(mV/A/m)			(mV/A/m)		
		r	x	z	r	x	z	r	x	z	r	x	z	r	x	z	r	x	z	r	x	z
1	46	46			46			–			40			40			40			–		
1.5	31	31			31			–			26			26			26			–		
2.5	18	18			18			–			16			16			16			–		
4	12	12			12			–			10			10			10			–		
6	7.7	7.7			7.7			–			6.7			6.7			6.7			–		
10	4.6	4.6			4.6			–			4.0			4.0			4.0			–		
16	2.9	2.9			2.9			–			2.5			2.5			2.5			–		
25	1.80	1.85	0.32	1.90	1.85	0.20	1.85	1.85	0.29	1.85	1.60	0.28	1.65	1.60	0.175	1.60	1.60	0.25	1.60	1.60	0.32	1.65
35	1.30	1.35	0.31	1.40	1.30	0.195	1.35	1.30	0.28	1.35	1.15	0.27	1.20	1.15	0.170	1.15	1.15	0.24	1.15	1.15	0.32	1.20
50	0.95	1.00	0.30	1.05	0.97	0.190	0.99	0.97	0.28	1.00	0.87	0.26	0.91	0.84	0.165	0.86	0.84	0.24	0.88	0.84	0.32	0.90
70	0.65	0.68	0.29	0.74	0.65	0.185	0.69	0.66	0.27	0.72	0.60	0.25	0.65	0.57	0.160	0.60	0.57	0.24	0.62	0.57	0.31	0.65
95	0.48	0.51	0.28	0.58	0.49	0.180	0.52	0.49	0.27	0.56	0.44	0.25	0.51	0.43	0.155	0.45	0.43	0.23	0.48	0.42	0.31	0.52
120	0.38	0.40	0.27	0.49	0.39	0.175	0.43	0.39	0.26	0.47	0.35	0.24	0.43	0.34	0.155	0.37	0.34	0.23	0.41	0.34	0.30	0.45
150	0.30	0.33	0.27	0.42	0.31	0.175	0.36	0.31	0.26	0.40	0.29	0.24	0.37	0.27	0.150	0.31	0.27	0.23	0.35	0.27	0.30	0.40
185	0.25	0.27	0.27	0.38	0.25	0.170	0.30	0.25	0.26	0.36	0.23	0.24	0.33	0.22	0.150	0.26	0.22	0.22	0.31	0.22	0.30	0.37
240	0.190	0.21	0.26	0.33	0.195	0.165	0.26	0.195	0.25	0.32	0.180	0.25	0.29	0.170	0.145	0.22	0.170	0.22	0.28	0.170	0.30	0.34
300	0.150	0.170	0.26	0.31	0.155	0.165	0.23	0.155	0.25	0.29	0.150	0.23	0.27	0.135	0.140	0.195	0.135	0.22	0.26	0.135	0.29	0.32
400	0.115	0.140	0.26	0.30	0.125	0.160	0.20	0.120	0.25	0.28	0.130	0.22	0.26	0.110	0.140	0.175	0.110	0.21	0.24	0.105	0.29	0.31
500	0.091	0.115	0.26	0.28	0.100	0.155	0.185	0.097	0.24	0.26	0.105	0.22	0.24	0.089	0.135	0.165	0.089	0.21	0.23	0.085	0.29	0.30
630	0.072	0.100	0.25	0.27	0.082	0.155	0.175	0.077	0.24	0.25	0.085	0.22	0.24	0.073	0.135	0.155	0.073	0.21	0.22	0.067	0.28	0.29

NOTE: * Spacings larger than those specified in Method 12 (see Table 4A1) will result in larger voltage drop.

TABLE 4F2A

Multicore 85 °C thermosetting (rubber) insulated cables with sheath, non-armoured
(COPPER CONDUCTORS)

Ambient temperature: 30 °C
Conductor operating temperature: 85 °C

CURRENT-CARRYING CAPACITY (amperes):

Conductor cross-sectional area	Reference Method 3 (enclosed)		Reference Method 1 (clipped direct)		Reference Method 11 (on a perforated cable tray) or Reference Method 13 (free air)	
	1 two-core cable, single-phase a.c. or d.c.	1 three- or four-core cable, three-phase a.c.	1 two-core cable, single-phase a.c. or d.c.	1 three- or four-core cable, three-phase a.c.	1 two-core cable, single-phase a.c. or d.c.	1 three- or four-core cable, three-phase a.c.
1	2	3	4	5	6	7
(mm²)	(A)	(A)	(A)	(A)	(A)	(A)
1	16.5	14.5	18	16	19.5	17.5
1.5	21	18.5	23	20	25	22
2.5	29	25	32	28	34	30
4	38	33	43	37	46	40
6	48	43	55	48	59	52
10	66	58	76	66	81	71
16	87	77	103	88	109	94
25	114	100	136	117	144	123
35	139	122	168	144	177	151
50	167	147	201	174	213	186
70	211	185	256	222	272	237
95	254	222	310	269	329	287
120	292	256	359	312	381	333
150	320	287	413	359	438	383
185	368	326	470	409	499	437
240	439	381	553	482	587	515
300	509	436	636	555	675	593

NOTES:

1. **Where the conductor is to be protected by a semi-enclosed fuse to BS 3036, see item 6.2 of the preface to this appendix.**

2. Where a conductor operates at a temperature exceeding 70 °C it shall be ascertained that the equipment connected to the conductor is suitable for the conductor operating temperature (see Regulation 512-02).

3. For cables in rigid pvc conduit the values stated in Table 4D2 are applicable (see Regulation 521-05).

4. Where cables in this table are connected to equipment or accessories designed to operate at a temperature rating not exceeding 70 °C, the current ratings given in the equivalent table for 70 °C thermoplastic (pvc) insulated cables (Table 4D2A) shall be used (see also Regulation 523-01-01).

TABLE 4F2B

VOLTAGE DROP (per ampere per metre): Conductor operating temperature: 85 °C

Conductor cross-sectional area	Two-core cable, d.c.	Two-core cable, single-phase a.c.			Three- or four-core cable, three-phase a.c.		
1	2	3			4		
(mm²)	(mV/A/m)	(mV/A/m)			(mV/A/m)		
1	46	46			40		
1.5	31	31			26		
2.5	19	19			16		
4	12	12			10		
6	7.7	7.7			6.7		
10	4.6	4.6			4.0		
16	2.9	2.9			2.5		
		r	x	z	r	x	z
25	1.80	1.85	0.175	1.85	1.60	0.150	1.60
35	1.30	1.30	0.170	1.35	1.15	0.150	1.15
50	0.95	0.97	0.170	0.99	0.84	0.145	0.86
70	0.65	0.66	0.165	0.68	0.58	0.140	0.59
95	0.48	0.49	0.160	0.52	0.43	0.140	0.45
120	0.38	0.39	0.160	0.42	0.34	0.135	0.36
150	0.30	0.31	0.155	0.35	0.27	0.135	0.30
185	0.25	0.25	0.155	0.30	0.22	0.130	0.26
240	0.190	0.195	0.150	0.25	0.170	0.130	0.22
300	0.150	0.155	0.150	0.22	0.135	0.130	0.185

TABLE 4H1A

60 °C thermosetting (rubber) insulated flexible cables with sheath, non-armoured

(COPPER CONDUCTORS)

CURRENT-CARRYING CAPACITY (amperes):   Ambient temperature: 30 °C

Conductor operating temperature: 60 °C

Conductor cross-sectional area	Single-phase a.c. or d.c. 1 two-core cable, with or without protective conductor	Three-phase a.c. 1 three-core, four-core or five-core cable	Single-phase a.c. or d.c. 2 single-core cables
1	2	3	4
(mm²)	(A)	(A)	(A)
4	30	26	–
6	39	34	–
10	51	47	–
16	73	63	–
25	97	83	–
35	–	102	140
50	–	124	175
70	–	158	216
95	–	192	258
120	–	222	302
150	–	255	347
185	–	291	394
240	–	343	471
300	–	394	541
400	–	–	644
500	–	–	738
630	–	–	861

NOTES:

1. The current ratings tabulated are for cables in free air but may also be used for cables resting on a surface. If the cable is to be wound on a drum on load the ratings should be reduced in accordance with NOTE 3 below and for cables which may be covered, NOTE 4 below.

2. **Where the conductor is to be protected by a semi-enclosed fuse to BS 3036, see item 6.2 of the preface to this appendix.**

3. *Flexible cables wound on reeling drums*

    The current ratings of cables used on reeling drums are to be reduced by the following factors:

    a) Radial type drum
       ventilated: 85 %
       unventilated: 75 %

    b) Ventilated cylindrical type drum
       1 layer of cable: 85 %
       2 layers of cable: 65 %
       3 layers of cable: 45 %
       4 layers of cable: 35 %

    A radial type drum is one where spiral layers of cable are accommodated between closely spaced flanges; if fitted with solid flanges the ratings given above should be reduced and the drum is described as non-ventilated and if the flanges have suitable apertures as ventilated.

    A ventilated cylindrical cable drum is one where layers of cable are accommodated between widely spaced flanges and the drum and end flanges have suitable ventilating apertures.

4. Where cable may be covered over or coiled up whilst on load, or the air movement over the cable restricted, the current rating should be reduced.

    It is not possible to specify the amount of reduction but the table of rating factors for reeling drums can be used as a guide.

TABLE 4H1B

VOLTAGE DROP (per ampere per metre):

Conductor operating temperature: 60 °C

Conductor cross-sectional area	Two-core cable, d.c.	Two-core cable, single-phase a.c.			1 three-core, four-core or five-core cable, three-phase a.c.			2 single-core cables, touching			
								d.c.	Single-phase a.c.*		
1	2	3			4			5	6		
(mm²)	(mV/A/m)	(mV/A/m)			(mV/A/m)			(mV/A/m)	(mV/A/m)		
		r	x	z	r	x	z		r	x	z
4	12	12			10			-	-	-	-
6	7.8	7.8			6.7			-	-	-	-
10	4.6	4.6			4.0			-	-	-	-
16	2.9	2.9			2.5			-	-	-	-
25	1.80	1.80	0.175	1.85	1.55	0.150	1.55	-	-	-	-
35	-	-	-	-	1.10	0.150	1.15	1.31	1.31	0.21	1.32
50	-	-	-	-	0.83	0.145	0.84	0.91	0.91	0.21	0.93
70	-	-	-	-	0.57	0.140	0.58	0.64	0.64	0.20	0.67
95	-	-	-	-	0.42	0.135	0.44	0.49	0.49	0.195	0.53
120	-	-	-	-	0.33	0.135	0.36	0.38	0.38	0.190	0.43
150	-	-	-	-	0.27	0.130	0.30	0.31	0.31	0.190	0.36
185	-	-	-	-	0.22	0.130	0.26	0.25	0.25	0.190	0.32
240	-	-	-	-	0.170	0.130	0.21	0.190	0.195	0.185	0.27
300	-	-	-	-	0.135	0.125	0.185	0.150	0.155	0.180	0.24
400	-	-	-	-	-	-	-	0.115	0.120	0.175	0.21
500	-	-	-	-	-	-	-	0.090	0.099	0.170	0.20
630	-	-	-	-	-	-	-	0.068	0.079	0.170	0.185

NOTE: * A larger voltage drop will result if the cables are spaced.

TABLE 4H2A

85 °C and 180 °C thermosetting (rubber) insulated flexible cables with sheath, non-armoured

(COPPER CONDUCTORS)

CURRENT-CARRYING CAPACITY (amperes): Ambient temperature: 30 °C
Conductor operating temperature: 85 °C

Conductor cross-sectional area	d.c. or single-phase a.c. (1 two-core cable, with or without protective conductor)	Three-phase a.c. (1 three-core, four-core or five-core cable)	Single-phase a.c. or d.c., 2 single-core cables, touching
1	2	3	4
(mm²)	(A)	(A)	(A)
4	41	36	-
6	53	47	-
10	73	64	-
16	99	86	-
25	131	114	-
35	-	140	192
50	-	170	240
70	-	216	297
95	-	262	354
120	-	303	414
150	-	348	476
185	-	397	540
240	-	467	645
300	-	537	741
400	-	-	885
500	-	-	1017
630	-	-	1190

CORRECTION FACTOR FOR AMBIENT TEMPERATURE

85 °C thermosetting (rubber) insulated cables:

Ambient temperature	35 °C	40 °C	45 °C	50 °C	55 °C	60 °C	65 °C	70 °C	75 °C	80 °C
Correction factor	0.95	0.90	0.85	0.80	0.74	0.67	0.60	0.52	0.43	0.30

180 °C thermosetting (rubber) insulated cables:

Ambient temperature	35 to 85 °C	90 °C	95 °C	100 °C	105 °C	110 °C	115 °C	120 °C	125 °C	130 °C	135 °C	140 °C	145 °C
Correction factor	1.0	0.96	0.92	0.88	0.83	0.78	0.73	0.68	0.62	0.55	0.48	0.39	0.28

NOTES:

1. The current ratings tabulated are for cables in free air but may also be used for cables resting on a surface. If the cable is to be wound on a drum on load the ratings should be reduced in accordance with NOTE 3 below and for cables which may be covered, NOTE 4 below.

2. **Where the conductor is to be protected by a semi-enclosed fuse to BS 3036, see item 6.2 of the preface to this appendix.**

3. *Flexible cables wound on reeling drums*

   The current ratings of cables used on reeling drums are to be reduced by the following factors:

   a) Radial type drum

   ventilated: 85 %
   unventilated: 75 %

   b) Ventilated cylindrical type drum

   1 layer of cable: 85 %
   2 layers of cable: 65 %
   3 layers of cable: 45 %
   4 layers of cable: 35 %

   A radial type drum is one where spiral layers of cable are accommodated between closely spaced flanges; if fitted with solid flanges the ratings given above should be reduced and the drum is described as non-ventilated and if the flanges have suitable apertures as ventilated.

   A ventilated cylindrical cable drum is one where layers of cable are accommodated between widely spaced flanges and the drum and end flanges have suitable ventilating apertures.

4. Where cable may be covered over or coiled up whilst on load, or the air movement over the cable restricted, the current rating should be reduced.
   It is not possible to specify the amount of reduction but the table of rating factors for reeling drums can be used as a guide.

5. The temperature limits given in Table 52B should be taken into account when it is intended to operate these cables at maximum permissible temperature.

6. Where a conductor operates at a temperature exceeding 70 °C it shall be ascertained that the equipment connected to the conductor is suitable for the conductor operating temperature (see Regulation 512-02).

7. For 180 °C cables, the correction factors for ambient temperature allow a conductor operating temperature up to 150 °C. Consult the cable manufacturer for further information.

TABLE 4H2B

VOLTAGE DROP (per ampere per metre):

Conductor operating temperature: 85 °C

Conductor cross-sectional area	1 two-core or 2 single-core cables d.c.	Two-core cable single-phase a.c. 3 (mV/A/m)			1 three-core, four-core or five-core cable three-phase a.c. 4 (mV/A/m)			2 single-core cables touching, Single-phase a.c.* 5 (mV/A/m)		
(mm²) 1	2 (mV/A/m)	r	x	z	r	x	z	r	x	z
4	13	13			11			-		
6	8.4	8.4			7.3			-		
10	5.0	5.0			4.3			-		
16	3.1	3.1			2.7			-		
25	2.0	2.00	0.175	2.00	1.70	0.150	1.70	-	-	-
35	1.42	-	-	-	1.20	0.150	1.20	1.42	0.21	1.43
50	0.99	-	-	-	0.90	0.145	0.91	0.99	0.21	1.01
70	0.70	-	-	-	0.61	0.140	0.63	0.70	0.20	0.72
95	0.53	-	-	-	0.46	0.135	0.48	0.53	0.195	0.56
120	0.41	-	-	-	0.36	0.135	0.39	0.41	0.190	0.46
150	0.33	-	-	-	0.29	0.130	0.32	0.33	0.190	0.38
185	0.27	-	-	-	0.24	0.130	0.27	0.27	0.190	0.33
240	0.21	-	-	-	0.185	0.130	0.22	0.21	0.185	0.28
300	0.165	-	-	-	0.145	0.125	0.195	0.170	0.180	0.25
400	0.125	-	-	-	-	-	-	0.130	0.175	0.22
500	0.098	-	-	-	-	-	-	0.105	0.170	0.20
630	0.073	-	-	-	-	-	-	0.084	0.170	0.190

NOTES:

1. The voltage drop figures given above are based on a conductor operating temperature of 85 °C and are therefore not accurate when the operating temperature is in excess of 85 °C. In the case of the 180 °C cables with a conductor temperature of 150 °C the above resistive values should be increased by a factor of 1.2.

2. * A larger voltage drop will result if the cables are spaced.

TABLE 4H3A
Flexible cords, non-armoured
(COPPER CONDUCTORS)

CURRENT-CARRYING CAPACITY (amperes): and MASS SUPPORTABLE (kg):

| Conductor cross-sectional area | Current-carrying capacity | | Maximum mass supportable by twin flexible cord (see Regulation 522-08-06) |
| | Single-phase a.c. | Three-phase a.c. | |
1	2	3	4
(mm²)	(A)	(A)	(kg)
0.5	3	3	2
0.75	6	6	3
1	10	10	5
1.25	13	-	5
1.5	16	16	5
2.5	25	20	5
4	32	25	5

Where cable is on a reel see the notes to table 4H1A.

CORRECTION FACTOR FOR AMBIENT TEMPERATURE

60 °C thermoplastic (pvc) or thermosetting (rubber) insulated cords:

Ambient temperature	35 °C	40 °C	45 °C	50 °C	55 °C
Correction factor	0.91	0.82	0.71	0.58	0.41

85 °C and 90 °C thermoplastic (pvc) or thermosetting (rubber) insulated cords:

Ambient temperature	35 to 50 °C	55 °C	60 °C	65 °C	70 °C
Correction factor	1.0	0.96	0.83	0.67	0.47

180 °C thermosetting insulated cords:

Ambient temperature	35 to 120 °C	125 °C	130 °C	135 °C	140 °C	145 °C
Correction factor	1.0	0.96	0.85	0.74	0.60	0.42

Glass fibre cords:

Ambient temperature	35 to 150 °C	155 °C	160 °C	165 °C	170 °C	175 °C
Correction factor	1.0	0.92	0.82	0.71	0.57	0.40

TABLE 4H3B

VOLTAGE DROP (per ampere per metre):

Conductor operating temperature: 60 °C*

Conductor cross-sectional area	d.c. or single-phase a.c.	Three-phase a.c.
1	2	3
(mm^2)	(mV/A/m)	(mV/A/m)
0.5	93	80
0.75	62	54
1	46	40
1.25	37	–
1.5	32	27
2.5	19	16
4	12	10

NOTE: * The tabulated values above are for 60 °C thermoplastic (pvc) or thermosetting (rubber) insulated flexible cords and for other types of flexible cords they are to be multiplied by the following factors:

For		
85 °C and 90 °C thermoplastic or thermosetting insulated	1.09
180 °C thermosetting insulated	1.31
185 °C glass fibre	1.43

THIS PAGE HAS BEEN INTENTIONALLY LEFT BLANK

TABLE 4J1A
Mineral insulated cables bare and exposed to touch (see note 2)
or having an overall thermoplastic (pvc) covering.
(COPPER CONDUCTORS AND SHEATH)

Ambient temperature: 30 °C

CURRENT-CARRYING CAPACITY (amperes):

Sheath operating temperature: 70 °C

	REFERENCE METHOD 1 (CLIPPED DIRECT)							
Conductor cross-sectional area	2 single-core cables, or 1 two-core cable, single-phase a.c. or d.c.	3 single-core cables in trefoil, or 1 three-core cable, three-phase a.c.	3 single-core cables in flat formation, three-phase a.c.	1 four-core cable, three cores loaded three-phase a.c.	1 four-core cable, all cores loaded	1 seven-core cable, all cores loaded	1 twelve-core cable, all cores loaded	1 nineteen-core cable, all cores loaded
1	2	3	4	5	6	7	8	9
(mm²)	(A)	(A)	(A)	(A)	(A)	(A)	(A)	(A)
Light duty 500 V								
1	18.5	15	17	15	13	10	-	-
1.5	23	19	21	19.5	16.5	13	-	-
2.5	31	26	29	26	22	17.5	-	-
4	40	35	38	-	-	-	-	-
Heavy duty 750 V								
1	19.5	16	18	16.5	14.5	11.5	9.5	8.5
1.5	25	21	23	21	18	14.5	12.0	10.0
2.5	34	28	31	28	25	19.5	16.0	-
4	45	37	41	37	32	26	-	-
6	57	48	52	47	41	-	-	-
10	77	65	70	64	55	-	-	-
16	102	86	92	85	72	-	-	-
25	133	112	120	110	94	-	-	-
35	163	137	147	-	-	-	-	-
50	202	169	181	-	-	-	-	-
70	247	207	221	-	-	-	-	-
95	296	249	264	-	-	-	-	-
120	340	286	303	-	-	-	-	-
150	388	327	346	-	-	-	-	-
185	440	371	392	-	-	-	-	-
240	514	434	457	-	-	-	-	-

NOTES:
1. For single-core cables, the sheaths of the circuit are assumed to be connected together at both ends.
2. For bare cables exposed to touch, the tabulated values should be multiplied by 0.9.
3. *Deleted by BS 7671 : 1992, Amendment No 2.*

TABLE 4J1A (continued)

Mineral insulated cables bare and exposed to touch (see note 2)
or having an overall thermoplastic (pvc) covering.
(COPPER CONDUCTORS AND SHEATH)

CURRENT-CARRYING CAPACITY (amperes):

Ambient temperature: 30 °C
Sheath operating temperature: 70 °C

Conductor cross-sectional area	REFERENCE METHOD 11 (ON A PERFORATED CABLE TRAY, HORIZONTAL OR VERTICAL)											
	2 single-core cables, touching	1 two-core cable,	1 three-core cable, three-phase a.c.	1 four-core cable, three cores loaded three-phase a.c.	1 four-core cable, all cores loaded	1 seven-core cable, all cores loaded	1 twelve-core cable, all cores loaded	1 nineteen-core cable, all cores loaded	3 single-core cables, three-phase a.c.			
	Single-phase a.c. or d.c.								Vertical spaced	Horizontal spaced	Flat touching	Trefoil
1	10	11	12	13	14	15	16	17	18	19	20	21
(mm²)	(A)	(A)	(A)	(A)	(A)	(A)	(A)	(A)	(A)	(A)	(A)	(A)
Light duty 500 V												
1	18.5	19.5	16.5	16	14	11	-	-	19	22	17	16.5
1.5	24	25	21	21	18	14	-	-	25	28	22	21
2.5	31	33	28	28	24	19	-	-	32	37	29	28
4	42	44	37	-	-	-	-	-	43	48	39	37
Heavy duty 750 V												
1	20	21	17.5	18	16	12	10	9	21	24	19	17.5
1.5	25	26	22	23	20	15.5	13	11	27	30	25	22
2.5	34	36	30	30	27	21	17	-	35	41	32	30
4	45	47	40	40	35	28	-	-	47	53	43	40
6	57	60	51	51	44	-	-	-	59	67	54	51
10	78	82	69	68	59	-	-	-	80	90	73	69
16	104	109	92	89	78	-	-	-	105	119	97	92
25	135	142	120	116	101	-	-	-	135	154	125	120
35	165	174	147	-	-	-	-	-	164	187	153	147
50	204	215	182	-	-	-	-	-	202	230	188	182
70	251	264	223	-	-	-	-	-	246	279	229	223
95	301	317	267	-	-	-	-	-	294	333	275	267
120	346	364	308	-	-	-	-	-	335	382	314	308
150	395	416	352	-	-	-	-	-	380	431	358	352
185	448	472	399	-	-	-	-	-	424	482	405	399
240	524	552	466	-	-	-	-	-	472	537	471	466

NOTES:
1. For single-core cables, the sheaths of the circuit are assumed to be connected together at both ends.
2. For bare cables exposed to touch, the tabulated values should be multiplied by 0.9.
3. *Deleted by BS 7671 : 1992, Amendment No 2.*

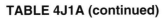

TABLE 4J1A (continued)

Mineral insulated cables bare and exposed to touch (see note 2) or having an overall thermoplastic (pvc) covering.
(COPPER CONDUCTORS AND SHEATH)

Ambient temperature: 30 °C
Sheath operating temperature: 70 °C

CURRENT-CARRYING CAPACITY (amperes):

Conductor cross-sectional area	2 single-core cables, or 1 two-core cable, single-phase a.c. or d.c.	3 single-core cables in trefoil, or 1 three-core cable, three phase a.c.	1 four-core cable, three cores loaded three-phase a.c.	1 four-core cable, all cores loaded	1 seven-core cable, all cores loaded	1 twelve-core cable, all cores loaded	1 nineteen-core cable, all cores loaded	3 single-core cables, three-phase a.c.		
								Vertical spaced	Horizontal spaced	Touching
1	22	23	24	25	26	27	28	29	30	31
(mm²)	(A)	(A)	(A)	(A)	(A)	(A)	(A)	(A)	(A)	(A)
Light duty 500 V										
1	19.5	16.5	16	14	11	-	-	20	23	18
1.5	25	21	21	18	14	-	-	26	29	23
2.5	33	28	28	24	19	-	-	34	39	31
4	44	37	-	-	-	-	-	45	51	41
Heavy duty 750 V										
1	21	17.5	18	16	12	10	9	22	25	20
1.5	26	22	23	20	15.5	13	11	28	32	26
2.5	36	30	30	27	21	17	-	37	43	34
4	47	40	40	35	28	-	-	49	56	45
6	60	51	51	44	-	-	-	62	71	57
10	82	69	68	59	-	-	-	84	95	77
16	109	92	89	78	-	-	-	110	125	102
25	142	120	116	101	-	-	-	142	162	132
35	174	147	-	-	-	-	-	173	197	161
50	215	182	-	-	-	-	-	213	242	198
70	264	223	-	-	-	-	-	259	294	241
95	317	267	-	-	-	-	-	309	351	289
120	364	308	-	-	-	-	-	353	402	331
150	416	352	-	-	-	-	-	400	454	377
185	472	399	-	-	-	-	-	446	507	426
240	552	466	-	-	-	-	-	497	565	496

REFERENCE METHODS 12 and 13 (FREE AIR)

NOTES:
1. For single-core cables, the sheaths of the circuit are assumed to be connected together at both ends.
2. For bare cables exposed to touch, the tabulated values should be multiplied by 0.9.
3. *Deleted by BS 7671 : 1992, Amendment No 2.*

TABLE 4J1B
Mineral insulated cables bare and exposed to touch or having an overall thermoplastic (pvc) covering
(COPPER CONDUCTORS AND SHEATH)

VOLTAGE DROP (per ampere per metre) for single-phase a.c. or d.c.:

Sheath operating temperature: 70 °C

Conductor cross-sectional area	Two single-core cables, touching			One two-core or multicore* cable		
1	2			3		
(mm²)	(mV/A/m)			(mV/A/m)		
1	42			42		
1.5	28			28		
2.5	17			17		
4	10			10		
6	7			7		
10	4.2			4.2		
16	2.6			2.6		
	r	x	z	r	x	z
25	1.65	0.200	1.65	1.65	0.145	1.65
35	1.20	0.195	1.20	–	–	–
50	0.89	0.185	0.91	–	–	–
70	0.62	0.180	0.64	–	–	–
95	0.46	0.175	0.49	–	–	–
120	0.37	0.170	0.41	–	–	–
150	0.30	0.170	0.34	–	–	–
185	0.25	0.165	0.29	–	–	–
240	0.190	0.160	0.25	–	–	–

NOTE: * Multiple single-phase a.c. or d.c. circuits in a multicore cable

TABLE 4J1B (continued)

Mineral insulated cables bare and exposed to touch or having an overall thermoplastic (pvc) covering (COPPER CONDUCTORS AND SHEATH)

Sheath operating temperature: 70 °C

VOLTAGE DROP (per ampere per metre) for three-phase operation:

Conductor cross-sectional area	Three single-core cables									One three-core or four-core or multicore* cable		
	Trefoil touching			Flat formation								
				Touching			Spaced 1 cable diameter apart					
1	2			3			4			5		
(mm²)	(mV/A/m)			(mV/A/m)			(mV/A/m)			(mV/A/m)		
1	36			36			36			36		
1.5	24			24			24			24		
2.5	14			14			14			14		
4	9.1			9.1			9.1			9.1		
6	6.0			6.0			6.0			6.0		
10	3.6			3.5			3.6			3.6		
16	2.3			2.3			2.3			2.3		
	r	x	z	r	x	z	r	x	z	r	x	z
25	1.45	0.170	1.45	1.45	0.25	1.45	1.45	0.32	1.50	1.45	0.125	1.45
35	1.05	0.165	1.05	1.05	0.24	1.10	1.05	0.31	1.10	–	–	–
50	0.78	0.160	0.80	0.79	0.24	0.83	0.82	0.31	0.87	–	–	–
70	0.54	0.155	0.56	0.55	0.23	0.60	0.58	0.30	0.65	–	–	–
95	0.40	0.150	0.43	0.41	0.22	0.47	0.44	0.29	0.53	–	–	–
120	0.32	0.150	0.36	0.33	0.22	0.40	0.36	0.28	0.46	–	–	–
150	0.26	0.145	0.30	0.29	0.21	0.36	0.32	0.27	0.42	–	–	–
185	0.21	0.140	0.26	0.25	0.21	0.32	0.28	0.26	0.39	–	–	–
240	0.165	0.140	0.22	0.21	0.20	0.29	0.26	0.25	0.36	–	–	–

NOTE: * Multiple three-phase circuits in a multicore cable

TABLE 4J2A
Mineral insulated cables bare and neither exposed to touch
nor in contact with combustible materials
(COPPER CONDUCTORS AND SHEATH)

CURRENT-CARRYING CAPACITY (amperes):

Ambient temperature: 30 °C
Sheath operating temperature: 105 °C

	REFERENCE METHOD 1 (CLIPPED DIRECT)							
Conductor cross-sectional area	2 single-core cables, or 1 two-core cable, single-phase a.c. or d.c.	3 single-core cables in trefoil, or 1 three-core cable, three-phase a.c	3 single-core cables in flat formation, three-phase a.c.	1 four-core cable, three cores loaded three-phase a.c.	1 four-core cable, all cores loaded	1 seven-core cable, all cores loaded	1 twelve-core cable, all cores loaded	1 nineteen-core cable, all cores loaded
1	2	3	4	5	6	7	8	9
(mm²)	(A)	(A)	(A)	(A)	(A)	(A)	(A)	(A)
Light duty 500 V								
1	22	19	21	18.5	16.5	13	-	-
1.5	28	24	27	24	21	16.5	-	-
2.5	38	33	36	33	28	22	-	-
4	51	44	47	-	-	-	-	-
Heavy duty 750 V								
1	24	20	24	20	17.5	14	12	10.5
1.5	31	26	30	26	22	17.5	15.5	13
2.5	42	35	41	35	30	24	20	-
4	55	47	53	46	40	32	-	-
6	70	59	67	58	50	-	-	-
10	96	81	91	78	68	-	-	-
16	127	107	119	103	90	-	-	-
25	166	140	154	134	117	-	-	-
35	203	171	187	-	-	-	-	-
50	251	212	230	-	-	-	-	-
70	307	260	280	-	-	-	-	-
95	369	312	334	-	-	-	-	-
120	424	359	383	-	-	-	-	-
150	485	410	435	-	-	-	-	-
185	550	465	492	-	-	-	-	-
240	643	544	572	-	-	-	-	-

NOTES:

1. For single-core cables, the sheaths of the circuit are assumed to be connected together at both ends.
2. No correction factor for grouping need be applied.
3. Where a conductor operates at a temperature exceeding 70 °C it shall be ascertained that the equipment connected to the conductor is suitable for the conductor operating temperature (see Regulation 512-02).

TABLE 4J2A (continued)
Mineral insulated cables bare and neither exposed to touch nor in contact with combustible materials
(COPPER CONDUCTORS AND SHEATH)

Ambient temperature: 30 °C
Sheath operating temperature: 105 °C

CURRENT-CARRYING CAPACITY (amperes):

REFERENCE METHODS 12 and 13 (FREE AIR)										
Conductor cross-sectional area	2 single-core cables, or 1 two-core cable, single-phase a.c. or d.c.	3 single-core cables in trefoil, or 1 three-core cable, three-phase a.c.	1 four-core cable, three cores loaded three-phase a.c.	1 four-core cable, all cores loaded	1 seven-core cable, all cores loaded	1 twelve-core cable, all cores loaded	1 nineteen-core cable, all cores loaded	3 single-core cables, three-phase a.c.		
								Vertical spaced	Horizontal spaced	Touching
1	10	11	12	13	14	15	16	17	18	19
(mm²)	(A)	(A)	(A)	(A)	(A)	(A)	(A)	(A)	(A)	(A)
Light duty 500 V										
1	24	21	20	18	14	-	-	26	29	23
1.5	31	26	26	22	18	-	-	33	37	29
2.5	41	35	35	30	24	-	-	43	49	39
4	54	46	-	-	-	-	-	56	64	51
Heavy duty 750 V										
1	26	22	22	19	15	13	11	28	32	25
1.5	33	28	28	24	19	16.5	14	35	40	32
2.5	45	38	37	32	26	22	-	47	54	43
4	60	50	49	43	34	-	-	61	70	56
6	76	64	63	54	-	-	-	78	89	71
10	104	87	85	73	-	-	-	105	120	96
16	137	115	112	97	-	-	-	137	157	127
25	179	150	146	126	-	-	-	178	204	164
35	220	184	-	-	-	-	-	216	248	200
50	272	228	-	-	-	-	-	266	304	247
70	333	279	-	-	-	-	-	323	370	300
95	400	335	-	-	-	-	-	385	441	359
120	460	385	-	-	-	-	-	441	505	411
150	526	441	-	-	-	-	-	498	565	469
185	596	500	-	-	-	-	-	557	629	530
240	697	584	-	-	-	-	-	624	704	617

NOTES:
1. For single-core cables, the sheaths of the circuit are assumed to be connected together at both ends.
2. No correction factor for grouping need be applied.
3. Where a conductor operates at a temperature exceeding 70 °C it shall be ascertained that the equipment connected to the conductor is suitable for the conductor operating temperature (see Regulation 512-02).

TABLE 4J2B

Mineral insulated cables bare and neither exposed to touch nor in contact with combustible materials
(COPPER CONDUCTORS AND SHEATH)

VOLTAGE DROP (per ampere per metre) for single-phase a.c. or d.c.:   Sheath operating temperature: 105 °C

Conductor cross-sectional area	Two single-core cables touching			One two-core or multicore* cable		
1	2			3		
(mm²)	(mV/A/m)			(mV/A/m)		
1	47			47		
1.5	31			31		
2.5	19			19		
4	12			12		
6	7.8			7.8		
10	4.7			4.7		
16	3.0			3.0		
	r	x	z	r	x	z
25	1.85	0.180	1.85	1.85	0.145	1.85
35	1.35	0.175	1.35	–	–	–
50	1.00	0.170	1.00	–	–	–
70	0.69	0.165	0.71	–	–	–
95	0.51	0.160	0.54	–	–	–
120	0.41	0.160	0.44	–	–	–
150	0.33	0.155	0.36	–	–	–
185	0.27	0.150	0.31	–	–	–
240	0.21	0.150	0.26	–	–	–

NOTE: * Multiple single-phase a.c. or d.c. circuits in a multicore cable

TABLE 4J2B (continued)

Mineral insulated cables bare and neither exposed to touch nor in contact with combustible materials (COPPER CONDUCTORS AND SHEATH)

VOLTAGE DROP (per ampere per metre) for three-phase operation:

Sheath operating temperature: 105 °C

Conductor cross-sectional area	Three single-core cables									One three-core or four-core or multicore* cable		
	Trefoil touching			Flat formation								
				Touching			Spaced 1 cable diameter apart					
1	2			3			4			5		
(mm²)	(mV/A/m)			(mV/A/m)			(mV/A/m)			(mV/A/m)		
1	40			40			40			40		
1.5	27			27			27			27		
2.5	16			16			16			16		
4	10			10			10			10		
6	6.8			6.8			6.8			6.8		
10	4.1			4.1			4.1			4.1		
16	2.6			2.6			2.6			2.6		
	r	x	z	r	x	z	r	x	z	r	x	z
25	1.60	0.160	1.65	1.60	0.23	1.65	1.60	0.31	1.65	1.60	0.125	1.60
35	1.15	0.155	1.20	1.15	0.23	1.20	1.20	0.30	1.25	–	–	–
50	0.87	0.150	0.88	0.88	0.22	0.91	0.90	0.29	0.95	–	–	–
70	0.60	0.145	0.62	0.61	0.22	0.65	0.63	0.29	0.70	–	–	–
95	0.45	0.140	0.47	0.46	0.21	0.50	0.48	0.28	0.56	–	–	–
120	0.36	0.135	0.38	0.37	0.21	0.42	0.39	0.28	0.48	–	–	–
150	0.29	0.135	0.32	0.31	0.20	0.37	0.34	0.27	0.43	–	–	–
185	0.23	0.130	0.27	0.26	0.20	0.33	0.29	0.26	0.39	–	–	–
240	0.180	0.130	0.22	0.22	0.195	0.29	0.26	0.25	0.36	–	–	–

NOTE: * Multiple three-phase circuits in a multicore cable

ALUMINIUM CONDUCTORS

TABLE 4K1A

Single-core 70 °C thermoplastic (pvc) insulated cables, non-armoured, with or without sheath
(ALUMINIUM CONDUCTORS)

CURRENT-CARRYING CAPACITY (amperes):

Ambient temperature: 30 °C
Conductor operating temperature: 70 °C

Conductor cross-sectional area	Reference Method 4 (enclosed in conduit in thermally insulating wall etc.)		Reference Method 3 (enclosed in conduit on a wall or in trunking etc.)		Reference Method 1 (clipped direct)		Reference Method 11 (on a perforated cable tray horizontal or vertical)		Reference Method 12 (free air)		
	2 cables, single-phase a.c. or d.c.	3 or 4 cables, three-phase a.c.	2 cables, single-phase a.c. or d.c.	3 or 4 cables, three-phase a.c.	2 cables, single-phase a.c. or d.c. flat and touching	3 or 4 cables, three-phase a.c. flat and touching or trefoil	2 cables, single-phase a.c. or d.c. flat and touching	3 or 4 cables, three-phase a.c. flat and touching or trefoil	Horizontal flat spaced 2 cables, single-phase a.c. or d.c. or 3 cables three-phase a.c.	Vertical flat spaced 2 cables, single-phase a.c. or d.c. or 3 cables three-phase a.c.	Trefoil 3 cables trefoil, three-phase a.c.
1	2	3	4	5	6	7	8	9	10	11	12
(mm²)	(A)	(A)	(A)	(A)	(A)	(A)	(A)	(A)	(A)	(A)	(A)
50	93	84	118	104	134	123	144	132	163	148	128
70	118	107	150	133	172	159	185	169	210	191	165
95	142	129	181	161	210	194	225	206	256	234	203
120	164	149	210	186	245	226	261	240	298	273	237
150	189	170	234	204	283	261	301	277	344	317	274
185	215	194	266	230	324	299	344	317	394	364	316
240	252	227	312	269	384	354	407	375	466	432	375
300	289	261	358	306	444	410	469	433	538	501	435
380	-	-	413	352	511	472	543	502	625	584	507
480	-	-	477	405	591	546	629	582	726	680	590
600	-	-	545	462	679	626	722	669	837	787	680
740	-	-	-	-	771	709	820	761	956	902	776
960	-	-	-	-	900	823	953	886	1125	1066	907
1200	-	-	-	-	1022	926	1073	999	1293	1229	1026

NOTE:
Where the conductor is to be protected by a semi-enclosed fuse to BS 3036, see item 6.2 of the preface to this appendix.

VOLTAGE DROP (per ampere per metre): Conductor operating temperature: 70 °C

TABLE 4K1B

Conductor cross-sectional area	2 cables, d.c.	2 cables, single-phase a.c.									3 or 4 cables, three-phase a.c.												
		Reference Methods 3 & 4 (enclosed in conduit etc. in or on a wall)			Reference Methods 1 & 11 (clipped direct or on trays, touching)			Reference Method 12 (spaced*)			Reference Methods 3 & 4 (enclosed in conduit etc. in or on a wall)			Reference Methods 1, 11 & 12 (in trefoil touching)			Reference Methods 1 & 11 (flat touching)			Reference Method 12 (flat spaced*)		
	(mV/A/m)	(mV/A/m)			(mV/A/m)			(mV/A/m)			(mV/A/m)			(mV/A/m)			(mV/A/m)			(mV/A/m)		
(mm²)		r	x	z	r	x	z	r	x	z	r	x	z	r	x	z	r	x	z	r	x	z
50	1.55	1.60	0.30	1.60	1.55	0.190	1.55	1.55	0.28	1.55	1.35	0.26	1.40	1.35	0.165	1.35	1.35	0.24	1.35	1.35	0.32	1.43
70	1.05	1.10	0.30	1.15	1.05	0.185	1.05	1.05	0.27	1.10	0.94	0.26	0.97	0.91	0.160	0.92	0.91	0.24	0.94	0.91	0.31	0.95
95	0.77	0.81	0.29	0.86	0.77	0.185	0.79	0.77	0.27	0.82	0.70	0.25	0.74	0.67	0.160	0.69	0.67	0.23	0.71	0.67	0.31	0.74
120	0.61	0.64	0.29	0.70	0.61	0.180	0.64	0.61	0.27	0.67	0.55	0.25	0.61	0.53	0.155	0.55	0.53	0.23	0.58	0.53	0.31	0.61
150	0.49	0.51	0.28	0.59	0.49	0.175	0.52	0.49	0.26	0.55	0.45	0.24	0.51	0.42	0.155	0.45	0.42	0.23	0.48	0.42	0.30	0.52
185	0.39	0.42	0.28	0.50	0.40	0.175	0.43	0.39	0.26	0.47	0.36	0.24	0.44	0.34	0.150	0.37	0.34	0.23	0.41	0.34	0.30	0.46
240	0.30	0.32	0.27	0.42	0.30	0.170	0.35	0.30	0.26	0.43	0.28	0.24	0.37	0.26	0.150	0.30	0.26	0.22	0.35	0.26	0.30	0.40
300	0.24	0.26	0.27	0.37	0.24	0.170	0.30	0.24	0.26	0.35	0.23	0.23	0.32	0.21	0.145	0.26	0.21	0.22	0.31	0.21	0.30	0.36
380	0.190	0.22	0.27	0.35	0.195	0.165	0.26	0.195	0.25	0.32	0.190	0.23	0.30	0.170	0.145	0.22	0.170	0.22	0.28	0.170	0.29	0.34
480	0.150	0.180	0.26	0.32	0.155	0.165	0.23	0.155	0.25	0.29	0.155	0.23	0.27	0.140	0.140	0.195	0.140	0.22	0.26	0.135	0.29	0.32
600	0.120	0.150	0.26	0.30	0.130	0.160	0.21	0.125	0.25	0.28	0.125	0.22	0.26	0.110	0.140	0.180	0.110	0.22	0.24	0.110	0.29	0.31
740	0.099	-	-	-	0.105	0.160	0.190	0.100	0.25	0.27	-	-	-	0.094	0.135	0.165	0.094	0.21	0.23	0.089	0.29	0.30
960	0.075	-	-	-	0.086	0.155	0.180	0.082	0.24	0.26	-	-	-	0.077	0.135	0.155	0.077	0.21	0.22	0.071	0.29	0.29
1200	0.060	-	-	-	0.074	0.155	0.170	0.068	0.24	0.25	-	-	-	0.066	0.135	0.150	0.066	0.21	0.22	0.059	0.28	0.29

NOTE: * Spacings larger than those specified in Method 12 (see Table 4A1) will result in a larger voltage drop.

TABLE 4K2A
Multicore 70 °C thermoplastic (pvc) insulated cables, non-armoured
(ALUMINIUM CONDUCTORS)

Ambient temperature: 30 °C
Conductor operating temperature: 70 °C

CURRENT-CARRYING CAPACITY (amperes):

Conductor cross-sectional area	Reference Method 4 (enclosed in an insulating wall etc.)		Reference Method 3 (enclosed in conduit on a wall or ceiling, or in trunking)		Reference Method 1 (clipped direct)		Reference Method 11 (on a perforated cable tray) or Reference Method 13 (free air)	
	1 two-core cable, single-phase a.c. or d.c.	1 three- or four-core cable, three-phase a.c.	1 two-core cable, single-phase a.c. or d.c.	1 three- or four-core cable, three-phase a.c.	1 two-core cable, single-phase a.c. or d.c.	1 three- or four-core cable, three-phase a.c.	1 two-core cable, single-phase a.c. or d.c.	1 three- or four-core cable, three-phase a.c.
1	2	3	4	5	6	7	8	9
(mm²)	(A)	(A)	(A)	(A)	(A)	(A)	(A)	(A)
16	44	41	54	48	66	59	73	61
25	58	53	71	62	83	73	89	78
35	71	65	86	77	103	90	111	96
50	86	78	104	92	125	110	135	117
70	108	98	131	116	160	140	173	150
95	130	118	157	139	195	170	210	183
120	-	135	-	160	-	197	-	212
150	-	155	-	184	-	227	-	245
185	-	176	-	210	-	259	-	280
240	-	207	-	248	-	305	-	330
300	-	237	-	285	-	351	-	381

NOTE:
Where the conductor is to be protected by a semi-enclosed fuse to BS 3036, see item 6.2 of the preface to this appendix.

TABLE 4K2B

VOLTAGE DROP (per ampere per metre): Conductor operating temperature: 70 °C

Conductor cross-sectional area	Two-core cable, d.c.	Two-core cable, single-phase a.c.			Three- or four-core cable, three-phase a.c.		
1	2	3			4		
(mm²)	(mV/A/m)	(mV/A/m)			(mV/A/m)		
16	4.5	4.5			3.9		
		r	x	z	r	x	z
25	2.9	2.9	0.175	2.9	2.5	0.150	2.5
35	2.1	2.1	0.170	2.1	1.80	0.150	1.80
50	1.55	1.55	0.170	1.55	1.35	0.145	1.35
70	1.05	1.05	0.165	1.05	0.90	0.140	0.92
95	0.77	0.77	0.160	0.79	0.67	0.140	0.68
120	-	-	-	-	0.53	0.135	0.55
150	-	-	-	-	0.42	0.135	0.44
185	-	-	-	-	0.34	0.135	0.37
240	-	-	-	-	0.26	0.130	0.30
300	-	-	-	-	0.21	0.130	0.25

TABLE 4K3A

Single-core 70 °C armoured thermoplastic (pvc) insulated cables (non-magnetic armour)
(ALUMINIUM CONDUCTORS)

CURRENT-CARRYING CAPACITY (amperes):

Ambient temperature: 30 °C
Conductor operating temperature: 70 °C

NOTE:
Where the conductor is to be protected by a semi-enclosed fuse to BS 3036, see item 6.2 of the preface to this appendix.

Conductor cross-sectional area	Reference Method 1 (clipped direct)		Reference Method 11 (on a perforated cable tray)		Reference Method 12 (free air)						
					2 cables, single-phase a.c.		2 cables, d.c. spaced		3 or 4 cables, three-phase a.c.		
	2 cables, single-phase a.c. or d.c. flat and touching	3 or 4 cables, three-phase a.c. flat and touching	2 cables, single-phase a.c. or d.c. flat and touching	3 or 4 cables, three-phase a.c. flat and touching	Horizontal flat spaced	Vertical flat spaced	Horizontal	Vertical	Horizontal flat spaced	Vertical flat spaced	3 cables trefoil
1	2	3	4	5	6	7	8	9	10	11	12
(mm2)	(A)	(A)	(A)	(A)	(A)	(A)	(A)	(A)	(A)	(A)	(A)
50	143	133	152	141	168	159	167	157	169	155	131
70	183	168	194	178	212	200	214	202	213	196	168
95	221	202	234	214	259	245	261	247	255	236	205
120	255	233	270	246	299	285	303	288	293	272	238
150	294	267	310	282	340	323	349	333	335	312	275
185	334	303	352	319	389	371	400	382	379	354	315
240	393	354	413	374	457	437	472	452	443	415	372
300	452	405	474	427	520	498	545	523	505	475	430
380	518	452	543	479	583	559	638	613	551	518	497
480	586	501	616	534	655	629	742	715	604	568	568
600	658	550	692	589	724	696	859	828	656	618	642
740	728	596	769	642	802	770	986	952	707	666	715
960	819	651	868	706	866	832	1171	1133	770	726	808
1200	893	692	952	756	938	902	1360	1317	822	774	880

TABLE 4K3B

VOLTAGE DROP (per ampere per metre):

Conductor operating temperature: 70 °C

Conductor cross-sectional area	2 cables, d.c.	2 cables, single-phase a.c.						3 or 4 cables, three-phase a.c.								
		Reference Methods 1 & 11 (touching)			Reference Method 12 (spaced*)			Reference Methods 1, 11 & 12 (in trefoil touching)			Reference Methods 1 & 11 (flat and touching)			Reference Method 12 (flat spaced*)		
1	2	3			4			5			6			7		
(mm²)	(mV/A/m)	(mV/A/m)			(mV/A/m)			(mV/A/m)			(mV/A/m)			(mV/A/m)		
		r	x	z	r	x	z	r	x	z	r	x	z	r	x	z
50	1.55	1.55	0.23	1.55	1.55	0.31	1.55	1.35	0.195	1.35	1.35	0.27	1.35	1.30	0.34	1.35
70	1.05	1.05	0.22	1.10	1.05	0.30	1.10	0.92	0.190	0.93	0.93	0.26	0.96	0.95	0.33	1.00
95	0.77	0.78	0.21	0.81	0.81	0.29	0.86	0.68	0.185	0.70	0.70	0.25	0.75	0.73	0.32	0.80
120	0.61	0.62	0.21	0.66	0.65	0.29	0.71	0.54	0.180	0.57	0.57	0.25	0.62	0.60	0.32	0.58
150	0.49	0.50	0.20	0.54	0.53	0.28	0.60	0.44	0.175	0.47	0.46	0.24	0.52	0.50	0.31	0.58
185	0.39	0.41	0.195	0.45	0.44	0.28	0.52	0.35	0.170	0.39	0.38	0.24	0.45	0.42	0.30	0.51
240	0.30	0.32	0.190	0.37	0.34	0.27	0.44	0.28	0.165	0.32	0.30	0.23	0.38	0.33	0.29	0.44
300	0.24	0.26	0.185	0.32	0.28	0.26	0.39	0.22	0.160	0.27	0.24	0.23	0.34	0.28	0.29	0.40
380	0.190	0.22	0.185	0.28	0.26	0.25	0.36	0.185	0.155	0.24	0.22	0.22	0.32	0.27	0.26	0.38
480	0.150	0.180	0.180	0.25	0.22	0.25	0.33	0.155	0.155	0.22	0.195	0.22	0.29	0.24	0.25	0.35
600	0.120	0.150	0.175	0.23	0.195	0.24	0.31	0.130	0.150	0.200	0.170	0.21	0.27	0.21	0.24	0.32
740	0.097	0.135	0.170	0.22	0.180	0.23	0.29	0.115	0.145	0.185	0.160	0.20	0.26	0.200	0.22	0.30
960	0.075	0.115	0.160	0.200	0.165	0.21	0.27	0.100	0.140	0.175	0.150	0.185	0.24	0.190	0.195	0.27
1200	0.060	0.110	0.155	0.190	0.160	0.180	0.24	0.094	0.140	0.170	0.145	0.160	0.22	0.185	0.165	0.25

NOTE: * Spacings larger than those specified in Method 12 (see Table 4A1) will result in larger voltage drop.

TABLE 4K4A

Multicore 70 °C armoured thermoplastic (pvc) insulated cables
(ALUMINIUM CONDUCTORS)

Ambient temperature: 30 °C
Conductor operating temperature: 70 °C

CURRENT-CARRYING CAPACITY (amperes):

NOTE:
Where the conductor is to be protected by a semi-enclosed fuse to BS 3036, see item 6.2 of the preface to this appendix.

Conductor cross-sectional area	Reference Method 1 (clipped direct)		Reference Method 11 (on a perforated cable tray) or Reference Method 13 (free air)	
	1 two-core cable, single-phase a.c. or d.c.	1 three- or four-core cable, three-phase a.c.	1 two-core cable, single-phase a.c. or d.c.	1 three- or four-core cable, three-phase a.c.
1	2	3	4	5
(mm²)	(A)	(A)	(A)	(A)
16	68	58	71	61
25	89	76	94	80
35	109	94	115	99
50	131	113	139	119
70	165	143	175	151
95	199	174	211	186
120	-	202	-	216
150	-	232	-	250
185	-	265	-	287
240	-	312	-	342
300	-	360	-	399

TABLE 4K4B

VOLTAGE DROP (per ampere per metre):   Conductor operating temperature: 70 °C

Conductor cross-sectional area	Two-core cable, d.c.	Two-core cable, single-phase a.c.			Three- or four-core cable, three-phase a.c.		
1	2	3			4		
(mm²)	(mV/A/m)	(mV/A/m)			(mV/A/m)		
16	4.5	4.5			3.9		
		r	x	z	r	x	z
25	2.9	2.9	0.175	2.9	2.5	0.150	2.5
35	2.1	2.1	0.170	2.1	1.80	0.150	1.80
50	1.55	1.55	0.170	1.55	1.35	0.145	1.35
70	1.05	1.05	0.165	1.05	0.90	0.140	0.92
95	0.77	0.77	0.160	0.79	0.67	0.140	0.68
120	-	-	-	-	0.53	0.135	0.55
150	-	-	-	-	0.42	0.135	0.44
185	-	-	-	-	0.34	0.135	0.37
240	-	-	-	-	0.26	0.130	0.30
300	-	-	-	-	0.21	0.130	0.25

ALUMINIUM CONDUCTORS

TABLE 4L1A
Single-core 90 °C thermosetting insulated cables, unarmoured, with or without sheath (ALUMINIUM CONDUCTORS)

Ambient temperature: 30 °C
Conductor operating temperature: 90 °C

CURRENT-CARRYING CAPACITY (amperes):

Conductor cross-sectional area	Reference Method 4 (enclosed in conduit in thermally insulating wall etc.)		Reference Method 3 (enclosed in conduit on a wall or in trunking etc.)		Reference Method 1 (clipped direct)		Reference Method 11 (on a perforated cable tray horizontal or vertical)		Reference Method 12 (free air)		
	2 cables, single-phase a.c. or d.c.	3 or 4 cables, three-phase a.c.	2 cables, single-phase a.c. or d.c.	3 or 4 cables, three-phase a.c.	2 cables, single-phase a.c. or d.c. flat and touching	3 or 4 cables, three-phase a.c. flat and touching or trefoil	2 cables, single-phase a.c. or d.c. flat and touching	3 or 4 cables, three-phase a.c. flat and touching or trefoil	Horizontal flat spaced — 2 cables, single-phase a.c. or d.c. or 3 cables, three-phase a.c.	Vertical flat spaced — 2 cables, single-phase a.c. or d.c. or 3 cables, three-phase a.c.	Trefoil — 3 cables trefoil, three-phase a.c.
1	2	3	4	5	6	7	8	9	10	11	12
(mm2)	(A)	(A)	(A)	(A)	(A)	(A)	(A)	(A)	(A)	(A)	(A)
50	125	113	157	140	169	149	180	165	210	188	159
70	158	142	200	179	215	189	231	211	271	244	206
95	191	171	242	217	265	234	281	258	332	300	253
120	220	197	281	251	308	273	326	300	387	351	296
150	253	226	-	-	353	314	376	346	448	408	343
185	288	256	-	-	410	366	430	396	515	470	395
240	338	300	-	-	489	438	509	469	611	561	471
300	387	344	-	-	564	507	586	541	708	652	544
380	-	-	-	-	658	594	679	628	798	742	638
480	-	-	-	-	765	692	786	728	927	865	743
600	-	-	-	-	871	791	903	836	1058	990	849
740	-	-	-	-	1001	911	1025	951	1218	1143	979
960	-	-	-	-	1176	1072	1191	1108	1440	1355	1151
1200	-	-	-	-	1333	1217	1341	1249	1643	1550	1307

NOTES:
1. **Where the conductor is to be protected by a semi-enclosed fuse to BS 3036, see item 6.2 of the preface to this appendix.**
2. Where a conductor operates at a temperature exceeding 70 °C it shall be ascertained that the equipment connected to the conductor is suitable for the conductor operating temperature (see Regulation 512-02).
3. Where cables in this table are connected to equipment or accessories designed to operate at a temperature not exceeding 70 °C, the current ratings given in the equivalent table for 70 °C thermoplastic (pvc) insulated cables (Table 4K1A) shall be used (see also Regulation 523-01-01).

TABLE 4L1B

VOLTAGE DROP (per ampere per metre): Conductor operating temperature: 90 °C

		2 cables, single-phase a.c.										3 or 4 cables, three-phase a.c.											
Conductor cross-sectional area	2 cables, d.c.	Reference Methods 3 &4 (enclosed in conduit etc. in or on a wall)			Reference Methods 1 &11 (clipped direct or on trays, touching)			Reference Method 12 (spaced*)			Reference Methods 3 &4 (enclosed in conduit etc. in or on a wall)			Reference Methods 1, 11 &12 (in trefoil)			Reference Methods 1 &11 (flat and touching)			Reference Method 12 (flat spaced*)		
		3			4			5			6			7			8			9		
(mm²)	(mV/A/m)	(mV/A/m)			(mV/A/m)			(mV/A/m)			(mV/A/m)			(mV/A/m)			(mV/A/m)			(mV/A/m)		
1	2	r	x	z	r	x	z	r	x	z	r	x	z	r	x	z	r	x	z	r	x	z
50	1.65	1.70	0.30	1.72	1.65	0.190	1.66	1.65	0.28	1.68	1.44	0.26	1.46	1.44	0.165	1.45	1.44	0.24	1.46	1.44	0.32	1.48
70	1.13	1.17	0.30	1.21	1.12	0.185	1.14	1.12	0.27	1.15	1.00	0.26	1.04	0.97	0.160	0.98	0.97	0.24	1.00	0.97	0.31	1.02
95	0.82	0.86	0.29	0.91	0.82	0.185	0.84	0.82	0.27	0.94	0.75	0.25	0.79	0.71	0.160	0.73	0.71	0.23	0.75	0.71	0.31	0.78
120	0.65	0.68	0.29	0.74	0.65	0.180	0.67	0.65	0.27	0.70	0.59	0.25	0.64	0.57	0.155	0.59	0.57	0.23	0.61	0.57	0.31	0.64
150	0.53	0.54	0.28	0.61	0.52	0.175	0.55	0.52	0.26	0.58	0.48	0.24	0.54	0.45	0.155	0.47	0.45	0.23	0.50	0.45	0.30	0.54
185	0.42	0.45	0.28	0.53	0.43	0.175	0.46	0.42	0.26	0.49	0.38	0.24	0.45	0.36	0.150	0.39	0.36	0.23	0.43	0.36	0.30	0.47
240	0.32	0.34	0.27	0.43	0.32	0.170	0.36	0.32	0.26	0.41	0.30	0.24	0.38	0.28	0.150	0.32	0.28	0.22	0.35	0.28	0.30	0.41
300	0.26	0.28	0.27	0.38	0.26	0.170	0.31	0.26	0.26	0.36	0.25	0.23	0.34	0.22	0.145	0.27	0.22	0.22	0.31	0.22	0.30	0.37
380	0.20	-	-	-	0.21	0.165	0.27	0.21	0.25	0.33	0.20	0.23	0.31	0.180	0.145	0.23	0.180	0.22	0.28	0.180	0.29	0.34
480	0.160	-	-	-	0.170	0.165	0.23	0.165	0.25	0.30	0.165	0.23	0.28	0.150	0.140	0.20	0.150	0.22	0.27	0.145	0.29	0.32
600	0.130	-	-	-	0.140	0.160	0.21	0.135	0.25	0.28	0.135	0.22	0.26	0.120	0.140	0.185	0.120	0.22	0.25	0.120	0.29	0.31
740	0.105	-	-	-	0.115	0.160	0.19	0.110	0.25	0.27	-	-	-	0.100	0.135	0.170	0.100	0.21	0.23	0.095	0.29	0.30
960	0.080	-	-	-	0.092	0.155	0.18	0.087	0.24	0.26	-	-	-	0.082	0.135	0.160	0.082	0.21	0.23	0.076	0.29	0.30
1200	0.064	-	-	-	0.073	0.155	0.17	0.073	0.24	0.25	-	-	-	0.070	0.135	0.150	0.070	0.21	0.22	0.063	0.28	0.29

NOTE: * Spacings larger than those specified in Method 12 (see Table 4A1) will result in larger voltage drop.

ALUMINIUM CONDUCTORS

TABLE 4L2A
Multicore 90 °C thermosetting insulated cables, non-armoured
(ALUMINIUM CONDUCTORS)

CURRENT-CARRYING CAPACITY (amperes):

Ambient temperature: 30 °C

Conductor operating temperature: 90 °C

Conductor cross-sectional area	Reference Method 4 (enclosed in an insulated wall etc.)		Reference Method 3 (enclosed in conduit on a wall or ceiling, or in trunking)		Reference Method 1 (clipped direct)		Reference Method 11 (on a perforated cable tray) or Reference Method 13 (free air)	
	1 two-core cable, single-phase a.c. or d.c.	1 three- or four-core cable, three-phase a.c.	1 two-core cable, single-phase a.c. or d.c.	1 three- or four-core cable, three-phase a.c.	1 two-core cable, single-phase a.c. or d.c.	1 three- or four-core cable, three-phase a.c.	1 two-core cable, single-phase a.c. or d.c.	1 three- or four-core cable, three-phase a.c.
1	2	3	4	5	6	7	8	9
(mm²)	(A)	(A)	(A)	(A)	(A)	(A)	(A)	(A)
16	60	55	72	64	84	76	91	77
25	78	71	94	84	101	90	108	97
35	96	87	115	103	126	112	135	120
50	115	104	138	124	154	136	164	146
70	145	131	175	156	198	174	211	187
95	175	157	210	188	241	211	257	227
120	-	180	-	216	-	245	-	263
150	-	206	-	240	-	283	-	304
185	-	233	-	272	-	323	-	347
240	-	273	-	318	-	382	-	409
300	-	313	-	364	-	440	-	471

NOTES:

1. Where the conductor is to be protected by a semi-enclosed fuse to BS 3036, see item 6.2 of the preface to this appendix.

2. Where a conductor operates at a temperature exceeding 70 °C it shall be ascertained that the equipment connected to the conductor is suitable for the conductor operating temperature (see Regulation 512-02).

3. Where cables in this table are connected to equipment or accessories designed to operate at a temperature not exceeding 70 °C, the current ratings given in the equivalent table for 70 °C thermoplastic (pvc) insulated cables (Table 4K2A) shall be used (see also Regulation 523-01-01).

TABLE 4L2B

VOLTAGE DROP (per ampere per metre): Conductor operating temperature: 90 °C

Conductor cross-sectional area	Two-core cable, d.c.	Two-core cable, single-phase a.c.			Three- or four-core cable, three-phase a.c.		
1	2	3			4		
(mm²)	(mVA/m)	(mV/A/m)			(mV/A/m)		
	4.8	4.8			4.2		
16							
		r	x	z	r	x	z
25	3.1	3.1	0.165	3.1	2.7	0.140	2.7
35	2.2	2.2	0.160	2.2	1.90	0.140	1.95
50	1.60	1.65	0.160	1.65	1.40	0.135	1.45
70	1.10	1.10	0.155	1.15	0.96	0.135	0.97
95	0.82	0.82	0.150	0.84	0.71	0.130	0.72
120	-	-	-	-	0.56	0.130	0.58
150	-	-	-	-	0.45	0.130	0.47
185	-	-	-	-	0.37	0.130	0.39
240	-	-	-	-	0.28	0.125	0.31
300	-	-	-	-	0.23	0.125	0.26

TABLE 4L3A

Single-core 90 °C armoured thermosetting insulated cables (non-magnetic armour)
(ALUMINIUM CONDUCTORS)

CURRENT-CARRYING CAPACITY (amperes):

Ambient temperature: 30 °C
Conductor operating temperature: 90 °C

Conductor cross-sectional area	Reference Method 1 (clipped direct)		Reference Method 11 (on a perforated cable tray)		Reference Method 12 (free air)						
	2 cables, single-phase a.c. or d.c., flat and touching	3 or 4 cables, three-phase a.c., flat and touching	2 cables, single-phase a.c. or d.c., flat and touching	3 or 4 cables, three-phase a.c., flat and touching	2 cables, single-phase a.c.		2 cables, d.c.		3 or 4 cables, three-phase a.c.		
					Horizontal flat spaced	Vertical flat spaced	Horizontal spaced	Vertical spaced	Horizontal flat spaced	Vertical flat spaced	3 cables trefoil
1	2	3	4	5	6	7	8	9	10	11	12
(mm²)	(A)	(A)	(A)	(A)	(A)	(A)	(A)	(A)	(A)	(A)	(A)
50	179	165	192	176	212	199	216	197	215	192	162
70	228	209	244	222	269	254	275	253	270	244	207
95	276	252	294	267	328	310	332	307	324	296	252
120	320	291	340	308	378	358	384	357	372	343	292
150	368	333	390	352	429	409	441	411	424	394	337
185	419	378	444	400	490	467	511	480	477	447	391
240	494	443	521	468	576	549	605	572	554	523	465
300	568	508	597	536	654	624	701	666	626	595	540
380	655	573	688	608	735	704	812	780	693	649	625
480	747	642	786	685	825	790	942	906	765	717	714
600	836	706	880	757	909	872	1076	1036	832	780	801
740	934	764	988	824	989	950	1250	1205	890	835	897
960	1056	838	1121	911	1094	1052	1488	1435	970	911	1014
1200	1163	903	1236	990	1187	1141	1715	1658	1043	980	1118

NOTES:

1. **Where the conductor is to be protected by a semi-enclosed fuse to BS 3036, see item 6.2 of the preface to this appendix.**

2. Where a conductor operates at a temperature exceeding 70 °C it shall be ascertained that the equipment connected to the conductor is suitable for the conductor operating temperature (see Regulation 512-02).

3. Where cables in this table are connected to equipment or accessories designed to operate at a temperature not exceeding 70°C, the current ratings given in the equivalent table for 70 °C thermoplastic (pvc) insulated cables (Table 4K3A) shall be used (see also Regulation 523-01-01).

TABLE 4L3B

VOLTAGE DROP (per ampere per metre):
Conductor operating temperature: 90 °C

Conductor cross-sectional area (mm²)	2 cables, d.c. (mV/A/m)	2 cables, single-phase a.c. Reference Methods 1 & 11 (touching) (mV/A/m)			Reference Method 12 (spaced*) (mV/A/m)			3 or 4 cables, three-phase a.c. Reference Methods 1 11 &12 (in trefoil touching) (mV/A/m)			Reference Methods 1 &11 (flat and touching) (mV/A/m)			Reference Method 12 (flat spaced*) (mV/A/m)		
1	2	3			4			5			6			7		
		r	x	z	r	x	z	r	x	z	r	x	z	r	x	z
50	1.60	1.60	0.22	1.60	1.60	0.30	1.60	1.40	0.185	1.40	1.40	0.26	1.40	1.35	0.34	1.40
70	1.10	1.10	0.21	1.15	1.10	0.29	1.15	0.96	0.180	0.98	0.97	0.25	1.00	0.99	0.33	1.05
95	0.82	0.83	0.20	0.85	0.85	0.29	0.90	0.71	0.175	0.74	0.74	0.25	0.78	0.76	0.32	0.85
120	0.65	0.66	0.20	0.69	0.69	0.28	0.74	0.57	0.170	0.60	0.60	0.24	0.64	0.63	0.31	0.70
150	0.52	0.53	0.195	0.57	0.56	0.28	0.62	0.46	0.170	0.49	0.49	0.24	0.54	0.52	0.30	0.60
185	0.42	0.43	0.190	0.47	0.46	0.27	0.54	0.38	0.165	0.41	0.40	0.24	0.47	0.44	0.30	0.53
240	0.32	0.34	0.185	0.39	0.37	0.27	0.45	0.29	0.160	0.34	0.32	0.23	0.39	0.35	0.29	0.45
300	0.26	0.27	0.185	0.33	0.30	0.26	0.40	0.24	0.160	0.29	0.26	0.23	0.34	0.29	0.29	0.41
380	0.21	0.23	0.180	0.29	0.26	0.25	0.36	0.195	0.155	0.25	0.23	0.22	0.32	0.27	0.27	0.38
480	0.160	0.185	0.175	0.25	0.23	0.25	0.34	0.160	0.155	0.22	0.20	0.21	0.29	0.24	0.26	0.35
600	0.130	0.160	0.175	0.24	0.20	0.24	0.31	0.135	0.150	0.20	0.175	0.21	0.27	0.22	0.25	0.33
740	0.105	0.140	0.170	0.22	0.190	0.22	0.29	0.120	0.145	0.190	0.165	0.195	0.26	0.21	0.22	0.30
960	0.080	0.120	0.160	0.20	0.170	0.21	0.27	0.105	0.140	0.175	0.150	0.180	0.24	0.195	0.195	0.28
1200	0.064	0.105	0.160	0.190	0.155	0.20	0.25	0.093	0.135	0.165	0.140	0.175	0.22	0.180	0.185	0.26

NOTE: * Spacings larger than those specified in Method 12 (see Table 4A1) will result in larger voltage drop.

TABLE 4L4A

Multicore 90 °C armoured thermosetting insulated cables
(ALUMINIUM CONDUCTORS)

CURRENT-CARRYING CAPACITY (amperes):

Ambient temperature: 30 °C
Conductor operating temperature: 90 °C

Conductor cross-sectional area	Reference Method 1 (clipped direct)		Reference Method 11 (on a perforated cable tray) or Reference Method 13 (free air)	
	1 two-core cable, single-phase a.c. or d.c.	1 three- or four-core cable, three-phase a.c.	1 two-core cable, single-phase a.c. or d.c.	1 three- or four-core cable, three-phase a.c.
1	2	3	4	5
(mm²)	(A)	(A)	(A)	(A)
16	82	71	85	74
25	108	92	112	98
35	132	113	138	120
50	159	137	166	145
70	201	174	211	185
95	242	214	254	224
120	–	249	–	264
150	–	284	–	305
185	–	328	–	350
240	–	386	–	418
300	–	441	–	488

NOTES:

1. **Where the conductor is to be protected by a semi-enclosed fuse to BS 3036, see item 6.2 of the preface to this appendix.**

2. Where a conductor operates at a temperature exceeding 70 °C it shall be ascertained that the equipment connected to the conductor is suitable for the conductor operating temperature (see Regulation 512-02).

3. Where cables in this table are connected to equipment or accessories designed to operate at a temperature not exceeding 70°C, the current ratings given in the equivalent table for 70 °C thermoplastic (pvc) insulated cables (Table 4K4A) shall be used (see also Regulation 523-01-01).

TABLE 4L4B

VOLTAGE DROP (per ampere per metre): Conductor operating temperature: 90 °C

Conductor cross-sectional area	Two-core cable, d.c.		Two-core cable, single-phase a.c.				Three- or four-core cable, three-phase a.c.		
1	2		3				4		
(mm²)	(mV/A/m)		(mV/A/m)				(mV/A/m)		
16	4.8		4.8				4.2		
		r	x	z		r	x	z
25	3.1	3.1	0.165	3.1		2.7	0.140	2.7
35	2.2	2.2	0.160	2.2		1.90	0.140	1.95
50	1.60	1.65	0.160	1.65		1.40	0.135	1.45
70	1.10	1.10	0.155	1.15		0.96	0.135	0.97
95	0.82	0.82	0.150	0.84		0.71	0.130	0.72
120	-	-	-	-		0.56	0.130	0.58
150	-	-	-	-		0.45	0.130	0.47
185	-	-	-	-		0.37	0.130	0.39
240	-	-	-	-		0.28	0.125	0.31
300	-	-	-	-		0.23	0.125	0.26

273

APPENDIX 5

CLASSIFICATION OF EXTERNAL INFLUENCES
(Chapters 32 and 52)

This Appendix gives the classification and codification of external influences developed for IEC Publication 364-3, Second Edition 1993.

Each condition of external influence is designated by a code comprising a group of two capital letters and a number, as follows:

The first letter relates to the general category of external influence:

A   Environment

B   Utilisation

C   Construction of buildings

The second letter relates to the nature of the external influence:

...   **A**

...   **B**

...   **C**

The number relates to the class within each external influence:

...   ...   **1**

...   ...   **2**

...   ...   **3**

For example, the code **AA4** signifies:

A   = Environment

AA   = Environment - Ambient temperature

AA4   = Environment - Ambient temperature in the range of -5 °C to +40 °C.

NOTE: The codification given in this Appendix is not intended to be used for marking equipment.

APPENDIX 5
CONCISE LIST OF EXTERNAL INFLUENCES

A ENVIRONMENT

AA *Ambient (°C)*

AA1	-60 °C	+5 °C
AA2	-40 °C	+5 °C
AA3	-25 °C	+5 °C
AA4	-5 °C	+40 °C
AA5	+5 °C	+40 °C
AA6	+5 °C	+60 °C
AA7	-25 °C	+55 °C
AA8	-50 °C	+40 °C

AB *Temperature and humidity*

AC *Altitude (metres)*

AC1	≤ 2000 metres
AC2	> 2000 metres

AD *Water*

AD1	Negligible
AD2	Drops
AD3	Sprays
AD4	Splashes
AD5	Jets
AD6	Waves
AD7	Immersion
AD8	Submersion

AE *Foreign bodies*

AE1	Negligible
AE2	Small
AE3	Very small
AE4	Light dust
AE5	Moderate dust
AE6	Heavy dust

AF *Corrosion*

AF1	Negligible
AF2	Atmospheric
AF3	Intermittent
AF4	Continuous

AG *Impact*

AG1	Low
AG2	Medium
AG3	High

AH *Vibration*

AH1	Low
AH2	Medium
AH3	High

AJ *Other mechanical stresses*

AK *Flora*

AK1	No hazard
AK2	Hazard

AL *Fauna*

AL1	No hazard
AL2	Hazard

AM *Radiation*

AM1	Electromagnetic, ...
AM2	Signalling voltages
AM3	Voltage amplitude variations
AM4	Voltage unbalance
AM5	Power frequency variations
AM6	Induced low-frequency voltages
AM7	DC in AC networks
AM8	Radiated magnetic fields
AM9	Electric fields
AM21	High-frequency etc...
AM22	Conducted...nano...
AM23	Conducted...micro...
AM24	Conducted oscillatory...
AM25	Radiated HF phenomena
AM31	Electrostatic discharges
AM41	Ionization

AN *Solar*

AN1	Low
AN2	Medium
AN3	High

AP *Seismic*

AP1	Negligible
AP2	Low
AP3	Medium
AP4	High

AQ *Lightning*

AQ1	Negligible
AQ2	Indirect
AQ3	Direct

AR *Movement of air*

AR1	Low
AR2	Medium
AR3	High

AS *Wind*

AS1	Low
AS2	Medium
AS3	High

B UTILIZATION

BA *Capability*

BA1	Ordinary
BA2	Children
BA3	Handicapped
BA4	Instructed
BA5	Skilled

BB *Resistance*

BC *Contact with earth*

BC1	None
BC2	Low
BC3	Frequent
BC4	Continuous

BD *Evacuation*

BD1	Normal
BD2	Difficult
BD3	Crowded
BD4	Difficult and crowded

BE *Materials*

BE1	No risk
BE2	Fire risk
BE3	Explosion risk
BE4	Contamination risk

C BUILDING

CA *Materials*

CA1	Non-combustible
CA2	Combustible

CB *Structure*

CB1	Negligible
CB2	Fire propagation
CB3	Structural movement
CB4	Flexible

Environment:

Code	Class designation	Characteristics	Applications and examples
	Ambient temperature		
		The ambient temperature is that of the ambient air where the equipment is to be installed.	
		It is assumed that the ambient temperature includes the effects of all other equipment installed in the same location.	
		The ambient temperature to be considered for the equipment is the temperature at the place where the equipment is to be installed resulting from the influence of all other equipment in the same location, when operating, not taking into account the thermal contribution of the equipment to be installed.	
		Lower and upper limits of the ranges of ambient temperature:	
AA1		-60 °C +5 °C	
AA2		-40 °C +5 °C	
AA3		-25 °C +5 °C	
AA4		-5 °C +40 °C	
AA5		+5 °C +40 °C	
AA6		+5 °C +60 °C	
AA7		-25 °C +55 °C	
AA8		-50 °C +40 °C	
		Ambient temperature classes are applicable only where humidity has no influence.	
		The average temperature over a 24-hour period must not exceed 5 °C below the upper limits.	
		Combination of two ranges to define some environments may be necessary. Installations subject to temperatures outside the ranges require special consideration	

Environment continued:

Code	Class designation	Characteristics						Applications and examples
		Ambient climatic conditions (combined influence of temperature and humidity)						
		Low air temperature °C	High air temperature °C	Low relative humidity %	High relative humidity %	Low absolute humidity g/m^3	High absolute humidity g/m^3	
AB1		-60	+5	3	100	0.003	7	Indoor and outdoor locations with extremely low ambient temperatures
AB2		-40	+5	10	100	0.1	7	Indoor and outdoor locations with low ambient temperatures
AB3		-25	+5	10	100	0.5	7	Indoor and outdoor locations with low ambient temperatures
AB4		-5	+40	5	95	1	29	Weather protected locations having neither temperature nor humidity control. Heating may be used to raise low ambient temperatures
AB5		+5	+40	5	85	1	25	Weather protected locations with temperature control
AB6		+5	+60	10	100	1	35	Indoor and outdoor locations with extremely high ambient temperature, influence of cold ambient temperature is prevented. Occurrence of solar and heat radiation
AB7		-25	+55	10	100	0.5	29	Indoor weather protected locations having neither temperature nor humidity control, the locations may have openings directly to the open air or be subjected to solar radiation
AB8		-50	+40	15	100	0.04	36	Outdoor and non-weather protected locations, with low and high temperatures

NOTES:

1. All specified values are maximum or limit values which will have a low probability of being exceeded.

2. The low and high relative humidities are limited by the low and high absolute humidities, so that the limit values given do not occur simultaneously. See IEC 364-3 for climatograms which describe the interdependence of air temperature, relative humidity and absolute humidity for the climate classes specified.

Environment continued:

Code	Class designation	Characteristics	Applications and examples
	Altitude		
AC1 AC2		≤ 2000 m > 2000 m	
	Presence of water		
AD1	Negligible	Probability of presence of water is negligible	Location in which the walls do not generally show traces of water but may do so for short periods, for example in the form of vapour which good ventilation dries rapidly
AD2	Free-falling drops	Possibility of vertically falling drops	Location in which water vapour occasionally condenses as drops or where steam may occasionally be present
AD3	Sprays	Possibility of water falling as a spray at an angle up to 60 degrees from the vertical	Locations in which sprayed water forms a continuous film on floors and/or walls
AD4	Splashes	Possibility of splashes from any direction	Locations where equipment may be subjected to splashed water; this applies, for example, to certain external luminaires, construction site equipment
AD5	Jets	Possibility of jets of water from any direction	Locations where hosewater is used regularly (yards, car-washing bays)
AD6	Waves	Possibility of water waves	Seashore locations such as piers, beaches, quays, etc.
AD7	Immersion	Possibility of intermittent partial or total covering by water	Locations which may be flooded and/or where water may be at maximum 150 mm above the highest point of equipment, the lowest part of equipment being not more than 1 m below the water surface
AD8	Submersion	Possibility of permanent and total covering by water	Locations such as swimming pools where electrical equipment is permanently and totally covered with water under a pressure greater than 0.1 bar
	Presence of foreign solid bodies		
AE1	Negligible	The quantity or nature of dust or foreign solid bodies is not significant	
AE2	Small objects	Presence of foreign solid bodies where the smallest dimension is not less than 2.5 mm	Tools and small objects are examples of foreign bodies of which the smallest dimension is at least 2.5 mm
AE3	Very small objects	Presence of foreign solid bodies where the smallest dimension is not less than 1 mm	Wires are examples of foreign solid bodies of which the smallest dimension is not less than 1 mm
AE4	Light dust	Presence of light deposits of dust $10 < \frac{\text{deposit of dust}}{} \leq 35$ mg/m^2 a day	

Environment continued:

Code	Class designation	Characteristics	Applications and examples
AE5	Moderate	Presence of medium deposits of dust $35 < \begin{smallmatrix}\text{deposit}\\\text{of dust}\end{smallmatrix} \leq 350$ mg/m^2 a day	
AE6	Heavy dust	Presence of large deposits of dust $350 < \begin{smallmatrix}\text{deposit}\\\text{of dust}\end{smallmatrix} \leq 1000$ mg/m^2 a day	
	Presence of corrosive or polluting substances		
AF1	Negligible	The quantity or nature of corrosive or polluting substances is not significant	
AF2	Atmospheric	The presence of corrosive or polluting substances of atmospheric origin is significant	Installations situated by the sea or near industrial zones producing serious atmospheric pollution, such as chemical works, cement works; this type of pollution arises especially in the production of abrasive, insulating or conductive dusts
AF3	Intermittent or accidental	Intermittent or accidental subjection to corrosive or polluting chemical substances being used or produced	Locations where some chemical products are handled in small quantities and where these products may come only accidentally into contact with electrical equipment; such conditions are found in factory laboratories, other laboratories or in locations where hydrocarbons are used (boiler-rooms, garages, etc.)
AF4	Continuous	Continuously subject to corrosive or polluting chemical substances in substantial quantity	For example, chemical works
	Mechanical stress		
	Impact		
AG1	Low severity		Household and similar conditions
AG2	Medium severity		Usual industrial conditions
AG3	High severity		Severe industrial conditions
	Vibration		
AH1	Low severity		Household and similar conditions where the effects of vibration are generally negligible
AH2	Medium severity		Usual industrial conditions
AH3	High severity		Industrial installations subject to severe conditions

279

Environment continued:

Code	Class designation	Characteristics	Applications and examples
	Other mechanical stresses		
AJ	(Classification under consideration)		
	Presence of flora and/or mould growth		
AK1	No hazard	No harmful hazard or flora and/or mould growth	
AK2	Hazard	Harmful hazard or flora and/or mould growth	The hazard depends on local conditions and the nature of flora. Distinction should be made between harmful growth of vegetation or conditions for promotion of mould growth
	Presence of fauna		
AL1	No hazard	No harmful hazard from fauna	
AL2	Hazard	Harmful hazard from fauna (insects, birds, small animals)	The hazard depends on the nature of the fauna. Distinction should be made between: - presence of insects in harmful quantity or of an aggressive nature - presence of small animals or birds in harmful quantity or of an aggressive nature
	Electromagnetic, electrostatic or ionizing influence		
AM1	*Electromagnetic, electrostatic or ionizing influences* *Low-frequency electromagnetic phenomena (conducted or radiated)* *Harmonics, interharmonics*		
AM1-1	Controlled level	Controlled situation	Medical apparatus Measuring instruments
AM1-2	Normal level	Low voltage networks	Residential Commercial Light industry
AM1-3	High level	Disturbed networks	Industrial systems or large commercial buildings supplied by dedicated HV/LV substations
AM2	*Signalling voltages (superimposed voltages for control purposes eg ripple-free control units)*		
AM2-1	Controlled level	Residual signals only	Protected installation or protected part of an installation
AM2-2	Medium level	Presence of signalling voltages	Residential Commercial Industrial
AM2-3	High level	Resonance	Special cases

Environment continued:

Code	Class designation	Characteristics	Applications and examples
AM3	*Voltage amplitude variations*		
AM3-1	Controlled level	Use of UPS	Sensitive loads such as information technology equipment
AM3-2	Normal level	Voltage fluctuations Voltage dips and interruptions	Residential Commercial Industrial
AM4	*Voltage unbalance*		
AM4-1	Normal level		
AM5	*Power frequency variations*		
AM5-1	Normal level	Slight frequency variations	General case
AM6	*Induced low-frequency voltages*		
AM6-1	No class	Generated continuously or during fault conditions	General case
AM7	*Direct current in AC networks*		
AM7-1	No class	Fault conditions downstream of rectifiers	General case
AM8	*Radiated magnetic fields*		
AM8-1	Medium level	Produced by power lines, transformers and other apparatus at the power frequency and its harmonics	Residential Commercial Light industrial
AM8-2	High level	Close vicinity of the above-mentioned apparatus or similar ones	Heavy industrial HV/LV stations Switchboards Vicinity of railway tracks
AM9	*Electric fields*		
AM9-1	Negligible level	General case	
AM9-2	Medium level	According to the value of the voltage and the location, indoor or outdoor	Vicinity of high voltage overhead lines or HV station
AM9-3	High level		
AM9-4	Very high level		
AM21	*High-frequency electromagnetic phenomena conducted, induced or radiated (continuous or transient)* *Induced oscillatory voltages or currents*		
AM21-1	No class	Mainly common mode disturbances generated by continuous AM-or FM-modulated electromagnetic fields	General case
AM22	*Conducted unidirectional transients of the nanosecond time scale*		
AM22-1	Negligible level	Protected environment	Computer rooms
AM22-2	Medium level	Protected environment	Control rooms
AM22-3	High level	Switching of small inductive loads, bouncing of relay contacts Dielectric breakdowns	Low voltage network
AM22-4	Very high level	HV/LV stations Gas-insulated switchgear or vacuum switchgear	Heavy industrial Main or intermediate distribution boards

Environment continued:

Code	Class designation	Characteristics	Applications and examples
AM23	*Conducted unidirectional transients of microsecond to millisecond time scale*		
AM23-1	Controlled level	Circuits or installations protected by surge arresters, transformers with link to earth	Controlled situations
AM23-2	Medium level	Far lightning (more than 1 km): wave shape 10/1000 μs and source impedance 20-300 Ω. Switching, e.g. clearing of a fault by a fuse; wave shape 0.1/1 ms and source impedance 50 Ω	Lightning far from an underground network
AM23-3	High level	Close lightning (less than 1km) wave shape 1.2/50 μs and source impedance 1-10 Ω	Lightning close to an overhead network or to a building
AM24	*Conducted oscillatory transients*		
AM24-1	Medium level	Indoor switching phenomena	Residential Commercial Industrial
AM24-2	High level	Switching phenomena	HV/MV substations
AM25	*Radiated high-frequency phenomena*		
AM25-1	Negligible level	Radio television stations at more than 1 km	Residential Commercial
AM25-2	Medium level	Portable transceivers not closer than 1 m	Light industrial
AM25-3	High level	High-power transceivers in the vicinity	Heavy industry Good reliable applications
AM31	*Electrostatic discharges*		
AM31-1	Low level	Particularly generated by people walking on synthetic carpets	According to the required reliability
AM31-2	Medium level	Level related to the type of carpet and humidity	
AM31-3	High level		
AM31-4	Very high level		
AM41	*Ionization*		
AM41-1	Ionization	Harmful presence of ionizing radiations	
	Solar radiation		
AN1	Low	Intensity ≤ 500 W/m^2	
AN2	Medium	500 < intensity ≤ 700 W/m^2	
AN3	High	700 < intensity ≤ 1120 W/m^2	

Environment continued:

Code	Class designation	Characteristics	Applications and examples
	Seismic effects		
AP1	Negligible	Acceleration ≤ 30 Gal	1 Gal = 1 cm/s^2
AP2	Low severity	30 < acceleration ≤ 300 Gal	
AP3	Medium severity	300 < acceleration ≤ 600 Gal	
AP4	High severity	600 < acceleration	Vibration which may cause the destruction of the building is outside the classification Frequency is not taken into account in the classification, however, if the seismic wave resonates with the building, seismic effects must be specially considered. In general, the frequency of seismic acceleration is between 0 Hz and 10 Hz
	Lightning, ceraunic level		
AQ1	Negligible	≤ 25 days per year	
AQ2	Indirect exposure	> 25 days per year Hazard from supply arrangement	Installations supplied by overhead lines
AQ3	Direct	Hazard from exposure of equipment	Parts of installations located outside buildings. The risks AQ2 and AQ3 relate to regions with a particularly high level of thunderstorm activity
	Movement of air		
AR1	Low	Speed ≤ 1 m/s	
AR2	Medium	1 m/s < speed ≤ 5 m/s	
AR3	High	5 m/s < speed ≤ 10 m/s	
	Wind		
AS1	Low	Speed ≤ 20 m/s	
AS2	Medium	20 m/s < speed ≤ 30 m/s	
AS3	High	30 m/s < speed ≤ 50 m/s	

Utilisation:

Code	Class designation	Characteristics	Applications and examples	
	Capability of persons			
BA1	Ordinary	Uninstructed persons		
BA2	Children	Children in locations intended for their occupation NOTE - This class does not necessarily apply to family dwellings	Nurseries	Requirement for inaccessibility of electrical equipment. Limitation of temperature of accessible surfaces
BA3	Handicapped	Persons not in command of all their physical and intellectual abilities (sick person, old persons)	Hospitals	Requirement for inaccessibility of electrical equipment. Limitation of temperature of accessible surfaces
BA4	Instructed	Persons adequately advised or supervised by skilled persons to enable them to avoid dangers which electricity may create (operating and maintenance staff)	Electrical operating areas	
BA5	Skilled	Persons with technical knowledge or sufficient experience to enable them to avoid dangers which electricity may create (engineers and technicians)	Closed electrical operating areas	
	Electrical resistance of the human body			
BB	(Classification under consideration)			
	Contact of persons with earth potential			
BC1	None	Persons in non-conducting situation	Non-conducting locations	
BC2	Low	Persons who do not in usual conditions make contact with extraneous-conductive-parts or stand on conducting surfaces		
BC3	Frequent	Persons who are frequently in touch with extraneous-conductive-parts or stand on conducting surfaces	Locations with extraneous-conductive-parts, either numerous or of large area	
BC4	Continuous	Persons who are in permanent contact with metallic surroundings and for whom the possibility of interrupting contact is limited.	Metallic surroundings such as boilers and tanks	

Utilisation continued:

Code	Class designation	Characteristics	Applications and examples
Conditions of evacuation in an emergency			
BD1	Normal	Low density occupation, easy conditions of evacuation	Buildings of normal or low height used for habitation
BD2	Difficult	Low density occupation, difficult conditions of evacuation	High-rise buildings
BD3	Crowded	High density occupation, easy conditions of evacuation	Locations open to the public (theatres, cinemas, department stores, etc.)
BD4	Difficult and crowded	High density occupation, difficult conditions of evacuation	High-rise buildings open to the public (hotels, hospitals, etc.)
Nature of processed or stored materials			
BE1	No significant risk		
BE2	Fire risks	Manufacture, processing or storage of flammable materials including presence of dust	Barns, woodworking shops, paper factories
BE3	Explosion risks	Processing or storage of explosive or low flash-point materials including presence of explosive dusts	Oil refineries, hydrocarbon stores
BE4	Contamination risks	Presence of unprotected foodstuffs, pharmaceutics, and similar products without protection	Foodstuff industries, kitchens. Certain precautions may be necessary, in the event of fault, to prevent processed materials being contaminated by electrical equipment, e.g. by broken lamps

Construction of buildings:

Code	Class designation	Characteristics	Applications and examples
	Construction of buildings		
CA1	Non-combustible		
CA2	Combustible	Buildings mainly constructed of combustible materials	Wooden buildings
	Building design		
CB1	Negligible risks		
CB2	Propagation of fire	Buildings of which the shape and dimensions facilitate the spread of fire (e.g. chimney effects)	High-rise buildings. Forced ventilation systems
CB3	Movement	Risks due to structural movement (e.g. displacement between different parts of a building or between a building and the ground, or settlement of ground of building foundations)	Buildings of considerable length or erected on unstable ground
CB4	Flexible or unstable	Structures which are weak or subject to movement (e.g. oscillation)	Tents, air-support structures, false ceilings, removable partitions. Installations to be structurally self-supporting

APPENDIX 6

MODEL FORMS FOR CERTIFICATION AND REPORTING

Introduction

(i) The Electrical Installation Certificate required by Part 7 shall be made out and signed or otherwise authenticated by a competent person or persons in respect of the design, construction, inspection and testing of the work.

(ii) The Minor Works Certificate required by Part 7 shall be made out and signed or otherwise authenticated by a competent person in respect of the inspection and testing of an installation.

(iii) The Periodic Inspection Report required by Part 7 shall be made out and signed or otherwise authenticated by a competent person in respect of the inspection and testing of an installation.

(iv) Competent persons will, as appropriate to their function under (i) (ii) and (iii) above, have a sound knowledge and experience relevant to the nature of the work undertaken and to the technical standards set down in this British Standard, be fully versed in the inspection and testing procedures contained in this Standard and employ adequate testing equipment.

(v) Electrical Installation Certificates will indicate the responsibility for design, construction, inspection and testing, whether in relation to new work or further work on an existing installation.

Where design, construction and inspection and testing is the responsibility of one person a Certificate with a single signature declaration in the form shown below may replace the multiple signatures section of the model form.

FOR DESIGN, CONSTRUCTION, INSPECTION & TESTING.

I being the person responsible for the Design, Construction, Inspection & Testing of the electrical installation (as indicated by my signature below), particulars of which are described above, having exercised reasonable skill and care when carrying out the Design, Construction, Inspection & Testing, hereby CERTIFY that the said work for which I have been responsible is to the best of my knowledge and belief in accordance with BS 7671 : ...., amended to ....(date) except for the departures, if any, detailed as follows.

(vi) A Minor Works Certificate will indicate the responsibility for design, construction, inspection and testing of the work described in Part 4 of the certificate.

(vii) A Periodic Inspection Report will indicate the responsibility for the inspection and testing of an installation within the extent and limitations specified on the report.

(viii) A schedule of inspections and a schedule of test results as required by Part 7 shall be issued with the associated Electrical Installation Certificate or Periodic Inspection Report.

(ix) When making out and signing a form on behalf of a company or other business entity, individuals shall state for whom they are acting.

(x) Additional forms may be required as clarification, if needed by non-technical persons, or in expansion, for larger or more complex installations.

(xi) The IEE Guidance Note 3 provides further information on inspection and testing on completion and for periodic inspections.

ELECTRICAL INSTALLATION CERTIFICATE

(REQUIREMENTS FOR ELECTRICAL INSTALLATIONS - BS 7671 [IEE WIRING REGULATIONS])

DETAILS OF THE CLIENT

....

INSTALLATION ADDRESS

....

....

DESCRIPTION AND EXTENT OF THE INSTALLATION Tick boxes as appropriate

Description of installation:

Extent of installation covered by this Certificate:

New installation	☐
Addition to an existing installation	☐
Alteration to an existing installation	☐

(Use continuation sheet if necessary)   see continuation sheet No: ....

FOR DESIGN

I/We being the person(s) responsible for the design of the electrical installation (as indicated by my/our signatures below), particulars of which are described above, having exercised reasonable skill and care when carrying out the design hereby CERTIFY that the design work for which I/we have been responsible is to the best of my/our knowledge and belief in accordance with BS 7671 : ...., amended to .... (date) except for the departures, if any, detailed as follows:

Details of departures from BS 7671 (Regulations 120-01-03, 120-02):

The extent of liability of the signatory or the signatories is limited to the work described above as the subject of this Certificate.

For the DESIGN of the installation: **(Where there is mutual responsibility for the design)

Signature: ....   Date: ....   Name (IN BLOCK LETTERS): .... Designer No 1

Signature: ....   Date: ....   Name (IN BLOCK LETTERS): .... Designer No 2**

FOR CONSTRUCTION

I/We being the person(s) responsible for the construction of the electrical installation (as indicated by my/our signatures below), particulars of which are described above, having exercised reasonable skill and care when carrying out the construction hereby CERTIFY that the construction work for which I/we have been responsible is to the best of my/our knowledge and belief in accordance with BS 7671 : ...., amended to ....(date) except for the departures, if any, detailed as follows:

Details of departures from BS 7671 (Regulations 120-01-03, 120-02):

The extent of liability of the signatory is limited to the work described above as the subject of this Certificate.

For CONSTRUCTION of the installation:

Signature: ....   Date: ....   Name (IN BLOCK LETTERS): .... Constructor

FOR INSPECTION & TESTING

I/We being the person(s) responsible for the inspection & testing of the electrical installation (as indicated by my/our signatures below), particulars of which are described above, having exercised reasonable skill and care when carrying out the inspection & testing hereby CERTIFY that the work for which I/we have been responsible is to the best of my/our knowledge and belief in accordance with BS 7671 : ...., amended to ....(date) except for the departures, if any, detailed as follows:

Details of departures from BS 7671 (Regulations 120-01-03, 120-02):

The extent of liability of the signatory is limited to the work described above as the subject of this Certificate.

For INSPECTION AND TEST of the installation:

Signature: ....   Date: ....   Name (IN BLOCK LETTERS): .... Inspector

NEXT INSPECTION

I/We the designer(s), recommend that this installation is further inspected and tested after an interval of not more than ....
years/months.

PARTICULARS OF SIGNATORIES TO THE ELECTRICAL INSTALLATION CERTIFICATE

Designer (No 1)

Name: .... Company: ....

Address: ....

.... Postcode: .... Tel No: ....

Designer (No 2)
(if applicable)

Name: .... Company: ....

Address: ....

.... Postcode: .... Tel No: ....

Constructor

Name: .... Company: ....

Address: ....

.... Postcode: .... Tel No: ....

Inspector

Name: .... Company: ....

Address: ....

.... Postcode: .... Tel No: ....

SUPPLY CHARACTERISTICS AND EARTHING ARRANGEMENTS   Tick boxes and enter details, as appropriate

Earthing arrangements	Number and Type of Live Conductors	Nature of Supply Parameters	Supply Protective Device Characteristics
TN-C ☐ TN-S ☐ TN-C-S ☐ TT ☐ IT ☐	a.c. ☐ d.c. ☐ 1-phase, 2-wire ☐ 2-pole ☐ 2-phase, 3-wire ☐ 3-pole ☐ 3-phase, 3-wire ☐ other ☐ 3-phase, 4-wire ☐	Nominal voltage, U/U_o [(1)] ....V Nominal frequency, f [(1)] ....Hz Prospective fault current, I_{pf} [(2)] ....kA External loop impedance, Z_e [(2)] ....Ω (Note: (1) by enquiry, (2) by enquiry or by measurement)	Type: .... Nominal current rating ....A

Alternative source ☐ of supply (to be detailed on attached schedules)

PARTICULARS OF INSTALLATION REFERRED TO IN THE CERTIFICATE   Tick boxes and enter details, as appropriate

Means of Earthing	Maximum Demand
Distributor's facility ☐	Maximum demand (load) .... Amps

Details of Installation Earth Electrode (where applicable)

Installation earth electrode ☐

Type (e.g. rod(s), tape etc)	Location	Electrode resistance to earth
....	....	.... Ω

Main Protective Conductors

Earthing conductor: material .... csa ....   connection verified ☐

Main equipotential bonding conductors   material .... csa ....   connection verified ☐

To incoming water and/or gas service ☐   To other elements: ....

Main Switch or Circuit-breaker

BS, Type and No. of poles ....   Current rating ....A   Voltage rating V

Location ....   Fuse rating or setting.................A

Rated residual operating current $I_{\Delta n}$ = ... mA, and operating time of .... ms (at $I_{\Delta n}$) (applicable only where an RCD is suitable and is used as a main circuit-breaker)

COMMENTS ON EXISTING INSTALLATION (in the case of an alteration or additions see Section 743):

....

....

....

....

SCHEDULES

The attached Schedules are part of this document and this Certificate is valid only when they are attached to it.

.... Schedules of Inspections and .... Schedules of Test Results are attached.

(Enter quantities of schedules attached).

ELECTRICAL INSTALLATION CERTIFICATE
NOTES:

1. The Electrical Installation Certificate is to be used only for the initial certification of a new installation or for an alteration or addition to an existing installation where new circuits have been introduced.

    It is not to be used for a Periodic Inspection for which a Periodic Inspection Report form should be used. For an alteration or addition which does not extend to the introduction of new circuits, a Minor Electrical Installation Works Certificate may be used.

    The original Certificate is to be given to the person ordering the work (Regulation 742-01-03). A duplicate should be retained by the contractor.

2. This Certificate is only valid if accompanied by the Schedule of Inspections and the Schedule(s) of Test Results.

3. The signatures appended are those of the persons authorised by the companies executing the work of design, construction and inspection and testing respectively. A signatory authorised to certify more than one category of work should sign in each of the appropriate places.

4. The time interval recommended before the first periodic inspection must be inserted (see IEE Guidance Note 3 for guidance).

5. The page numbers for each of the Schedules of Test Results should be indicated, together with the total number of sheets involved.

6. The maximum prospective fault current recorded should be the greater of either the short-circuit current or the earth fault current.

7. The proposed date for the next inspection should take into consideration the frequency and quality of maintenance that the installation can reasonably be expected to receive during its intended life, and the period should be agreed between the designer, installer and other relevant parties.

ELECTRICAL INSTALLATION CERTIFICATE
GUIDANCE FOR RECIPIENTS (to be appended to the Certificate)

This safety Certificate has been issued to confirm that the electrical installation work to which it relates has been designed, constructed and inspected and tested in accordance with British Standard 7671 (the IEE Wiring Regulations).

You should have received an original Certificate and the contractor should have retained a duplicate Certificate. If you were the person ordering the work, but not the user of the installation, you should pass this Certificate, or a full copy of it including the schedules, immediately to the user.

The "original" Certificate should be retained in a safe place and be shown to any person inspecting or undertaking further work on the electrical installation in the future. If you later vacate the property, this Certificate will demonstrate to the new owner that the electrical installation complied with the requirements of British Standard 7671 at the time the Certificate was issued. The Construction (Design and Management) Regulations require that for a project covered by those Regulations, a copy of this Certificate, together with schedules is included in the project health and safety documentation.

For safety reasons, the electrical installation will need to be inspected at appropriate intervals by a competent person. The maximum time interval recommended before the next inspection is stated on Page 1 under "Next Inspection".

This Certificate is intended to be issued only for a new electrical installation or for new work associated with an alteration or addition to an existing installation. It should not have been issued for the inspection of an existing electrical installation. A "Periodic Inspection Report" should be issued for such a periodic inspection.

MINOR ELECTRICAL INSTALLATION WORKS CERTIFICATE
(REQUIREMENTS FOR ELECTRICAL INSTALLATIONS - BS 7671 [IEE WIRING REGULATIONS])
To be used only for minor electrical work which does not include the provision of a new circuit

---

PART 1 : Description of minor works

1. Description of the minor works

2. Location/Address

3. Date minor works completed

4. Details of departures, if any, from BS 7671

PART 2 : Installation details

1. System earthing arrangement   TN-C-S ☐   TN-S ☐   TT ☐

2. Method of protection against indirect contact

3. Protective device for the modified circuit   Type ....   Rating .... A

Comments on existing installation, including adequacy of earthing and bonding arrangements : (see Regulation 130-07)

PART 3 : Essential Tests

Earth continuity satisfactory   ☐

Insulation resistance:

        Phase/neutral .... MΩ

        Phase/earth .... MΩ

        Neutral/earth.................................... MΩ

Earth fault loop impedance ....Ω

Polarity satisfactory   ☐

RCD operation (if applicable). Rated residual operating current $I_{\Delta n}$ ....mA and operating time of ....ms (at $I_{\Delta n}$)

PART 4 : Declaration

I/We CERTIFY that the said works do not impair the safety of the existing installation, that the said works have been designed, constructed, inspected and tested in accordance with BS 7671 : .... (IEE Wiring Regulations), amended to .... and that the said works, to the best of my/our knowledge and belief, at the time of my/our inspection, complied with BS 7671 except as detailed in Part 1.

Name: ....

For and on behalf of: ....

Address: ....

....

....

Signature: ....

Position: ....

Date : ....

MINOR ELECTRICAL INSTALLATION WORKS CERTIFICATE
NOTES:

The Minor Works Certificate is intended to be used for additions and alterations to an installation that do not extend to the provision of a new circuit. Examples include the addition of a socket-outlet or lighting point to an existing circuit, the relocation of a light switch etc. This Certificate may also be used for the replacement of equipment such as accessories or luminaires, but not for the replacement of distribution boards or similar items. Appropriate inspection and testing, however, should always be carried out irrespective of the extent of the work undertaken.

MINOR ELECTRICAL INSTALLATION WORKS CERTIFICATE
GUIDANCE FOR RECIPIENTS (to be appended to the Certificate)

This Certificate has been issued to confirm that the electrical installation work to which it relates has been designed, constructed and inspected and tested in accordance with British Standard 7671, (the IEE Wiring Regulations).

You should have received an 'original' Certificate and the contractor should have retained a duplicate. If you were the person ordering the work, but not the owner of the installation, you should pass this Certificate, or a copy of it, to the owner. A separate Certificate should have been received for each existing circuit on which minor works have been carried out. This Certificate is not appropriate if you requested the contractor to undertake more extensive installation work, for which you should have received an Electrical Installation Certificate.

The Certificate should be retained in a safe place and be shown to any person inspecting or undertaking further work on the electrical installation in the future. If you later vacate the property, this Certificate will demonstrate to the new owner that the minor electrical installation work carried out complied with the requirements of British Standard 7671 at the time the Certificate was issued.

PERIODIC INSPECTION REPORT FOR AN ELECTRICAL INSTALLATION
(REQUIREMENTS FOR ELECTRICAL INSTALLATIONS - BS 7671 [IEE WIRING REGULATIONS])

DETAILS OF THE CLIENT

Client: ....

Address: ....

Purpose for which this Report is required: ....

DETAILS OF THE INSTALLATION Tick boxes as appropriate

Occupier: ....

Installation: ....

Address: ....

Description of Premises: Domestic ☐   Commercial ☐   Industrial ☐

Other ☐

Estimated age of the Electrical   .... years
Installation:

Evidence of Alterations or Additions: Yes ☐   No ☐   Not apparent ☐

If "Yes", estimate age: .... years

Date of last inspection: ....   Records available   Yes ☐   No ☐

EXTENT AND LIMITATIONS OF THE INSPECTION

Extent of electrical installation covered by this report: ....

....

....

Limitations: ....

....

....

This inspection has been carried out in accordance with BS 7671 : 2001 (IEE Wiring Regulations), amended to ....
Cables concealed within trunking and conduits, or cables and conduits concealed under floors, in roof spaces and generally within the fabric of the building or underground have not been inspected.

NEXT INSPECTION

I/We recommend that this installation is further inspected and tested after an interval of not more than .... months/years, provided that any observations 'requiring urgent attention' are attended to without delay.

DECLARATION

INSPECTED AND TESTED BY

Name: ....   Signature: ....

For and on behalf of: ....   Position: ....

Address: ....

....   Date: ....

....

293

SUPPLY CHARACTERISTICS AND EARTHING ARRANGEMENTS Tick boxes and enter details, as appropriate

Earthing arrangements	Number and Type of Live Conductors	Nature of Supply Parameters	Supply Protective Device Characteristics
TN-C ☐	a.c. ☐ d.c. ☐	Nominal voltage, U/U_o [(1)] V	Type: ....
TN-S ☐	1-phase, 2-wire ☐ 2-pole ☐	Nominal frequency, f [(1)] .... Hz	
TN-C-S ☐	2-phase, 3-wire ☐ 3-pole ☐	Prospective fault current, I_{pf} [(2)] .... kA	Nominal current rating ....A
TT ☐	3-phase, 3-wire ☐ other ☐	External loop impedance, Z_e [(2)] .... Ω	
IT ☐	3-phase, 4-wire ☐	(Note: (1) by enquiry, (2) by enquiry or by measurement)	

PARTICULARS OF INSTALLATION REFERRED TO IN THE REPORT Tick boxes and enter details, as appropriate

Means of Earthing
Distributor's facility ☐

Installation earth electrode ☐

Details of Installation Earth Electrode (where applicable)

Type   Location   Electrode resistance

(e.g. rod(s), tape etc)   to earth

.... Ω

Main Protective Conductors

Earthing conductor: material .... csa ....

Main equipotential bonding conductors   material .... csa ....

To incoming water service ☐   To incoming gas service ☐   To incoming oil service ☐   To structural steel ☐
To lightning protection ☐   To other incoming service(s) ☐   (state details...)

Main Switch or Circuit-breaker

BS, Type and number of poles ....   Current rating ....A   Voltage rating V

Location ....   Fuse rating or setting................A

Rated residual operating current $I_{\Delta n}$ = ... mA, and operating time of .... ms (at $I_{\Delta n}$) (applicable only where an RCD is suitable and is used as a main circuit-breaker)

OBSERVATIONS AND RECOMMENDATIONS Tick boxes as appropriate

Recommendations as detailed below

Referring to the attached Schedule(s) of Inspection and Test Results, and subject to the limitations specified at the Extent and Limitations of the Inspection section
☐ No remedial work is required   ☐ The following observations are made:

....

....

....

....

....

....

....

One of the following numbers, as appropriate, is to be allocated to each of the observations made above to indicate to the person(s) responsible for the installation the action recommended.

| 1 | requires urgent attention | 2 | requires improvement | 3 | requires further investigation |

| 4 | does not comply with BS 7671 : 2001 amended to .... This does not imply that the electrical installation inspected is unsafe.

SUMMARY OF THE INSPECTION

Date(s) of the inspection: ....

General condition of the installation: ....

....

....

....

Overall assessment: Satisfactory/Unsatisfactory

SCHEDULE(S)

The attached Schedules are part of this document and this Report is valid only when they are attached to it.
.... Schedules of Inspections and .... Schedules of Test Results are attached.
(Enter quantities of schedules attached).

PERIODIC INSPECTION REPORT
NOTES:

1. This Periodic Inspection Report form shall only be used for the reporting on the condition of an existing installation.

2. The Report, normally comprising at least four pages, shall include schedules of both the inspection and the test results. Additional sheets of test results may be necessary for other than a simple installation. The page numbers of each sheet shall be indicated, together with the total number of sheets involved.

3. The intended purpose of the Periodic Inspection Report shall be identified, together with the recipient's details in the appropriate boxes.

4. The maximum prospective fault current recorded should be the greater of either the short-circuit current or the earth fault current.

5. The 'Extent and Limitations' box shall fully identify the elements of the installation that are covered by the report and those that are not; this aspect having been agreed with the client and other interested parties before the inspection and testing is carried out.

6. The recommendation(s), if any, shall be categorised using the numbered coding 1-4 as appropriate.

7. The 'Summary of the Inspection' box shall clearly identify the condition of the installation in terms of safety.

8. Where the periodic inspection and testing has resulted in a satisfactory overall assessment, the time interval for the next periodic inspection and testing shall be given. The IEE Guidance Note 3 provides guidance on the maximum interval between inspections for various types of buildings. If the inspection and testing reveals that parts of the installation require urgent attention, it would be appropriate to state an earlier re-inspection date having due regard to the degree of urgency and extent of the necessary remedial work.

9. If the space available on the model form for information on recommendations is insufficient, additional pages shall be provided as necessary.

PERIODIC INSPECTION REPORT
GUIDANCE FOR RECIPIENTS (to be appended to the Report)

This Periodic Inspection Report form is intended for reporting on the condition of an existing electrical installation.

You should have received an original Report and the contractor should have retained a duplicate. If you were the person ordering this Report, but not the owner of the installation, you should pass this Report, or a copy of it, immediately to the owner.

The original Report is to be retained in a safe place and be shown to any person inspecting or undertaking work on the electrical installation in the future. If you later vacate the property, this Report will provide the new owner with details of the condition of the electrical installation at the time the Report was issued.

The 'Extent and Limitations' box should fully identify the extent of the installation covered by this Report and any limitations on the inspection and tests. The contractor should have agreed these aspects with you and with any other interested parties (Licensing Authority, Insurance Company, Building Society etc) before the inspection was carried out.

The Report will usually contain a list of recommended actions necessary to bring the installation up to the current standard. **For items classified as 'requires urgent attention', the safety of those using the installation may be at risk,** and it is recommended that a competent person undertakes the necessary remedial work without delay.

For safety reasons, the electrical installation will need to be re-inspected at appropriate intervals by a competent person. The maximum time interval recommended before the next inspection is stated in the Report under 'Next Inspection.'

SCHEDULE OF INSPECTIONS

Methods of protection against electric shock

(a) Protection against both direct and indirect contact:

☐ (i)   SELV

☐ (ii)   Limitation of discharge of energy

(b) Protection against direct contact:

☐ (i)   Insulation of live parts

☐ (ii)   Barriers or enclosures

☐ (iii) Obstacles

☐ (iv) Placing out of reach

☐ (v)   PELV

☐ (vi) Presence of RCD for supplementary protection

(c) Protection against indirect contact:

(i)   EEBADS including:

☐ Presence of earthing conductor

☐ Presence of circuit protective conductors

☐ Presence of main equipotential bonding conductors

☐ Presence of supplementary equipotential bonding conductors

☐ Presence of earthing arrangements for combined protective and functional purposes

☐ Presence of adequate arrangements for alternative source(s), where applicable

☐ Presence of residual current device(s)

☐ (ii)   Use of Class II equipment or equivalent insulation

☐ (iii) Non-conducting location: Absence of protective conductors

☐ (iv) Earth-free equipotential bonding: Presence of earth-free equipotential bonding conductors

☐ (v)   Electrical separation

Prevention of mutual detrimental influence

☐ (a) Proximity of non-electrical services and other influences

☐ (b) Segregation of band I and band II circuits or band II insulation used

☐ (c) Segregation of safety circuits

Identification

☐ (a) Presence of diagrams, instructions, circuit charts and similar information

☐ (b) Presence of danger notices and other warning notices

☐ (c) Labelling of protective devices, switches and terminals

☐ (d) Identification of conductors

Cables and conductors

☐ (a) Routing of cables in prescribed zones or within mechanical protection

☐ (b) Connection of conductors

☐ (c) Erection methods

☐ (d) Selection of conductors for current-carrying capacity and voltage drop

☐ (e) Presence of fire barriers, suitable seals and protection against thermal effects

General

☐ (a) Presence and correct location of appropriate devices for isolation and switching

☐ (b) Adequacy of access to switchgear and other equipment

☐ (c) Particular protective measures for special installations and locations

☐ (d) Connection of single-pole devices for protection or switching in phase conductors only

☐ (e) Correct connection of accessories and equipment

☐ (f) Presence of undervoltage protective devices

☐ (g) Choice and setting of protective and monitoring devices for protection against indirect contact and/or overcurrent

☐ (h) Selection of equipment and protective measures appropriate to external influences

☐ (i)   Selection of appropriate functional switching devices

Inspected by ....

Date ....

Notes:

✓   to indicate an inspection has been carried out and the result is satisfactory

✗   to indicate an inspection has been carried out and the result was unsatisfactory

N/A to indicate the inspection is not applicable

LIM to indicate that, exceptionally, a limitation agreed with the person ordering the work prevented the inspection or test being carried out.

SCHEDULE OF TEST RESULTS

Contractor: ....

Test Date: ....

Signature ....

Method of protection against indirect contact: ....

Equipment vulnerable to testing: ....

Address/Location of distribution board: ....

....

Type of Supply: TN-S/TN-C-S/TT

Ze at origin: ....ohms

PFC: ....kA

Instruments

loop impedance: ....

continuity: ....

insulation: ....

RCD tester: ....

Description of Work: ....

Circuit Description	Overcurrent Device			Wiring Conductors		Test Results										Remarks
	Short-circuit capacity: ....kA					Continuity			Insulation Resistance		Polarity	Earth Loop Impedance Z_s	Functional Testing		
	type	Rating I_n	live	cpc	$(R_1 + R_2)^*$	R_2^*	R_{ing}	Live/ Live	Live/ Earth			RCD time	Other	
		A	mm²	mm²	Ω	Ω		MΩ	MΩ		Ω	ms		
1	2	3	4	5	6	7	8	9	10	11	12	13	14	15

Deviations from Wiring Regulations and special notes:

* Complete column 6 or 7.

APPENDIX 7

HARMONIZED CABLE CORE COLOURS

1. Introduction

The requirements of BS 7671 have been harmonized with the technical intent of CENELEC Standard HD 384.5.514: *Identification*, including 514.3: *Identification of conductors*. The cable standards have been harmonized with CENELEC Harmonization Document HD 308 S2: 2001 *Identification of cores in cables and flexible cords*. These standards specify the cable core marking including cable core colours to be implemented in the CENELEC countries.

This appendix provides guidance on marking at the interface between old and harmonized colours, and general guidance on the colours to be used for conductors.

British Standards for fixed and flexible cables have been harmonized with the colours in HD 308 S2. BS 7671 has been modified to align with these cable colours, but also allows other suitable methods of marking connections by colours (tapes, sleeves or discs), or by alphanumerics (letters and/or numbers). Methods may be mixed within an installation.

2. Alteration or addition to an existing installation

2.1 *Single-phase*

An alteration or an addition made to a single-phase installation need not be marked at the interface provided that:

    i)   the old cables are correctly identified by the colour red for phase and black for neutral, and

    ii) the new cables are correctly identified by the colour brown for phase and blue for neutral.

2.2 *Two- or three-phase installation*

Where an alteration or an addition is made to a two- or a three-phase installation wired in the old core colours with cable to the new core colours, unambiguous identification is required at the interface. Cores shall be marked as follows:

> *Neutral conductors*
> Old and new conductors: N
>
> *Phase conductors*
> Old and new conductors: L1, L2, L3.

TABLE 7A
**Example of conductor marking at the interface for additions and alterations
to an a.c. installation identified with the old cable colours**

Function	Old conductor		New conductor	
	Colour	Marking	Marking	Colour
Phase 1 of a.c.	Red	L1	L1	Brown[1]
Phase 2 of a.c.	Yellow	L2	L2	Black[1]
Phase 3 of a.c.	Blue	L3	L3	Grey[1]
Neutral of a.c.	Black	N	N	Blue
Protective conductor	Green-and-Yellow			Green-and-Yellow

[1] Three single-core cables with insulation of the same colour may be used if identified at the terminations.

3. Switch wires in a new installation or an alteration or addition to an existing installation

Where a two-core cable with cores coloured brown and blue is used as a switch wire, both conductors being phase conductors, the blue conductors shall be marked brown or L at its terminations.

4. Intermediate and two-way switch wires in a new installation or an alteration or addition to an existing installation

Where a three-core cable with cores coloured brown, black and grey is used as a switch wire, all three conductors being phase conductors, the black and grey conductors shall be marked brown or L at their terminations.

5. Phase conductors in a new installation or an alteration or addition to an existing installation

Power circuit phase conductors should be coloured as in Table 51. Other phase conductors may be brown, black, red, orange, yellow, violet, grey, white, pink or turquoise.

In a two- or three-phase power circuit the phase conductors may all be of one of the permitted colours, either identified L1, L2, L3 or marked brown, black, grey at their terminations to show the phases.

6. Changes to cable core colour identification

TABLE 7B
Cable to BS 6004 (flat cable with bare cpc)

Cable type	Old core colours	New core colours
Single-core + bare cpc	Red or Black	Brown or Blue
Two-core + bare cpc	Red, Black	Brown, Blue
Alt. two-core + bare cpc	Red, Red	Brown, Brown
Three-core + bare cpc	Red, Yellow, Blue	Brown, Black, Grey

TABLE 7C
Standard 600/1000V armoured cable BS 6346, BS 5467 or BS 6724

Cable type	Old core colours	New core colours
Single-core	Red or Black	Brown or Blue
Two-core	Red, Black	Brown, Blue
Three-core	Red, Yellow, Blue	Brown, Black, Grey
Four core	Red, Yellow, Blue, Black	Brown, Black, Grey, Blue
Five-core	Red, Yellow, Blue, Black, Green-and-Yellow	Brown, Black, Grey, Blue, Green-and-Yellow

TABLE 7D
Flexible cable to BS 6500

Cable type	Old core colours	New core colours
Two-core	Brown, Blue	No change
Three-core	Brown, Blue, Green-and-Yellow	No change
Four-core	Black, Blue, Brown, Green-and-Yellow	Brown, Black, Grey, Green-and-Yellow
Five-core	Black, Blue, Brown, Black, Green-and-Yellow	Brown, Black, Grey, Blue, Green-and-Yellow

7. Alteration or addition to a d.c. installation

When an alteration or an addition is made to a d.c. installation wired in the old core colours with cable to the new core colours, unambiguous identification is required at the interface. Cores shall be marked as follows:

Neutral and mid-point conductors
Old and new conductors: M

Phase conductors
Old and new conductors: Brown or Grey, or
old and new conductors: L, L+ or L-.

TABLE 7E
Example of conductor marking at the interface for additions and alterations to a d.c. installation identified with the old cable colours

Function	Old conductor		New conductor	
	Colour	Marking	Marking	Colour
Two-wire unearthed d.c. power circuit				
Positive of two-wire circuit	Red	L+	L+	Brown
Negative of two-wire circuit	Black	L-	L-	Grey
Two-wire earthed d.c. power circuit				
Positive (of negative earthed) circuit	Red	L+	L+	Brown
Negative (of negative earthed) circuit	Black	M	M	Blue
Positive (of positive earthed) circuit	Black	M	M	Blue
Negative (of positive earthed) circuit	Blue	L-	L-	Grey
Three-wire d.c. power circuit				
Outer positive of two-wire circuit derived from three-wire system	Red	L+	L+	Brown
Outer negative of two-wire circuit derived from three-wire system	Red	L-	L-	Grey
Positive of three-wire circuit	Red	L+	L+	Brown
Mid-wire of three-wire circuit	Black	M	M	Blue
Negative of three-wire circuit	Blue	L-	L-	Grey

INDEX

H

I